TEST ITEM FILE
Jay Stubblefield North Carolina Wesleyan College

BUSINESS COMMUNICATION ESSENTIALS
Third Edition

Courtland Bovée
John Thill

PEARSON
Prentice
Hall

Upper Saddle River, New Jersey 07458

VP/Editorial Director: Jeff Shelstad
Executive Editor: David Parker
Product Development Manager: Ashley Santora
Associate Director, Manufacturing: Vincent Scelta
Production Editor & Buyer: Carol O'Rourke
Printer/Binder: Offset Paperback Manufacturing

Pearson Prentice Hall^{TM} **is a trademark of Pearson Education, Inc.**

10 9 8 7 6 5 4 3 2 1
ISBN-13: 978-0-13-232483-0
ISBN-10:   0-13-232483-0

Contents

CHAPTER 1
UNDERSTANDING BUSINESS COMMUNICATION IN TODAY'S WORKPLACE

Multiple Choice

1. Communication is the process of
    a. transferring knowledge.
    b. listening actively.
    c. sending and receiving messages.
    d. writing effective messages.

ANSWER: c. Communication is the process of sending and receiving messages. Only answer "c" contains the key dynamics of communication: sending and receiving.
DIFFICULTY: moderate; PAGE: 2; OBJECTIVE: 1; TYPE: concept

2. Your ability to communicate effectively as a business professional gives both you and your employer benefits in
    a. more efficient problem solving.
    b. increased productivity.
    c. enhanced professional images.
    d. all of the above.

ANSWER: d. The benefits of effective communication include all of the items listed here along with others listed on page 3.
DIFFICULTY: moderate; PAGE: 3; OBJECTIVE: 1; TYPE: concept

3. Communicating effectively yields all of the following benefits *except*
    a. better responses from colleagues, employees, customers, and other stakeholders.
    b. stronger business relationships.
    c. decreased need for teams in the workplace.
    d. stronger decision making.

ANSWER: c. Benefits include those above plus items on page 3.
DIFFICULTY: difficult; PAGE 3; OBJECTIVE 1; TYPE: concept

4. Communication is effective only if your message
    a. is understood.
    b. stimulates action.
    c. encourages the audience to think in new ways.
    d. all of the above

ANSWER: d. Effective communication is understood by the receiver; it stimulates audiences to think or take action.
DIFFICULTY: difficult; PAGE: 3; OBJECTIVE: 1; TYPE: concept

5. Good communication skills are more important today than ever in history because of
   a. advances in technology.
   b. the need to manage vast amounts of information.
   c. the growth of globalization.
   d. all of the above

ANSWER: d. Each item listed is one of the factors that make up the complex environment of the workplace.
DIFFICULTY: moderate; PAGE: 3; OBJECTIVE: 2; TYPE: concept

6. Good communication skills are vital today because
   a. people need to adapt to a constantly changing workplace.
   b. of an aging population.
   c. there are multiple sets of generations in the workplace that have different methods of communication.
   d. of the numerous kinds of media used to communicate.

ANSWER: a. There are many challenges in the workplace.
DIFFICULTY: moderate; PAGE 3; OBJECTIVE: 1; TYPE: concept

7. One of the greatest challenges that communicators face in the new age of information is
   a. effectively formatting their documents.
   b. successfully analyzing their audience.
   c. effectively catching their audience's attention.
   d. successfully editing for clarity.

ANSWER: c. People are so inundated with information that they tend to ignore messages they see as less important. It is a challenge to catch their attention.
DIFFICULTY: difficult; PAGE: 3; OBJECTIVE: 2; TYPE: concept

8. Communicating in team-based organizations requires that you
   a. listen well and understand how groups interact.
   b. be assertive and take charge.
   c. speed up the decision-making process.
   d. all of the above

ANSWER: a. To function effectively in team-based organizations you need to understand communication in groups, listen closely and interpret body language.
DIFFICULTY: difficult; PAGE: 4; OBJECTIVE: 2; TYPE: concept

9. In the communication process all of the following occur, *except*:
   a. the sender has an idea
   b. the sender transmits the message
   c. the receiver has an idea
   d. the receiver decodes the message

ANWER: c. The receiver sends feedback, but the initial idea is the sender's.
DIFFICULTY: moderate; PAGE: 5; OBJECTIVE: 3; TYPE: concept

10. When senders transmit a message, they must
    a. select a communication channel.
    b. choose a communication medium.
    c. analyze the message, the audience's location, the need for speed, and the formality required.
    d. all of the above

ANSWER: d. In order to select a channel and a mode, the sender must analyze several factors.
DIFFICULTY: difficult; PAGE: 5; OBJECTIVE: 3; TYPE: concept

11. When the receivers of a message respond in some way, they are providing _____ to the sender.
    a. an evaluation
    b. feedback
    c. attention
    d. an answer

ANSWER: b. A receiver's response provides feedback to the sender.
DIFFICULTY: moderate; PAGE: 5; OBJECTIVE: 3; TYPE: concept

12. Ethical communication is
    a. not deceptive in any way.
    b. designed to enhance public image.
    c. a strategy for increasing profits.
    d. a way to conceal errors.

ANSWER: a. Ethical communication is not deceptive in any way.
DIFFICULTY: moderate; PAGE: 6; OBJECTIVE: 4; TYPE: concept

13. Identify the characteristic that is *not* a part of ethical communication.
    a. It includes all relevant information.
    b. It is designed to hide some negative information.
    c. It is true in every sense.
    d. It is not deceptive in any way.

ANSWER: b. Ethical communication must always include the qualities noted in answers "a", "c", and "d".
DIFFICULTY: moderate; PAGE: 6; OBJECTIVE: 4; TYPE: application

14. Which of the following is the best definition of ethics?
    a. stealing someone else's words or work and claiming it as your own
    b. the accepted principles of conduct that govern a person or a group
    c. the belief that one's own culture is superior to others
    d. predicting individuals' behavior on the basis of their membership in a particular group

ANSWER: b. Ethics are the accepted principles of conduct that govern a person or a group.
DIFFICULTY: difficult; PAGE: 6; OBJECTIVE: 4; TYPE: concept

15. All of the following are examples of unethical communication practices *except*:
    a. distorting visuals
    b. using jargon
    c. plagiarism
    d. misquoting

ANSWER: b. While using jargon is not always an effective means of communication, it is not unethical.
DIFFICULTY: moderate; PAGE: 6; OBJECTIVE: 4; TYPE: concept

16. _____ occurs when the writer steals someone else's work and claims it as his/her own.
    a. Selective misquoting
    b. Distortion
    c. Plagiarism
    d. Copying

ANSWER: c. Plagiarism is stealing another's work and claiming it as your own.
DIFFICULTY: moderate; PAGE: 6; OBJECTIVE 4; TYPE: concept

17. Choosing between alternatives that aren't clear-cut is termed an:
    a. ethical lapse
    b. ethical dilemma
    c. ethical crime
    d. ethical misdeed

ANSWER: b. An ethical dilemma occurs when you must weigh the relative merits of the situation—there is no clear answer.
DIFFICULTY: moderate; PAGE: 6; OBJECTIVE: 5; TYPE: concept

18. When one person takes credit for the words and writing of another, it is called
    a. ethics.
    b. cultural diversity.
    c. plagiarism.
    d. ethnocentrism.

ANSWER: c. Plagiarism is claiming someone else's work as your own.
DIFFICULTY: moderate; PAGE: 6; OBJECTIVE: 6; TYPE: application

19. Identify the claim that is most true.
    a. ethical questions are always clear-cut
    b. ethical behavior will result in higher pay
    c. ethical dilemmas are never easy to solve
    d. ethical choices may lie somewhere in the gray area between right and wrong

ANSWER: d. Ethical dilemmas often include complex alternatives that may offer equally valid and ethical choices.
DIFFICULTY: easy; PAGE: 6-7; OBJECTIVE: 6; TYPE: concept

20. Making a clearly unethical or illegal choice is termed an:
    a. ethical lapse
    b. ethical dilemma
    c. ethical crime
    d. ethical misdeed

ANSWER: a. An ethical lapse is the term used for a clearly unethical or illegal choice.
DIFFICULTY: moderate; PAGE: 7; OBJECTIVE: 5; TYPE: concept

21. Miscommunication between cultures often occurs because
    a. the senders and receivers are encoding and decoding messages using the assumptions of their different cultures.
    b. the senders are encoding messages that the receivers will not be able to decode.
    c. the receivers are decoding messages that the senders were not able to encode.
    d. the senders and receivers are encoding and decoding messages that offend each other.

ANSWER: a. When you communicate with someone from another culture, you encode your message using the assumptions of your own culture. However, the audience will decode your message using the assumptions of their culture.
DIFFICULTY: difficult; PAGE: 9; OBJECTIVE: 4; TYPE: concept

22. You can improve your intercultural sensitivity by
    a. holding to the ethics of your own culture.
    b. recognizing cultural differences.
    c. insisting that any transaction be conducted in English only.
    d. all of the above

ANSWER: b. Only answer "b" satisfies the dynamics for effective intercultural communication.
DIFFICULTY: moderate; PAGE: 9; OBJECTIVE: 4; TYPE: application

23. Cultures like South Korea and Taiwan that rely less on verbal communication and more on context and setting to convey meaning are considered _____ cultures.
    a. basic-context
    b. moderate-context
    c. high-context
    d. low-context

ANSWER: c. South Korea and Taiwan are "high-context" cultures where context and setting convey meaning and where people are expected to recognize situational cues (such as gestures and tone of voice).
DIFFICULTY: moderate; PAGE: 9; OBJECTIVE: 6; TYPE: concept

24. Recognizing and accommodating cultural differences involves all of the following *except*:
   a. social customs
   b. ethics and laws
   c. nonverbal communication
   d. impact

ANSWER: d. Impact is not one of the cultural differences to consider.
DIFFICULTY: moderate; PAGE: 9; OBJECTIVE: 6; TYPE: concept

25. Cultural context is
   a. a pattern of physical cues.
   b. implicit understanding that conveys meaning.
   c. a pattern of environmental stimuli.
   d. all of the above

ANSWER: d. Cultural context is the pattern of cues and stimuli that convey meaning between members of a culture.
DIFFICULTY: difficult; PAGE: 9; OBJECTIVE: 6; TYPE: concept

26. All of the following are features found in low-context companies, *except*:
   a. Workers rely on detailed background information.
   b. Business and social relationships are discrete.
   c. Competence is valued.
   d. Information is shared with everyone.

ANSWER: d. See Figure 1.4 on page 9.
DIFFICULTY: difficult; PAGE 9; OBJECTIVE 6; TYPE: application

27. You will find all of the following features in a high-context company, *except*:
   a. Executive offices are shared and open to all.
   b. Information is centralized and controlled.
   c. Workers do not expect detailed information.
   d. Meetings are often called on short notice.

ANSWER: b. Features are listed in Figure 1.4 on page 9.
DIFFICULTY: difficult; PAGE: 9; OBJECTIVE 6: TYPE: application

28. The pattern of physical cues, environmental stimuli, and implicit understanding that conveys meaning between two members of the same culture is termed:
   a. ethics
   b. context
   c. social customs
   d. nonverbal communication

ANSWER: b. Context is the shared pattern of physical cues, environmental stimuli, and implicit understanding that convey meaning between two members of the same culture.
DIFFICULTY: moderate; PAGE: 9; OBJECTIVE: 6; TYPE: concept

29. Cultures like the U.S. and Germany that rely more on verbal communication and less on circumstance and cues to convey meaning are considered _____ cultures.
   a. basic-context
   b. moderate-context
   c. high-context
   d. low-context

ANSWER: d. The U.S. and Germany are "low-context" cultures where people rely more on verbal communication and less on context and cues to convey meaning.
DIFFICULTY: moderate; PAGE: 10; OBJECTIVE: 6; TYPE: concept

30. Rules and expectations are usually spelled out in _____ cultures.
   a. basic-context
   b. moderate-context
   c. high-context
   d. low-context

ANSWER: d. In "low-context" cultures, rules and expectations are usually spelled out through explicit statements.
DIFFICULTY: moderate; PAGE: 10; OBJECTIVE: 6; TYPE: concept

31. People in these cultures tend to view laws with flexibility.
   a. basic-context
   b. moderate-context
   c. high-context
   d. low-context

ANSWER: d. People in "low-context" cultures tend to view laws with flexibility.
DIFFICULTY: moderate; PAGE: 10; OBJECTIVE: 6; TYPE: concept

32. People in these cultures tend to adhere more strictly to the law.
   a. basic-context
   b. moderate-context
   c. high-context
   d. low-context

ANSWER: c. People in "high-context" cultures tend to adhere more strictly to the law.
DIFFICULTY: moderate; PAGE: 10; OBJECTIVE: 6; TYPE: concept

33. The U.S. is governed by this type of law.
   a. the King's Rules of common law
   b. the English common law
   c. Locke's code of law
   d. the Napoleonic code

ANSWER: b. Like the United Kingdom, the U.S. adheres to English common law.
DIFFICULTY: moderate; PAGE: 10; OBJECTIVE: 6; TYPE: concept

34. Law in Turkey presumes that you are
    a. guilty until proven innocent.
    b. innocent until proven guilty.
    c. neither guilty nor innocent until tried.
    d. innocent, as long as you can pay court costs.

ANSWER: a. As in Mexico, in Turkey someone is presumed guilty until proven innocent.
DIFFICULTY: moderate; PAGE: 10; OBJECTIVE: 6; TYPE: concept

35. All of the following are suggestions to help keep your message ethical when communicating across cultures *except*:
    a. seek mutual ground
    b. focus on profits
    c. show respect for cultural differences
    d. send messages that are honest

ANSWER: b. Focusing primarily on profits instead of on understanding will not further ethical intercultural communication.
DIFFICULTY: moderate; PAGE: 10; OBJECTIVE: 6; TYPE: concept

36. The formal rules of a culture that govern behavior, such as table manners at meals, are termed:
    a. ethics
    b. context
    c. social customs
    d. nonverbal communication

ANSWER: c. Formal social rules are specifically taught "rights" and "wrongs" of how to behave in common social situations (such as table manners at meals).
DIFFICULTY: easy; PAGE: 10; OBJECTIVE: 6; TYPE: concept

37. Nonverbal communication that differs from culture to culture includes things such as
    a. facial expressions.
    b. gestures.
    c. style of dress.
    d. all of the above.

ANSWER: d. All these nonverbal behaviors may have different meanings in different cultures.
DIFFICULTY: easy; PAGE: 10; OBJECTIVE: 6; TYPE: concept

38. Forming opinions on others based upon their affiliation or membership in a particular group is called
    a. stereotyping.
    b. ethics.
    c. ethnocentrism.
    d. context.

ANSWER: a. Assumptions made upon the basis of an individual's group membership come from stereotyping.
DIFFICULTY: moderate; PAGE: 11; OBJECTIVE: 6; TYPE: application

39. Ethnocentrism is
    a. predicting individuals' behavior or character based upon group affiliation.
    b. the belief that one's culture is superior to all others.
    c. the promotion of ethnic cultures.
    d. the formal rules that govern a culture's social behaviors.

ANSWER: b. Ethnocentrism is the belief that one's culture is superior to all others.
DIFFICULTY: moderate; PAGE: 11; OBJECTIVE: 6; TYPE: concept

40. To overcome ethnocentrism, follow all of these suggestions *except*:
    a. always hold to U.S. customs
    b. acknowledge distinctions
    c. avoid assumptions
    d. avoid judgments

ANSWER: a. Both parties must be flexible and avoid insisting that an interaction take place strictly in terms of one culture or another.
DIFFICULTY: moderate; PAGE: 11; OBJECTIVE: 6; TYPE: concept

41. When writing for multicultural audiences, it's important to
    a. use plain English.
    b. be clear.
    c. address international correspondence properly.
    d. all of the above

ANSWER: d. All of the items listed above are important in writing for multicultural audiences.
DIFFICULTY: moderate; PAGE: 11; OBJECTIVE: 6; TYPE: concept

42. _____ is the fear of foreigners and strangers, and can reduce the effectiveness of communication between two businesspeople from different cultures.
    a. Ethnocentrism
    b. Xenophobia
    c. Stereotyping
    d. Cultural Pluralism

ANSWER: b. This is the definition of xenophobia.
DIFFICULTY: easy; PAGE 11; OBJECTIVE 6; TYPE: concept

43. Identify the one item listed below that would *not* help you communicate effectively with people who speak English as a second language.
    a. try to eliminate noise
    b. always hold to U.S. customs and common greetings
    c. observe body language
    d. rephrase sentences where necessary

ANSWER: b. Both parties must be flexible and avoid insisting that an interaction take place strictly in terms of one culture or another.
DIFFICULTY: moderate; PAGE: 12-13; OBJECTIVE: 6; TYPE: concept

44. Identify the item from the list below that is *not* one of the basic principles for communicating across cultures.
    a. Show respect for cultural differences.
    b. Withhold judgment.
    c. Ignore body language.
    d. Recognize your own cultural biases.

ANSWER: c. Attending to body language gives you important feedback and is one more way to communicate effectively.
DIFFICULTY: easy; PAGE: 13-14; OBJECTIVE: 6; TYPE: concept

True/False

45. _____One challenge you will face as a business communicator is to get your audience's attention so they will read and act on your message.

ANSWER: True. Every business communicator faces the sometimes daunting task of "cutting through the clutter" to get an audience to read or hear a message.
DIFFICULTY: moderate; PAGE: 3; OBJECTIVE: 1; TYPE: concept

46. _____Stronger business relationships and stronger decision making are two of the benefits received from effective communication.

ANSWER: True. A list of benefits is on page 3.
DIFFICULTY: moderate; PAGE: 3; OBJECTIVE 1: TYPE: concept

47. _____Good communication skills are important because people need to adapt to a workplace that is culturally diverse.

ANSWER: True. This is one of the reasons for good communication skills.
DIFFICULTY: moderate; PAGE: 3-4; OBJECTIVE 1; TYPE: concept

48. _____Today's organizations often use teams and workgroups in order to collaborate and make fast decisions.

ANSWER: True. Team-based organizations are increasingly common.
DIFFICULTY: moderate; PAGE: 4; OBJECTIVE 2; TYPE: concept

49. _____The channel a communicator selects to transmit a message depends only on his or her personal preference.

ANSWER: False. How effective the channel of communication is depends on the message, the audience's location, the need for speed, and the formality required. Each element is important in deciding which channel to use.
DIFFICULTY: easy; PAGE: 5; OBJECTIVE: 1; TYPE: concept

50. _____Plagiarism is claiming someone else's work as your own.

ANSWER: True. Plagiarism is claiming someone else's work as your own.
DIFFICULTY: easy; PAGE: 6; OBJECTIVE: 5; TYPE: concept

51. _____Ethics are the accepted principles of conduct that govern a person or a group.

ANSWER: True. This is the definition given in the text.
DIFFICULTY: moderate; PAGE: 6; OBJECTIVE: 5; TYPE: concept

52. _____Ethical communication may state opinions as facts.

ANSWER: False. Ethical communication does not state opinions as facts, does not hide negative information behind an optimistic attitude, and does not portray graphic data unfairly.
DIFFICULTY: moderate; PAGE: 6; OBJECTIVE: 5; TYPE: application

53. _____An ethical dilemma may involve choosing between alternatives that are not clear-cut.

ANSWER: True. Ethical dilemmas often include complex alternatives that may offer equally valid and ethical choices, or the alternatives may lie somewhere in the gray area between right and wrong.
DIFFICULTY: moderate; PAGE: 6; OBJECTIVE: 5; TYPE: application

54. _____China, where speakers use indirectness and metaphor to convey meaning, is considered a high-context culture.

ANSWER: True. China is a high-context culture.
DIFFICULTY: moderate; PAGE: 9; OBJECTIVE: 6; TYPE: application

55. _____Members of high-context cultures put less emphasis on the written word and consider personal pledges more important than contracts.

ANSWER: True. Members of high-context cultures put less emphasis on the written word and consider personal pledges more important than contracts.
DIFFICULTY: moderate; PAGE: 9-10; OBJECTIVE: 6; TYPE: application

56. _____Germany, where business people want to make decisions as quickly and efficiently as possible, is considered a high-context culture.

ANSWER: False. Germany is a low-context culture where people rely more on verbal communications and less on circumstances and cues to convey meaning.
DIFFICULTY: moderate; PAGE: 10; OBJECTIVE: 6; TYPE: application

57. _____In low-context companies, exchanging information is the primary task of communication.

ANSWER: True. Exchanging information is the primary task of communication in low-context cultures.
DIFFICULTY: moderate; PAGE: 10; OBJECTIVE: 6; TYPE: application

58. _____ Differences in legal systems are particularly important if your firm must communicate about a legal dispute with another country.

ANSWER: True. For legal disputes to be resolved, negotiations must take place between differing legal systems and qualified personnel.
DIFFICULTY: easy; PAGE: 10; OBJECTIVE: 6; TYPE: application

59. _____ When communicating across cultures, both parties must determine whose code of ethics they will allow to guide their interactions.

ANSWER: False. Both parties must be flexible and avoid insisting that an interaction take place in terms of one culture or another.
DIFFICULTY: moderate; PAGE: 10; OBJECTIVE: 6; TYPE: concept

60. _____ Differences in social values are apparent in the way various cultures define manners, think about time, recognize status and value wealth.

ANSWER: True. One culture may condemn materialism and prize communal effort above that of the individual. Such differences are apparent in social customs and values.
DIFFICULTY: moderate; PAGE: 10; OBJECTIVE: 6; TYPE: concept

61. _____ A hand gesture in your culture may be interpreted quite differently in another culture.

ANSWER: True. The simplest hand gestures change meaning from culture to culture.
DIFFICULTY: easy; PAGE: 10; OBJECTIVE: 6; TYPE: concept

62. _____ To communicate successfully across cultures, you must hold to the customs and values of your home country.

ANSWER: False. To communicate across cultures successfully, you must be able to overcome the tendency to judge others by one's own standards.
DIFFICULTY: easy; PAGE: 11; OBJECTIVE: 6; TYPE: concept

63. _____ Ethnocentrism is the belief that one's own culture is superior to all others.

ANSWER: True. This is the definition given in the text.
DIFFICULTY: easy; PAGE: 11; OBJECTIVE: 6; TYPE: concept

64. _____ Ethnocentrism is predicting individuals' behavior or character on the basis of their membership in a particular group or class.

ANSWER: False. Ethnocentrism is the belief that one's culture is superior to all others.
DIFFICULTY: moderate; PAGE: 11; OBJECTIVE: 6; TYPE: concept

65. _____ Stereotyping is the belief that one's own culture is superior to all others.

ANSWER: False. Ethnocentrism is the belief that one's culture is superior to all others.
DIFFICULTY: moderate; PAGE: 11; OBJECTIVE: 6; TYPE: concept

66.   Stereotyping is assigning a wide range of generalized attributes to an individual on the basis of membership in a particular culture or group, without considering the individual's unique characteristics.

ANSWER: True. This is the definition given in the text.
DIFFICULTY: easy; PAGE: 11; OBJECTIVE: 6; TYPE: concept

67.   To overcome ethnocentrism, it's important to ignore the differences between your culture and another.

ANSWER: False. When communicating across cultures, it's important to acknowledge distinctions.
DIFFICULTY: moderate; PAGE: 11; OBJECTIVE: 6; TYPE: concept

68.   People often have cultural biases and beliefs that they're not even consciously aware of.

ANSWER: True. People are not always conscious of their cultural biases.
DIFFICULTY: moderate; PAGE: 11; OBJECTIVE: 6; TYPE: concept

69.   When communicating across cultures, it is important to use an impressive vocabulary.

ANSWER: False. When communicating across cultures, it's important to use short, precise words that say exactly what you mean.
DIFFICULTY: moderate; PAGE: 11; OBJECTIVE: 6; TYPE: concept

70.   When communicating across cultures, it is important to avoid using slang, idioms, jargon, and abbreviations.

ANSWER: True. Effective communication across cultures, whether written or spoken, requires the writer or speaker to avoid using slang, idioms, jargon, and abbreviations.
DIFFICULTY: moderate; PAGE: 11; OBJECTIVE: 6; TYPE: concept

71.   When speaking with people for whom English is a second language, an effective communicator will learn common greetings and a few simple phrases in the other person's native language.

ANSWER: True. Such accommodation shows simple respect and demonstrates interest in your listener's culture.
DIFFICULTY: moderate; PAGE: 12-13; OBJECTIVE: 6; TYPE: concept

72.   It's appropriate to follow-up a cross-culture conversation by writing a letter or a memo summarizing the conversation and thanking the person for meeting with you.

ANSWER: True. Such a strategy allows you to clarify what will happen next.
DIFFICULTY: moderate; PAGE: 13; OBJECTIVE: 6; TYPE: concept

73. _____Cultural diversity has little effect on how business messages are conceived, planned, sent, received, and interpreted in the workplace.

ANSWER: False. Cultural diversity has very important effects on how business messages are conceived, planned, sent, received, and interpreted in the workplace.
DIFFICULTY: moderate; PAGE: 13; OBJECTIVE: 6; TYPE: concept

74. _____To improve intercultural communication, it is important not to assume that others are very similar to you.

ANSWER: True. We tend to think everyone else is going to be like us; this results in miscommunication.
DIFFICULTY: moderate; PAGE: 13; OBJECTIVE: 6; TYPE: concept

Fill-in the Blank

75. The process of sending and receiving messages is called _____.

ANSWER: Communication
Difficulty: moderate; PAGE: 2; OBJECTIVE: 1; TYPE: concept

76. _____ is the last step in the communication process.

ANSWER: Feedback or the receiver sending feedback
DIFFICULTY: moderate; PAGE: 5; OBJECTIVE: 3; TYPE: concept

77. _____ refers to the accepted principles of conduct that govern a person or a group.

ANSWER: Ethics
DIFFICULTY: moderate; PAGE: 6; OBJECTIVE: 5; TYPE: concept

78. Stealing someone else's words or work and claiming it as your own is called _____.

ANSWER: Plagiarism
DIFFICULTY: moderate; PAGE: 6; OBJECTIVE: 5; TYPE: concept

79. Deliberately omitting damaging or unflattering comments to provide a better picture of your company is called _____ _____.

ANSWER: Selective Misquoting
DIFFICULTY: moderate; PAGE: 6; OBJECTIVE: 5; TYPE: concept

80. Unlike an ethical dilemma, an ethical _____ is making a clearly unethical or illegal choice.

ANSWER: Lapse
DIFFICULTY: moderate; PAGE: 6-7; OBJECTIVE: 5; TYPE: concept

81. One element of an audience-centered approach to communication is _____--the expected norms of behavior in a particular situation.

ANSWER: Etiquette
DIFFICULTY: moderate; PAGE: 7; OBJECTIVE: 4; TYPE: concept

82. Focusing on and caring about the receivers of your messages and making every effort to get your message across in a meaningful way is necessary to adopt a/an _____ approach.

ANSWER: Audience-Centered
DIFFICULTY: moderate; PAGE: 7; OBJECTIVE: 5; TYPE: concept

83. _____ _____ is the pattern of physical cues, environmental stimuli, and implicit understanding that conveys meaning between two members of the same culture.

ANSWER: Cultural Context
DIFFICULTY: moderate; PAGE: 9; OBJECTIVE: 6; TYPE: concept

84. South Korea and Taiwan are both considered _____-context cultures.

ANSWER: High
DIFFICULTY: moderate; PAGE: 9; OBJECTIVE: 6; TYPE: concept

85. In a/an _____-context culture, people rely less on verbal communication and more on the context of nonverbal actions and environmental setting to convey meaning.

ANSWER: High
DIFFICULTY: moderate; PAGE: 9-10; OBJECTIVE: 6; TYPE: concept

86. In a/an _____-context culture, people rely more on verbal communication and less on circumstances and cues to convey meaning.

ANSWER: Low
DIFFICULTY: moderate; PAGE: 9-10; OBJECTIVE: 6; TYPE: concept

87. Both the U.S. and Germany are considered _____-context cultures.

ANSWER: Low
DIFFICULTY: moderate; PAGE: 10; OBJECTIVE: 6; TYPE: concept

88. Because members of _____-context cultures value the written word, they consider written agreements binding.

ANSWER: Low
DIFFICULTY: moderate; PAGE: 10; OBJECTIVE: 6; TYPE: concept

89. Two major legal systems are the English _____ _____ and the _____ _____.

ANSWER: Common Law, Napoleonic Code
DIFFICULTY: difficult; PAGE 10; OBJECTIVE: 6; TYPE: concept

90. Rules that teach members of a culture how to behave in common social situations (such as table manners at meals) are considered _____ rules.

ANSWER: Formal
DIFFICULTY: moderate; PAGE: 10; OBJECTIVE: 6; TYPE: concept

91. Rules learned by watching how people behave and then imitating that behavior are termed _____ rules.

ANSWER: Informal
DIFFICULTY: moderate; PAGE: 10; OBJECTIVE: 6; TYPE: concept

92. _____ is the belief that one's own cultural background is superior to all others.

ANSWER: Ethnocentrism
DIFFICULTY: moderate; PAGE: 11; OBJECTIVE: 6; TYPE: concept

93. _____refers to a fear of strangers and foreigners.

ANSWER: Xenophobia
DIFFICULTY: moderate; PAGE: 11; OBJECTIVE: 6; TYPE: concept

94. Predicting individuals' behavior or character solely on the basis of their membership in a particular group or class is called _____.

ANSWER: Stereotyping
DIFFICULTY: moderate; PAGE: 11; OBJECTIVE: 6; TYPE: concept

95. Cultural _____ is the practice of accepting multiple cultures on their own terms.

ANSWER: Pluralism
DIFFICULTY: moderate; PAGE: 11; OBJECTIVE: 6; TYPE: concept

96. The workplace mixture of races, genders, ages, cultures, family structures, religions, and educational backgrounds is called cultural _____.

ANSWER: Diversity
DIFFICULTY: moderate; PAGE: 13; OBJECTIVE: 6; TYPE: concept

Short Answer/Essay

97. List four developments in the workplace that are intensifying the need to communicate effectively.

ANSWER: **First, there is the need to communicate amid advanced technology (such as instant messaging) that has revolutionized the way businesspeople communicate. Second, in today's workplace you must know how to find, evaluate, process, and share information effectively and efficiently. Third, businesspeople today must communicate globally and within culturally diverse workforces. Fourth, many successful companies today no longer limit decisions to a few managers at the top of a formal hierarchy. Instead, they rely on employees to work in teams.**
DIFFICULTY: difficult; PAGE: 3-4; OBJECTIVE: 2; TYPE: concept

98. List the six steps in the communication process.

ANSWER: **1) The sender has an idea. 2) The sender encodes the idea—decides on the message's form, length, organization, tone, and style. 3) The sender transmits the message— selects a communication channel and a medium depending on the audience's location, the need for speed and the formality required. 4) The receiver gets the message. 5) The receiver decodes the message—the receiver must understand the message and interpret it correctly. 6) The receiver sends feedback—responds in some way.**
DIFFICULTY: moderate; PAGE: 5; OBJECTIVE: 1; TYPE: concept

99. Briefly explain the difference between ethical communication and unethical communication.

ANSWER: **Ethical communication includes all relevant information, is true in every sense, and is not deceptive. It avoids plagiarism, misquoting, misrepresenting numbers, and distorting visuals. By contrast, unethical communication can include falsehoods and misleading information (or exclude important information).**
DIFFICULTY: moderate; PAGE: 6; OBJECTIVE: 1; TYPE: concept

100. Explain the difference between an "ethical dilemma" and an "ethical lapse."

ANSWER: **An ethical dilemma involves choosing between alternatives that aren't clear-cut. The right answer or action is not obvious. Two conflicting alternatives may lie somewhere in the gray area between right and wrong. An ethical lapse is making a clearly unethical or illegal choice.**

DIFFICULTY: moderate; PAGE: 6-7; OBJECTIVE: 5; TYPE: concept

101. List at least four questions to ask yourself in determining whether or not a message is ethical.

ANSWER: **1) Have you defined the situation fairly and accurately? 2) What is your intention in communicating this message? 3) What impact will this message have on the persons who receive it, or who might be affected by it? 4) Will the message achieve the greatest possible good while doing the least possible harm? 5) Will the assumptions you've made change over time? (Other questions listed in the chapter are also acceptable.)**
DIFFICULTY: difficult; PAGE: 7; OBJECTIVE: 5; TYPE: concept

102. Explain the difference between a "high-context" culture and a "low-context" culture. Be sure to give an example of each.

ANSWER: High-context cultures like South Korea or Japan reply less on verbal communication and more on the context of nonverbal actions and environmental setting to convey meaning. The rules of everyday life are rarely explicit. Instead, as individuals grow up, they learn how to recognize situational cues and how to respond as expected. In a low-context culture like Germany or the United States, people rely on verbal communication and less on circumstances and cues to convey meaning. Rules and expectations are spelled out through explicit statements.
DIFFICULTY: moderate; PAGE: 9-10; OBJECTIVE: 6; TYPE: concept

103. Briefly discuss the accommodations a speaker from a low-context culture might have to make to a speaker from a high-context culture. Give one example to illustrate your point.

ANSWER: Speakers from low-context cultures will have to pay more attention to nonverbal cues and to environmental factors when communicating with a person from a high-context culture. For example, they will have to realize that a high-context speaker will not come directly to the point. A Chinese speaker, for example, will expect the audience to discover the essence of a message and will use indirectness and metaphor to provide a web of meaning.
DIFFICULTY: moderate; PAGE: 9-10; OBJECTIVE: 6; TYPE: concept

104. Give at least four helpful tips for anyone needing to speak English to a person for whom English is not the native language.

ANSWER: Any four of these: 1) Use plain English. 2) Be clear. 3) Address international correspondence correctly. 4) Cite numbers carefully. 5) Avoid slang, idioms, jargon, and abbreviations. 6) Be brief. 7) Use short paragraphs. 8) Use transitional elements.
DIFFICULTY: moderate; PAGE: 11-12; OBJECTIVE: 6; TYPE: concept

105. Define "cultural diversity" and give examples to support your answer.

ANSWER: Cultural diversity includes all the elements that make people different from one another. This may include things like race, class, gender, ethnicity, language, family structure, religion, educational background, and more.
DIFFICULTY: moderate; PAGE: 13; OBJECTIVE: 6; TYPE: concept

CHAPTER 2
COMMUNICATING IN TEAMS AND MASTERING LISTENING AND NONVERBAL COMMUNICATION SKILLS

Multiple Choice

1.   Teams
      a.   are two or more people working together.
      b.   share a common goal.
      c.   are important in the workplace.
      d.   all of the above

ANSWER: d. These are all characteristics of a team.
DIFFICULTY: easy; PAGE: 28; OBJECTIVE: 1; TYPE: concept

2.   Identify the item listed below that is *not* an advantage of employees working in teams to help organizations succeed.
      a.   increased information and knowledge
      b.   increased groupthink among members
      c.   higher performance levels
      d.   increased diversity of views

ANSWER: b. Groupthink leads to poor decisions and ill-advised actions and can even induce people to act unethically.
DIFFICULTY: easy; PAGE: 29; OBJECTIVE: 1; TYPE: concept

3.   Teams can increase performance levels by
      a.   unleashing creativity and energy in workers who share a sense of purpose.
      b.   reducing boredom.
      c.   reducing tension between workers.
      d.   all of the above

ANSWER: d. All of these are ways that teamwork can increase performance.
DIFFICULTY: moderate; PAGE: 29; OBJECTIVE: 1; TYPE: concept

4.   Teams tend to be ineffective when there is/are
      a.   hidden agendas.
      b.   groupthink.
      c.   high coordination costs.
      d.   all of the above

ANSWER: d. All of these hinder team effectiveness.
DIFFICULTY: moderate; PAGE: 29; OBJECTIVE: 1; TYPE: concept

5. _____ occurs when individuals set aside their personal opinions in order to go along with everyone else.
   a. Free riding
   b. A hidden agenda
   c. Collaboration
   d. Groupthink

ANSWER: d. This is the definition of groupthink.
DIFFICULTY: easy; PAGE: 29; OBJECTIVE: 1; TYPE: concept

6. When a team member does not contribute his/her fair share to the group's activities, the team member is often called a/an
   a. non-participant.
   b. free rider.
   c. ineffective team player.
   d. person with a hidden agenda.

ANSWER: b. This is the definition of a free rider.
DIFFICULTY: easy; PAGE: 29; OBJECTIVE 1; TYPE: concept

7. When belonging to a team is more important to members than making the right decision, that team may develop what is termed
   a. diversity of views.
   b. increased performance levels.
   c. groupthink.
   d. effective team work.

ANSWER: c. When belonging to a team is more important to members than making the right decision, that team may develop what is termed "groupthink."
DIFFICULTY: moderate; PAGE: 29; OBJECTIVE: 1; TYPE: concept

8. Hidden agendas occur in teams when team members
   a. don't contribute their fair share.
   b. have private motives that affect the group's interaction.
   c. place greater value on belonging to a team than making right decisions.
   d. read one another's nonverbal messages.

ANSWER: b. Some team members can have private motives that affect the group's interaction.
DIFFICULTY: moderate; PAGE: 29; OBJECTIVE: 1; TYPE: concept

9. Effective teams do all of the following *except*:
   a. have a clear sense of purpose
   b. reach decisions by consensus
   c. think creatively
   d. all of the above

ANSWER: d. These are all characteristics of effective teams.
DIFFICULTY: moderate; PAGE: 29; OBJECTIVE: 1; TYPE: concept

10.	The key to productive meetings is careful planning of
	a.	purpose, participants, time, facilities, and agenda.
	b.	ethics, purpose, location, and agenda.
	c.	purpose, participants, location, and protocol.
	d.	ethics, purpose, rules of order, and location.

ANSWER: a. Only "a" offers the listing stated on pages 32-33.
DIFFICULTY: moderate; PAGE: 29; OBJECTIVE: 2; TYPE: concept

11.	The most common method for planning and running effective meetings is
	a.	the SEC Standard's of Ethics.
	b.	parliamentary procedure.
	c.	Robert's Rules of Order.
	d.	both b and c apply

ANSWER: d. Both "b" and "c" identify the valued method for planning and running effective meetings.
DIFFICULTY: moderate; PAGE: 31; OBJECTIVE: 3; TYPE: concept

12.	Organizational communication can be achieved most effectively through group meetings
	a.	Always.
	b.	when group dialogue stays between the team leader and individual.
	c.	when memos and individual conversations won't accomplish your goals.
	d.	only when an organization has expert communicators.

ANSWER: c. Often times, you can achieve your purpose most effectively with a phone call, a private conversation or through a memo.
DIFFICULTY: easy; PAGE: 32; OBJECTIVE: 1; TYPE: concept

13.	The two main types of meetings are
	a.	informational and decision-making.
	b.	problem and solution.
	c.	analytical and comprehensive.
	d.	focused and free-form.

ANSWER: a. Most meetings are either informational or decision-making.
DIFFICULTY: moderate; PAGE: 32; OBJECTIVE: 2; TYPE: concept

14.	When selecting participants for a team meeting, you should
	a.	include everyone who might possibly have any connection to the topic at hand.
	b.	include only the senior level workers on the project.
	c.	include only those people whose presence is essential.
	d.	include as many people as you can fit in the room where the meeting will be.

ANSWER: c. Only include those people who are essential to the project. You will waste anyone else's time.
DIFFICULTY: moderate; PAGE: 32; OBJECTIVE: 2; TYPE: application

15. Generally, morning meetings are more productive and should be used for
    a. meetings in which information is shared with others.
    b. those times when large groups of people must meet.
    c. customer meetings.
    d. work sessions.

ANSWER: d. For work sessions, morning meetings are more productive.
DIFFICULTY: moderate; PAGE: 32; OBJECTIVE: 2; TYPE: concept

16. The key to productive meetings is careful planning of
    a. purpose.
    b. participants.
    c. facilities and agenda.
    d. all of the above

ANSWER: d. The key to productive meetings is careful planning of purpose, participants, facilities and agenda.
DIFFICULTY: moderate; PAGE: 32-33; OBJECTIVE: 2; TYPE: concept

17. An effective agenda answers which of the following questions?
    a. What do we need to do in this meeting to accomplish our goals?
    b. What issues will be of greatest importance to all the participants?
    c. What needs do each of the participants have?
    d. both a and b

ANSWER: d. "A" and "B" are two of the three key questions an effective meeting agenda answers.
DIFFICULTY: difficult; PAGE: 33; OBJECTIVE: 2; TYPE: concept

18. Identify the one trait that does *not* characterize a responsible leader of a meeting.
    a. keeps the meeting on track
    b. paces the presentation and discussion
    c. encourages discussion from less vocal participants
    d. dominates the meeting

ANSWER: d. A responsible leader guides, mediates, probes, stimulates and summarizes, but most of all allows others to contribute ideas.
DIFFICULTY: easy; PAGE: 33-34; OBJECTIVE: 3; TYPE: concept

19. Parliamentary procedure is the same as
    a. the SEC Standard's of Ethics.
    b. Robert's Rules of Order.
    c. the Business Code of Order.
    d. Iacoca's Rules of Order.

ANSWER: b. Robert's Rules of Order constitute parliamentary procedure.
DIFFICULTY: moderate; PAGE: 34; OBJECTIVE: 3; TYPE: concept

20. Strictly following parliamentary procedure
    a. is especially important with larger groups.
    b. can help maintain order in a group.
    c. can protect individual rights.
    d. all of the above

ANSWER: d. These are all true of parliamentary procedure.
DIFFICULTY: moderate; PAGE: 34; OBJECTIVE: 3; TYPE: concept

21. As a leader, if one person is dominating the meeting and not letting others contribute, you should
    a. ask that person to leave the meeting.
    b. ignore the situation but not invite that person to the next meeting.
    c. politely point out that time is limited and that others need to be heard from too.
    d. all of the above

ANSWER: c. Politely let someone who is talking too much know that others need to have time to contribute too.
DIFFICULTY: moderate; PAGE: 34; OBJECTIVE: 3; TYPE: application

22. To close a meeting effectively you should
    a. summarize the group's conclusions.
    b. list the actions to be taken.
    c. review who has agreed to do what.
    d. all of the above

ANSWER: d. All of these steps will create an effective closing to a meeting.
DIFFICULTY: easy; PAGE: 34; OBJECTIVE: 3; TYPE: application

23. Minutes should be taken
    a. at every meeting.
    b. only at more formal meetings.
    c. only at smaller or more informal meetings.
    d. only when some members of the group cannot be present.

ANSWER: b. Minutes are needed for larger, more formal meetings.
DIFFICULTY: moderate; PAGE: 34; OBJECTIVE: 3; TYPE: concept

24. Using one's own values, beliefs, ideas, and expectations to assign meaning to sounds and words is called _____ in the listening process.
    a. receiving
    b. evaluating
    c. interpreting
    d. analyzing

ANSWER: c. Interpreting is assigning meaning to words.
DIFFICULTY: moderate; PAGE: 37; OBJECTIVE: 4; TYPE: concept

25. Most of us listen
    a. very effectively since it is such an easy skill.
    b. very ineffectively, remembering about half of what we hear.
    c. better when we are tired.
    d. better when the subject matter is complex.

ANSWER: b. Most of us remember only about half of what we hear and of that we forget another half within 48 hours.
DIFFICULTY: easy; PAGE: 37; OBJECTIVE: 4; TYPE: concept

26. All of the following are elements in the listening process *except*:
    a. interpreting
    b. remembering
    c. focusing
    d. evaluating

ANSWER: c. Focusing is not an element in the listening process.
DIFFICULTY: difficult; PAGE: 37-38; OBJECTIVE: 4; TYPE: concept

27. Which of the following is *not* a barrier to effective listening?
    a. self-centeredness
    b. focusing on the content of the message rather than the style of delivery
    c. prejudging and operating on assumptions
    d. listening selectively

ANSWER: b. Effective listeners overlook stylistic differences and focus on the speaker's message.
DIFFICULTY: easy; PAGE: 38; OBJECTIVE: 5; TYPE: concept

28. In selective listening, the listeners
    a. distort the message by tuning out anything that doesn't confirm their assumptions.
    b. tend to take control of the conversation.
    c. tune out until they hear something that gets their attention.
    d. all of the above

ANSWER: c. Selective listeners let their attention wander. They remember what they think the speaker said.
DIFFICULTY: moderate; PAGE: 38; OBJECTIVE: 5; TYPE: concept

29. Which of the following is *not* a trait of good listening?
    a. finding areas of interest in common with the speaker
    b. not interrupting the speaker
    c. listening to other sounds while someone is speaking
    d. paraphrasing the speaker's ideas at key pauses

ANSWER: c. Effective listeners block out competing distractions.
DIFFICULTY: easy; PAGE: 38; OBJECTIVE: 5; TYPE: application

30. Which listener tunes out dry subjects?
    a. the good listener
    b. the bad listener
    c. the reluctant listener
    d. the surface listener

ANSWER: b. The bad listener tunes out dry subjects.
DIFFICULTY: easy; PAGE: 38; OBJECTIVE: 5; TYPE: concept

31. Which listener takes careful notes?
    a. the good listener
    b. the bad listener
    c. the reluctant listener
    d. the surface listener

ANSWER: a. The good listener takes careful notes.
DIFFICULTY: easy; PAGE: 38; OBJECTIVE: 5; TYPE: concept

32. Which listener listens passively?
    a. the good listener
    b. the bad listener
    c. the reluctant listener
    d. the surface listener

ANSWER: b. The poor listener listens passively.
DIFFICULTY: moderate; PAGE: 38; OBJECTIVE: 5; TYPE: concept

33. Which listener adjusts his/her listening style to the situation?
    a. the good listener
    b. the bad listener
    c. the reluctant listener
    d. the surface listener

ANSWER: a. The good listener engages in content, critical, or empathic listening according to the situation.
DIFFICULTY: easy; PAGE: 38; OBJECTIVE: 5; TYPE: concept

34. Which listener listens actively?
    a. the good listener
    b. the bad listener
    c. the reluctant listener
    d. the surface listener

ANSWER: a. The good listener engages the speaker by listening actively.
DIFFICULTY: easy; PAGE: 38; OBJECTIVE: 5; TYPE: concept

35. Which listener resists giving nonverbal feedback to the speaker?
   a. the good listener
   b. the bad listener
   c. the reluctant listener
   d. the surface listener

ANSWER: b. The bad listener does not provide nonverbal feedback.
DIFFICULTY: moderate; PAGE: 38; OBJECTIVE: 5; TYPE: concept

36. Effective listeners will engage in all of the following *except*:
   a. making eye contact with the speaker
   b. giving the speaker nonverbal cues
   c. interrupting when they disagree
   d. looking for opportunities to learn

ANSWER: c. Table 2.1 lists actions of effective listeners.
DIFFICULTY: difficult; PAGE 38; OBJECTIVE: 5; TYPE: application.

37. Ineffective listeners will engage in all of the following activities, *except*:
   a. not taking notes
   b. allowing their mind to wander
   c. being judgmental and becoming distracted by stylistic differences
   d. making distinctions between main points and supporting details

ANSWER: d. See Table 2.1 for lists of actions of ineffective listeners.
DIFFICULTY: difficult; PAGE: 38; OBJECTIVE 5; TYPE: application

38. Listeners who engage in selective perception
   a. focus on the speaker's appearance.
   b. mold messages to fit what they already believe about the subject.
   c. let their attention wander.
   d. do all of the above

ANSWER: b. Selective perception involves molding a speaker's message to fit what the listener already believes about the subject.
DIFFICULTY: moderate; PAGE: 39; OBJECTIVE: 5; TYPE: concept

39. In part, poor listening is caused because
   a. people think faster than they speak.
   b. people are uninterested in the subject matter.
   c. people are unable to think originally.
   d. all of the above

ANSWER: a. People's minds tend to wander because they can think faster than they speak.
DIFFICULTY: moderate; PAGE: 39; OBJECTIVE: 5; TYPE: concept

40. Which of the following is *not* a form of nonverbal communication?
    a. education
    b. gesture and posture
    c. vocal characteristics
    d. touching behavior

ANSWER: a. All of these items but "a" are forms of nonverbal communication.
DIFFICULTY: easy; PAGE: 40-41; OBJECTIVE: 5; TYPE: concept

41. Which of the following is *not* an example of nonverbal communication?
    a. British listeners staring at the speaker and blinking their eyes to indicate understanding
    b. An American leaving a telephone voice message
    c. Germans tossing their head back to call someone to come closer
    d. A Greek nodding slightly upward to signal 'no'

ANSWER: b. A telephone message is an example of verbal communication.
DIFFICULTY: difficulty; PAGE: 40-41; OBJECTIVE 6; TYPE: application.

42. Identify the one item that is *not* a valid claim concerning touching behavior.
    a. conveys warmth, comfort, and reassurance
    b. accepted norms for touching behavior vary
    c. is governed by varying social customs
    d. all of the above

ANSWER: d. All of these statements are true of touching behavior.
DIFFICULTY: easy; PAGE: 41; OBJECTIVE: 5; TYPE: concept

43. Identify the one item that is *not* a method for improving your nonverbal communication.
    a. pay close attention to your vocal characteristics
    b. expect business professionals to share the same attitudes toward time
    c. maintain the eye contact your audience expects
    d. use touch only when appropriate

ANSWER: b. Be aware of varying attitudes toward time.
DIFFICULTY: easy; PAGE: 41; OBJECTIVE: 5; TYPE: concept

True/False

44. _____ Teams contribute to higher performance levels by giving employees a common purpose and boosting morale.

ANSWER: True. Team membership gives workers a common purpose and improves morale.
DIFFICULTY: easy; PAGE: 29; OBJECTIVE: 1; TYPE: concept

45. _____ While working in teams is productive for the individual, the group effort is less creative than an individual effort.

ANSWER: False. Working in teams can unleash vast amounts of creativity and energy in workers who share a sense of purpose and mutual accountability.
DIFFICULTY: moderate; PAGE: 29; OBJECTIVE: 1; TYPE: concept

46. _____ Groupthink leads team members to set aside their personal opinions and go along with everyone else, even if everyone else is wrong.

ANSWER: True. When belonging to a team is more important to members than making the right decision, that team may develop groupthink.
DIFFICULTY: easy; PAGE: 29; OBJECTIVE: 1; TYPE: concept

47. _____ A weak handshake reveals a great deal about one's personality.

ANSWER: True. It's important to adopt a handshake that matches your personality and intention.
DIFFICULTY: easy; PAGE: 30-31; OBJECTIVE: 7; TYPE: concept

48. _____ Small-group meetings are almost always productive.

ANSWER: False. Managers report that little more than half of their meetings are actually productive.
DIFFICULTY: moderate; PAGE: 32; OBJECTIVE: 1; TYPE: concept

49. _____ Some managers report that a little more than half of their meetings were actually productive and that a quarter of them could have been handled by a phone call or memo.

ANSWER: True. Some managers report that a little more than half of their meetings were actually productive and that a quarter of them could have been handled by a phone call or memo.
DIFFICULTY: easy; PAGE: 32; OBJECTIVE: 1; TYPE: concept

50. _____ You can always achieve the purpose of organizational communication most effectively through group meetings.

ANSWER: False. Sometimes memos and individual conversations achieve communication goals.
DIFFICULTY: easy; PAGE: 32; OBJECTIVE: 1; TYPE: concept

51. _____ Effective teams have a clear sense of purpose.

ANSWER: True. As well as having a clear sense of purpose, effective teams communicate openly and honestly, reach decisions by consensus, think creatively, remain focused, and resolve conflict effectively.
DIFFICULTY: moderate; PAGE: 32; OBJECTIVE: 1; TYPE: concept

52. _____ If a meeting is purely for informational purposes and one person will be doing most of the talking, you can include a relatively large group.

ANSWER: True. Problem solving meetings or those for the purpose of developing a plan or reaching a decision are best limited to six to twelve people.
DIFFICULTY: moderate; PAGE: 32; OBJECTIVE: 2; TYPE: concept

53. _____ For work sessions, afternoon and even night meetings are most productive.

ANSWER: False. For work sessions, morning meetings are usually more productive than afternoon sessions.
DIFFICULTY: easy; PAGE: 32; OBJECTIVE: 2; TYPE: concept

54. _____ In decision-making meetings participants persuade, analyze, and solve problems.

ANSWER: True. In decision-making meetings participants persuade, analyze, and solve problems.
DIFFICULTY: easy; PAGE: 32; OBJECTIVE: 3; TYPE: concept

55. _____ Even small, informal meetings can benefit from an agenda.

ANSWER: True. Even in small, informal meetings agendas help prepare participants.
DIFFICULTY: easy; PAGE: 33; OBJECTIVE: 1; TYPE: concept

56. _____ A well-written agenda shows respect for meeting participants and their time.

ANSWER: True. A clear agenda helps keep meetings on track and aids all participants.
DIFFICULTY: easy; PAGE: 33; OBJECTIVE: 2; TYPE: concept

57. _____ It's important to limit the time spent on each agenda item.

ANSWER: True. To cover all items on an agenda, it is important to limit the time spent on each.
DIFFICULTY: easy; PAGE: 33-34; OBJECTIVE: 3; TYPE: concept

58. _____ Parliamentary procedure can be effectively used in both large and small group meetings.

ANSWER: True. Used correctly, parliamentary procedure can serve participants in both small and large group meetings.
DIFFICULTY: easy; PAGE: 34; OBJECTIVE: 3; TYPE: concept

59. _____ Summarizing the conclusions of the discussion at the end of a meeting wastes valuable time.

ANSWER: False. Wrapping things up ensures that all participants agree on the outcome and gives people a chance to clear up any misunderstandings.
DIFFICULTY: easy; PAGE: 34; OBJECTIVE: 3; TYPE: concept

60. _____ It is appropriate for the leader of a meeting to ask shy individuals for their input on certain issues.

ANSWER: True. It is important for everyone to participate in most meetings.
DIFFICULTY: moderate; PAGE 34; OBJECTIVE 3; TYPE: concept

61. _____ It is important to have minutes of both formal and informal meetings.

ANSWER: False. Informal meetings usually do not require minutes.
DIFFICULTY: moderate; PAGE: 34; OBJECTIVE: 3; TYPE: concept

62. _____ Your ability to listen effectively is directly related to your success in meetings, conversations, phone calls, and other group relationships.

ANSWER: True. Your ability to listen effectively is directly related to your success.
DIFFICULTY: easy; PAGE: 37; OBJECTIVE: 4; TYPE: concept

63. _____ Effective listening requires the listener to separate fact from opinion and evaluate the quality of the evidence.

ANSWER: True. Effective listening requires applying critical thinking skills to weigh the speaker's remarks.
DIFFICULTY: easy; PAGE: 37; OBJECTIVE: 1; TYPE: concept

64. _____ Effective listening allows an organization to manage growing diversity both in the workforce and in the customers it serves.

ANSWER: True. Effective listening allows this benefit and strengthens organizational relationships, enhances product delivery, and alerts the organization to innovation from both internal and external sources.
DIFFICULTY: easy; PAGE: 37; OBJECTIVE: 5; TYPE: concept

65. _____ Prejudgment, interpreting, and selective listening are barriers to being a good listener.

ANSWER: False. Prejudgment, selective perception, and selective listening are barriers.
DIFFICULTY: difficulty; PAGE: 38-39; OBJECTIVE: 5; TYPE: concept

66. _____ People often speak much faster than they can think.

ANSWER: False. People can process information, or think, far faster than they can speak.
DIFFICULTY: easy; PAGE: 39; OBJECTIVE: 1; TYPE: concept

67. _____ Actions really do speak louder than words.

ANSWER: True. Nonverbal cues (gestures, etc.) can cancel the meaning of the words that accompany them.
DIFFICULTY: easy; PAGE: 39; OBJECTIVE: 7; TYPE: concept

68. _____ You can avoid giving others conflicting signals by paying attention to your nonverbal cues.

ANSWER: True. You can avoid giving others conflicting signals by paying attention to your nonverbal cues.
DIFFICULTY: easy; PAGE: 39; OBJECTIVE: 7; TYPE: concept

69. _____ Your tone and facial expressions shape the way others perceive you and your messages.

ANSWER: True. These non-verbal signals communicate important messages to your receivers.
DIFFICULTY: easy; PAGE: 40; OBJECTIVE: 6; TYPE: concept

70. _____ In Australia, the thumbs-up gesture indicates "great job" or "all is okay".

ANSWER: False. Thumbs-up in Australia is an obscene gesture.
DIFFICULTY: moderate; PAGE: 40; OJBECTIVE: 7; TYPE: application.

71. _____ In many cultures, it's important to maintain eye contact with your audience.

ANSWER: True. Eye contact is one of the most important nonverbal modes of communicating.
DIFFICULTY: easy; PAGE: 40; OBJECTIVE: 7; TYPE: concept

72. _____ Making other people wait is one way for you to assert your importance.

ANSWER: True. Touch, time, or space can be used to assert authority or importance.
DIFFICULTY: moderate; PAGE: 41; OBJECTIVE: 7; TYPE: application

Fill-in the Blank

73. A unit of two or more people who work together to achieve a goal is a/an _____.

ANSWER: Team
DIFFICULTY: easy; PAGE: 28; OBJECTIVE: 1; TYPE: concept

74. The willingness of individuals to set aside their personal opinions and go along with everyone else, even if everyone else is wrong, is termed _____.

ANSWER: Groupthink
DIFFICULTY: moderate; PAGE: 29; OBJECTIVE: 1; TYPE: concept

75. Individuals with private motives that affect a group's interaction are said to have _____ _____.

ANSWER: Hidden Agendas
DIFFICULTY: moderate; PAGE: 29; OBJECTIVE 1; TYPE: concept

76. Meetings in which participants persuade, analyze, and solve problems are called _____ meetings.

ANSWER: Decision-making
DIFFICULTY: moderate; PAGE: 32; OBJECTIVE: 1; TYPE: concept

77. A(n) _____ is an important tool for guiding the progress of a meeting.

ANSWER: Agenda
DIFFICULTY: moderate; PAGE: 33; OBJECTIVE: 3; TYPE: concept

78. The most common guide to parliamentary procedure is _____.

ANSWER: Robert's Rules of Order
DIFFICULTY: difficult; PAGE: 34; OBJECTIVE: 1; TYPE: concept

79. Members of a _____ team work in different locations and interact electronically, often through web-based meeting systems.

ANSWER: Virtual
DIFFICULTY: moderate; PAGE: 35; OBJECTIVE: 4; TYPE: concept

80. '_____' is the Hawaiian word for "quick," and refers to a website technology that allows team members to revise the content of a website as they get new ideas.

ANSWER: Wiki
DIFFICULTY: moderate; PAGE: 35; OBJECTIVE: 4; TYPE: concept

81. _____ is an umbrella term for systems that let people communicate, share files, present materials, and work on documents simultaneously.

ANSWER: Groupware
DIFFICULTY: moderate; PAGE: 36; OBJECTIVE: 4; TYPE: concept

82. One popular feature of shared workspaces is _____ _____, which allows only one person at a time to check out a given file or document and prevents ending up with two versions of the same file.

ANSWER: Revision control
DIFFICULTY: moderate; PAGE: 36; OBJECTIVE: 4; TYPE: concept

83. _____ _____ occurs when you let your mind wander and tune out what someone else is saying until you hear something that gets your attention.

ANSWER: Selective listening
DIFFICULTY: moderate; PAGE: 38; OBJECTIVE 5; TYPE: concept

84. Taking notes and not interrupting are actions of a person who is a(n) ____ _____.

ANSWER: Effective listener
DIFFICULTY: difficulty; PAGE: 38; OBJECTIVE: 5; TYPE: concept

85. The _____ listener takes careful notes and waits until an appropriate time to ask questions.

ANSWER: Good or effective
DIFFICULTY: moderate; PAGE: 38; OBJECTIVE: 5; TYPE: concept

86. The _____ listener makes little or no eye contact with the speaker.

ANSWER: Bad or poor
DIFFICULTY: moderate; PAGE: 38; OBJECTIVE: 5; TYPE: concept

87. _____ communication is the process of sending and receiving information without using written or spoken language.

ANSWER: Nonverbal
DIFFICULTY: easy; PAGE: 39; OBJECTIVE: 7; TYPE: concept

88. Cues, gestures, facial expressions, spatial relationships, and attitudes toward time are all elements of _____ communication.

ANSWER: Nonverbal
DIFFICULTY: moderate; PAGE: 39; OBJECTIVE: 7; TYPE: concept

89. Most people can deceive others much more easily with _____ than they can with their bodies.

ANSWER: Words or speech
DIFFICULTY: moderate; PAGE: 40-41; OBJECTIVE: 7; TYPE: concept

90. _____, _____, and _____ are three additional forms of nonverbal communication.

ANSWER: Facial expressions, gestures, posture, tone, attitude, personal appearance, touching behavior and use of time and space: any three of these forms of nonverbal communication will serve.
DIFFICULTY: moderate; PAGE: 40; OBJECTIVE: 7; TYPE: concept

91. _____, _____, and _____ are three forms of nonverbal communication.

ANSWER: Facial expressions, gestures, posture, tone, attitude, personal appearance, touching behavior and use of time and space: any three of these forms of nonverbal communication will serve.
DIFFICULTY: moderate; PAGE: 40-41; OBJECTIVE: 7; TYPE: concept

92. Your _____ is the primary site for nonverbally expressing your emotions.

ANSWER: Face
DIFFICULTY: moderate; PAGE: 41; OBJECTIVE: 7; TYPE: concept

93. _____ is an important way to convey warmth, comfort, and reassurance.

ANSWER: Touching
DIFFICULTY: moderate; PAGE: 41; OBJECTIVE: 7; TYPE: concept

Short Answer/Essay

94. Discuss at least two ways that teams help an organization succeed.

ANSWER: Any two of the following should be listed. 1) Increasing information and knowledge. 2) Increasing the diversity of views. 3) Increasing the acceptance of a solution. 4) Increasing performance levels.
DIFFICULTY: moderate; PAGE: 29; OBJECTIVE: 1; TYPE: concept

95. Outline the four elements necessary to plan a productive meeting.

ANSWER: 1) Decide on your purpose—informative or decision-making. 2) Select participants—involve only those whose presence is essential. 3) Choose an appropriate location—consider time, and seating arrangements. 4) Set and follow an agenda—distribute it ahead of time.
DIFFICULTY: moderate; PAGE: 32-33; OBJECTIVE: 2; TYPE: concept

96. List and briefly describe 3 important forms of meeting technologies in use today.

ANSWER: 1) Groupware is an umbrella term for systems that let people communicate, share files, present materials, and collaborate. 2) Shared workspaces are "virtual offices" that give everyone on a team access to the same set of resources and information. 3) Videoconferencing combines audio communication with live video, letting team members see each other, demonstrate products, and transmit other visual information.
DIFFICULTY: difficult; PAGE: 35-36; OBJECTIVE: 4; TYPE: concept

97. List and explain at least three phases of the listening process.

ANSWER: The listening process includes the following steps: 1) Receiving—hearing and taking note of the message. 2) Interpreting—assigning meaning to sounds; determining what the speaker really means. 3) Remembering—retaining what you hear. 4) Evaluating—applying critical thinking skills to weigh the speaker's remarks. 5) Responding—reacting to the speaker's message.
DIFFICULTY: difficult; PAGE: 37-38; OBJECTIVE: 4; TYPE: concept

98. List the three barriers to effective listening.

ANSWER: 1) Prejudgment—distorting messages by tuning out anything that doesn't confirm your assumptions. 2) Selective perception—molding a message to fit what you already believe about a particular subject. 3) Selective listening—letting your mind wander; tuning out until you hear something that gets your attention.
DIFFICULTY: difficult; PAGE: 38-39; OBJECTIVE: 5; TYPE: concept

99.   List four techniques to help store new information in long-term memory.

ANSWER: 1) Associate new information with something closely related to it. 2) Categorize the new information into logical groups. 3) Visualize words and ideas as pictures. 4) Create mnemonics such as acronyms or rhymes.
DIFFICULTY: moderate; PAGE: 39; OBJECTIVE: 5; TYPE: concept

100.   List four of the six categories of nonverbal communication.

ANSWER: The six categories include: facial expression; gesture and posture; vocal characteristics; personal appearance; touching behavior; use of time and space.
DIFFICULTY: difficult; PAGE: 40-41; OBJECTIVE: 5; TYPE: concept

CHAPTER 3
PLANNING BUSINESS MESSAGES

Multiple Choice

1. Which of the following correctly lists the three-step writing process?
    a. planning, writing, sending
    b. planning, writing, revising
    c. planning, writing, completing
    d. planning, writing, designing the page

ANSWER: c. "C" includes the other tasks in the word "completing," as noted in the text.
DIFFICULTY: moderate; PAGE: 53; OBJECTIVE: 1; TYPE: concept

2. The first stage of the writing process includes
    a. clarifying your purpose.
    b. analyzing audience members.
    c. gathering information.
    d. all of the above

ANSWER: d. These are all part of the planning stage of writing.
DIFFICULTY: moderate; PAGE: 53; OBJECTIVE: 1; TYPE: concept

3. The second stage of the writing process includes
    a. gathering information that will inform, persuade, or motivate your audience.
    b. organizing your ideas and composing the first draft.
    c. revising and rewriting until the message is clear and effective.
    d. adapting your message to the audience's needs.

ANSWER: b. The second stage of the writing process is organizing and writing the first draft.
DIFFICULTY: moderate; PAGE: 53; OBJECTIVE: 1; TYPE: concept

4. When do you step back to review the message to make sure it is clear, concise, and correct?
    a. planning
    b. writing
    c. completing
    d. revising

ANSWER: c. Only "c" notes the stage in which the tasks listed are undertaken.
DIFFICULTY: moderate; PAGE: 53; OBJECTIVE: 1; TYPE: application

5. The activities of revising, producing, and proofreading take place in the _____ stage of the message writing process.
    a. writing
    b. completing
    c. planning
    d. responding

ANSWER: b. These are the three activities of the completing stage.
DIFFICULTY: difficult; PAGE 53; OBJECTIVE: 1; TYPE: concept

6. The planning stage should take about
    a. 10% of the time you have to produce the message.
    b. 30% of the time you have to produce the message.
    c. 50% of the time you have to produce the message.
    d. 70% of the time you have to produce the message.

ANSWER: c. Devote about half of your time to planning the message.
DIFFICULTY: difficult; PAGE: 53; OBJECTIVE: 1; TYPE: application

7. The general purpose of a business message is to
    a. inform, persuade, and collaborate with your audience.
    b. inform, persuade, and sell your product to your audience.
    c. inform, persuade, and promote your professional reputation.
    d. inform, persuade, and eliminate the competition.

ANSWER: a. The general purpose of a business message is to inform, persuade, and collaborate with your audience.
DIFFICULTY: moderate; PAGE: 54; OBJECTIVE: 1; TYPE: concept

8. When deciding if your purpose is worth pursuing, ask yourself:
    a. Is the purpose realistic?
    b. What are audience attitudes toward the purpose?
    c. What likely response will it receive?
    d. all of the above

ANSWER: a. Considering if the purpose is realistic is an important step when analyzing your purpose. The other answers analyze audience.
DIFFICULTY: difficult; PAGE: 54; OBJECTIVE: 2; TYPE: application

9. As part of determining your purpose, you must also consider
    a. when to deliver your message.
    b. how your message will be delivered.
    c. where your message will be delivered.
    d. all of the above

ANSWER: a. The timing of your message can profoundly impact its effectiveness.
DIFFICULTY: difficult; PAGE: 54; OBJECTIVE: 2; TYPE: concept

10. Which of the following is *not* a general purpose common to business communication?
   a. to inform
   b. to persuade
   c. to negotiate
   d. to collaborate

ANSWER: c. The general purpose of a business message can be to inform, persuade, or collaborate. DIFFICULTY: moderate; PAGE: 54; OBJECTIVE: 2; TYPE: concept

11. An example of a specific purpose for a business message would be to
   a. impart information to the audience.
   b. inform employees about the new vacation policy.
   c. persuade readers to take an action.
   d. obtain audience participation and collaboration.

ANSWER: b. Other choices are examples of general purposes. DIFFICULTY: moderate; PAGE: 54; OBJECTIVE: 2; TYPE: application

12. An audience-centered message will consider the audience's
   a. needs.
   b. size.
   c. probable reaction.
   d. all of the above

ANSWER: d. These are all characteristics of an audience-centered message.
DIFFICULTY: easy; PAGE: 54-55; OBJECTIVE: 1; TYPE: concept

13. A good audience profile contains analysis of which of the following questions?
   a. Who are your audience members?
   b. What are their attitudes?
   c. What do they need to know?
   d. all of the above

ANSWER d. Each of these questions is listed as key to compiling an audience profile.
DIFFICULTY: moderate; PAGE: 55-56; OBJECTIVE: 3; TYPE: concept

14. All of the following questions are important in developing an audience profile *except*:
   a. What is your audience's level of understanding?
   b. Where is your audience located?
   c. How big is your audience?
   d. What is your audience's probable reaction?

ANSWER: b. In addition to a, c, and d, other questions include: Who is your primary audience? What is your audience's composition?
DIFFICULTY: difficult; PAGE: 55-56; OBJECTIVE 3; TYPE: concept

15. An effective audience analysis contains information about
    a. common interests that tie audience members together.
    b. education, status, or attitude.
    c. geographic distribution.
    d. all of the above

ANSWER: d. Each audience characteristic given is listed in the textbook.
DIFFICULTY: moderate; PAGE: 55-56; OBJECTIVE: 1; TYPE: concept

16. Good sources of information you might need for a particular memo or e-mail message might come from
    a. annual reports.
    b. financial statements.
    c. news releases.
    d. all of the above

ANSWER: d. Each item listed can be a solid source of information for the business communicator.
DIFFICULTY: moderate; PAGE: 56; OBJECTIVE: 1; TYPE: concept

17. When deciding what information to include in your message, be sure your information is
    a. complete.
    b. accurate.
    c. ethical.
    d. all of the above

ANSWER: d. All of these are important characteristics of the information you include in your message.
DIFFICULTY: easy; PAGE: 57; OBJECTIVE: 3; TYPE: concept

18. A message can be unethical if it
    a. misleads the audience.
    b. leaves some information out.
    c. provides inaccurate information.
    d. all of the above

ANSWER: d. All of these practices can lead to unethical messages.
DIFFICULTY: moderate; PAGE: 57; OBJECTIVE: 3; TYPE: concept

19. Which of the following formats is the most formal?
    a. E-mail
    b. memo
    c. phone
    d. all are equal in formality

ANSWER: b. Memos are more formal than e-mails or phone.
DIFFICULTY: moderate; PAGE: 57; OBJECTIVE: 4; TYPE: concept

20. When you need immediate feedback, which of these channels is most effective?
   a. written media
   b. oral media
   c. electronic forms
   d. presentations

ANSWER: b. Use oral media when you want immediate feedback.
DIFFICULTY: easy; PAGE: 57; OBJECTIVE: 4; TYPE: application

21. Written media include which of the following?
   a. e-mail
   b. letters, memos, and reports
   c. teleconferencing
   d. all of the above

ANSWER: b. E-mail and teleconferencing are electronic media.
DIFFICULTY: easy; PAGE: 57-59; OBJECTIVE: 4; TYPE: concept

22. Oral media include all of the following *except*:
   a. speeches
   b. presentations
   c. informal scribbled notes
   d. face-to-face conversations

ANSWER: c. Notes are a written medium.
DIFFICULTY: moderate; PAGE: 57-58; OBJECTIVE 4; TYPE: concept

23. The main advantage of written media is that they
   a. let you plan and control the message.
   b. are more confidential.
   c. allow for immediate feedback.
   d. all of the above

ANSWER: a. Written channels allow you more control when planning and writing your message.
DIFFICULTY: moderate; PAGE: 58; OBJECTIVE: 4; TYPE: concept

24. When you need no immediate feedback, which of these channels is most effective?
   a. written media
   b. oral media
   c. electronic forms
   d. presentations

ANSWER: a. Use written media when you need no immediate feedback.
DIFFICULTY: easy; PAGE: 58; OBJECTIVE: 4; TYPE: concept

25. When you need a permanent, verifiable record, which of these media is the most effective?
   a. written media
   b. oral media
   c. electronic media
   d. presentations

ANSWER: a. Use written media when you need a permanent, verifiable record.
DIFFICULTY: easy; PAGE: 58; OBJECTIVE: 4; TYPE: application

26. When you want to minimize the distortion that can occur when messages pass orally from person to person, which of these media is the most effective?
   a. written media
   b. oral media
   c. electronic media
   d. presentations

ANSWER: a. Use written media when you want to minimize the distortion that can occur when messages pass orally from person to person.
DIFFICULTY: easy; PAGE: 58; OBJECTIVE: 4; TYPE: application

27. When you must reach a dispersed audience personally, which of these media is most effective?
   a. written media
   b. oral media
   c. electronic media
   d. either 'a' or 'c'

ANSWER: d. Use electronic or written media when you must reach a dispersed audience personally.
DIFFICULTY: moderate; PAGE: 58-59; OBJECTIVE: 4; TYPE: application

28. One of the drawbacks of using e-mail is
   a. its high cost.
   b. its slow speed.
   c. its lack of privacy.
   d. all of the above

ANSWER: c. Like other electronic media, e-mail often lacks privacy. DIFFICULTY: easy;
PAGE: 59; OBJECTIVE: 5; TYPE: concept

29. Which of the following is *not* a disadvantage of electronic media?
   a. high cost
   b. potential for inadvertently creating tension and conflict
   c. tendency for employees to overuse them
   d. all of the above

ANSWER: a. This is not a disadvantage of electronic media. DIFFICULTY: moderate;
PAGE: 59; OBJECTIVE: 5; TYPE: concept

30. When your message is detailed, complex, and requires careful planning, which of these channels is most effective?
   a. written media
   b. oral media
   c. electronic forms
   d. presentations

ANSWER: a. Use written media when your message is detailed, complex, and requires careful planning.
DIFFICULTY: easy; PAGE: 60; OBJECTIVE: 4; TYPE: application

31. When your message is relatively straightforward and easy to accept, which of these channels is most effective?
   a. written media
   b. oral media
   c. electronic forms
   d. presentations

ANSWER: b. Use oral media when your message is relatively simple and easy to accept.
DIFFICULTY: easy; PAGE: 60; OBJECTIVE: 4; TYPE: application

32. When you want to encourage interaction to solve a problem or reach a group decision, which of these media is the most effective?
   a. written media
   b. oral media
   c. electronic media
   d. teleconferencing

ANSWER: b. Use oral media when you want to encourage interaction to solve a problem or reach a group decision.
DIFFICULTY: easy; PAGE: 60; OBJECTIVE: 4; TYPE: application

33. When your message has limited emotional component, which of these media is the most effective?
   a. written media
   b. oral media
   c. electronic media
   d. presentations

ANSWER: a. Use written media when your message has no emotional component.
DIFFICULTY: moderate; PAGE: 60; OBJECTIVE: 4; TYPE: application

34. When you want to read the audience's body language or hear the tone of their response, which of these media is most effective?
    a. written media
    b. oral media
    c. electronic media
    d. teleconferencing

ANSWER: b. Use oral media when you want to encourage interaction to solve a problem or reach a group decision.
DIFFICULTY: easy; PAGE: 60; OBJECTIVE: 4; TYPE: application

35. When you want to give the audience an opportunity to edit the message, which of these media is most effective?
    a. written media
    b. oral media
    c. electronic media
    d. presentations

ANSWER: c. Use electronic media when you want the audience to edit your message.
DIFFICULTY: easy; PAGE: 60; OBJECTIVE: 4; TYPE: application

36. When your message has an emotional component, which of these media is the most effective?
    a. written media
    b. oral media
    c. electronic media
    d. presentations

ANSWER: b. Use oral media when your message has an emotional component.
DIFFICULTY: easy; PAGE: 60; OBJECTIVE: 4; TYPE: application

37. Leaner media are best used for messages that
    a. are routine.
    b. are highly emotional.
    c. are nonroutine.
    d. require feedback.

ANSWER: a. The other options describe messages that require richer media.
DIFFICULTY: moderate; PAGE: 60; OBJECTIVE: 5; TYPE: concept

38. Media richness depends on
    e. the cost of using a specific medium.
    f. a medium's ability to facilitate feedback.
    a. how well a medium repeats the main idea.
    b. none of the above

ANSWER: b. This is one of several aspects of media richness. DIFFICULTY: moderate;
PAGE: 60; OBJECTIVE: 5; TYPE: concept

39. The richest communication medium is
     a. a phone call.
     b. a memo.
     c. an e-mail.
     d. a face-to-face conversation.

ANSWER: d. A face-to-face conversation allows for immediate feedback and is the richest of all media. DIFFICULTY: moderate; PAGE: 60; OBJECTIVE: 5; TYPE: concept

40. Which of the following are important to consider when choosing a communication medium?
     a. message formality
     b. media richness
     c. urgency and cost
     d. all of the above

ANSWER: d. All of these factors are important. DIFFICULTY: moderate; PAGE: 60-61; OBJECTIVE: 5; TYPE: concept

41. In high-context cultures, _____ media are often more effective than _____ ones.
     a. leaner, richer
     b. oral, written
     c. foreign, domestic
     d. none of the above

ANSWER: b. High-context cultures rely heavily on nonverbal communication.
DIFFICULTY: moderate; PAGE: 61; OBJECTIVE: 5; TYPE: concept

42. You can improve the organization of your message by
     a. repeating important points throughout your message.
     b. leaving out information your audience may not like.
     c. limiting its scope.
     d. putting a positive 'spin' on negative information.

ANSWER: c. Limiting the scope of a message improves its organization and increases its overall effectiveness. DIFFICULTY: moderate; PAGE: 61; OBJECTIVE: 6; TYPE: concept

43. The fact that the Japanese prefer oral communications is an example of:
     a. audience perception
     b. time availability
     c. need for audience feedback
     d. audience expectation

ANSWER: d. Audience expectation refers to the type of media the audience expects or prefers.
DIFFICULTY: difficult; PAGE: 61; OBJECTIVE: 4; TYPE: application

44. When it comes to business messages, good organization
    a. means the same thing regardless of culture.
    b. is less important than it is in academic writing.
    c. is defined differently, depending on the culture.
    d. is only important in upward-traveling messages.

ANSWER: c. Good organization can mean different things in high- and low-context cultures. DIFFICULTY: moderate; PAGE: 61; OBJECTIVE: 3; TYPE: concept

45. Whatever the length of your message, you should limit the number of major support points to roughly
    a. two
    b. three
    c. six
    d. ten

ANSWER: c. Messages that contain more than six major points are difficult for audiences to understand and remember. DIFFICULTY: moderate; OBJECTIVE: 2; PAGE: 63; TYPE: concept

46. Brainstorming
    a. is useful in the completing stage of writing messages.
    b. wastes valuable time.
    c. is not helpful when several people are collaborating on a message.
    d. none of the above

ANSWER: d. Brainstorming is useful for generating ideas, and can be helpful when writing collaboratively or on your own. DIFFICULTY: moderate; PAGE: 63; OBJECTIVE: 4; TYPE: concept

47. The direct approach is best when
    a. your audience is likely to be receptive to your message.
    b. your audience is likely to react negatively to your message.
    c. you do not know your audience well.
    d. your message is highly emotional.

ANSWER: a. The direct approach works well for routine, positive, and noncontroversial messages. DIFFICULTY: moderate; PAGE: 63-64; OBJECTIVE: 6; TYPE: concept

True/False

48. _____ Writing is a two-step process.

ANSWER: False. Writing is a three-step process.
DIFFICULTY: easy; PAGE: 52-53; OBJECTIVE: 1; TYPE: concept

49.   _____ Clarifying the purpose of your message, gathering necessary information, and tailoring your message to the needs and expectations of your audience takes place in the "writing" stage of the writing process.

ANSWER: False. These activities take place in the planning stage.
DIFFICULTY: moderate; PAGE: 53; OBJECTIVE: 1; TYPE: concept

50.   _____ The second stage of the writing process is organizing and writing the first draft.

ANSWER: True. The second stage of the writing process is organizing and writing the first draft.
DIFFICULTY: easy; PAGE: 53; OBJECTIVE: 1; TYPE: concept

51.   _____ Gathering information through formal or informal methods is usually done in the writing stage.

ANSWER: False. Gathering information is done in the planning stage.
DIFFICULTY: difficult; PAGE 53; OBJECTIVE 1; TYPE: concept

52.   _____ You should spend about half of your time actually writing the document in the writing process.

ANSWER: False. Spend less than one-quarter of your time writing.
DIFFICULTY: moderate; PAGE: 53-54; OBJECTIVE 1; TYPE: concept

53.   _____ The general purpose of a business message is to inform, persuade, and collaborate with your audience.

ANSWER: True. The general purpose of a business message is to inform, persuade, and collaborate with your audience.
DIFFICULTY: easy; PAGE: 54; OBJECTIVE: 2; TYPE: concept

54.   _____ In any business message, you should do your best to fulfill your audience's expectations and preferences.

ANSWER: True. Do your best to project your audience's expectations and preferences.
DIFFICULTY: moderate; PAGE: 55; OBJECTIVE: 5; TYPE: concept

55.   _____ If you expect an unfavorable response to your message, it is quite effective to state your conclusions and recommendations up front.

ANSWER: False. If you expect an unfavorable response to your message, introduce conclusions gradually, with sufficient support evidence and proof for your claims.
DIFFICULTY: difficult; PAGE: 55; OBJECTIVE: 5; TYPE: concept

56.   _____ Planning complex messages often requires you to conduct formal research to locate and analyze all the information you need for your purpose and audience.

ANSWER: True. Formal reports often require you to conduct formal research to locate and analyze all the information you need for your purpose and audience.
DIFFICULTY: moderate; PAGE: 56; OBJECTIVE: 3; TYPE: concept

57.   Company documents may be a good source for the information you need for a particular memo or e-mail message.

ANSWER: True. Company documents may be a good source for the information you need for a particular memo or e-mail message.
DIFFICULTY: moderate; PAGE: 56; OBJECTIVE: 3; TYPE: concept

58.   _____ Talking with supervisors, colleagues, or customers will customarily give you distorted and questionable information.

ANSWER: False. Chatting with supervisors, colleagues, or customers can help you gather information.
DIFFICULTY: moderate; PAGE: 56; OBJECTIVE: 3; TYPE: concept

59.   _____ It is not a good strategy to use the journalistic approach of seeing if your message answers *who, what, when, where, why,* and *how.*

ANSWER: False. The journalistic approach is one good way to test the thoroughness of your messages.
DIFFICULTY: moderate; PAGE: 56-57; OBJECTIVE: 5; TYPE: concept

60.   _____ Messages can be unethical simply because information is omitted.

ANSWER: True. You must include enough detail to avoid misleading your audience.
DIFFICULTY: easy; PAGE: 57; OBJECTIVE: 5; TYPE: concept

61.   _____ A letter or a memo is more formal than an e-mail message.

ANSWER: True. You can emphasize the formality of a message by using a more formal medium than an e-mail message, such as a letter or a memo.
DIFFICULTY: easy; PAGE: 57; OBJECTIVE: 4; TYPE: concept

62.   _____ Saving documents in PDF format makes them more vulnerable to viruses than word processor files.

ANSWER: False. PDFs are more secure and less vulnerable to viruses.
DIFFICULTY: moderate; PAGE: 58; OBJECTIVE: 5; TYPE: application

63.   _____ The main advantage of written communication is that the writer has an opportunity to plan and control the message.

ANSWER: True. Written media give you more control over messages than oral media.
DIFFICULTY: moderate; PAGE: 58; OBJECTIVE: 5; TYPE: concept

64.   _____ 'RSS' stands for Really Simple Syndication.

ANSWER: True. This is a useful tool for automatically delivering updated blog content.
DIFFICULTY: moderate; PAGE: 59; OBJECTIVE: 5; TYPE: concept

65. _____ The biggest drawback to e-mail is that it is underutilized.

ANSWER: False. E-mail (like other electronic media) is often overused.
DIFFICULTY: moderate; PAGE: 59; OBJECTIVE: 5; TYPE: concept

66. _____ One advantage of e-mail is its high level of privacy.

ANSWER: False. E-mail and other electronic media often lack privacy.
DIFFICULTY: moderate; PAGE: 59; OBJECTIVE: 5; TYPE: concept

67. _____ An important advantage of electronic media is the privacy they provide.

ANSWER: False. Electronic media often lack privacy.
DIFFICULTY: easy; PAGE: 59; OBJECTIVE: 4; TYPE: concept

68. _____ The richest form of feedback is the face-to-face conversation.

ANSWER: True. The richest form of feedback is the face-to-face conversation.
DIFFICULTY: moderate; PAGE: 60; OBJECTIVE: 5; TYPE: concept

69. _____ Media richness refers to the relative costs of advertising in the various mass media.

ANSWER: False. Media richness is a medium's ability to convey a message through more than one informational cue, to facilitate feedback, and establish personal focus.
DIFFICULTY: moderate; PAGE: 60; OBJECTIVE: 5; TYPE: concept

70. _____ You can expect your audience to adapt to any medium that fits your purpose.

ANSWER: False. You need to select a medium that balances your needs and your audience's needs and expectations.
DIFFICULTY: moderate; PAGE: 60-61; OBJECTIVE: 4; TYPE: concept

71. If a message is urgent, a blog or podcast would not be an appropriate medium to use.

ANSWER: False. These newer media options make it easy to deliver messages quickly at low cost.
DIFFICULTY: moderate; PAGE: 61; OBJECTIVE 4; TYPE: application

72. _____ People in the US and Germany prefer oral messages rather than written ones.

ANSWER: False. People in the US and Germany prefer written messages rather than oral ones.
DIFFICULTY: difficult; PAGE: 61; OBJECTIVE: 4; TYPE: concept

73. _____ Culture influences media preferences.

ANSWER: True. Culture influences media preferences.
DIFFICULTY: moderate; PAGE: 61; OBJECTIVE: 4; TYPE: concept

74. _____ People in Japan prefer oral messages.

ANSWER: True. People in Japan prefer oral messages.
DIFFICULTY: difficult; PAGE: 61; OBJECTIVE: 4; TYPE: concept

75. _____ In the United States and Canada, good organization generally means creating a linear message that proceeds point by point.

ANSWER: True. This is true of most low-context cultures.
DIFFICULTY: moderate; PAGE: 61; OBJECTIVE: 7; TYPE: application

76. _____ The urgency of your message should help you decide what medium to use.

ANSWER: True. This is one of several factors to consider in choosing a medium for your message.
DIFFICULTY: moderate; PAGE: 61; OBJECTIVE: 5; TYPE: concept

Fill-in the Blank

77. Clarifying the purpose of your message, gathering necessary information, and tailoring your message to the needs and expectations of your audience takes place in the _____ stage of the writing process.

ANSWER: Planning
DIFFICULTY: moderate; PAGE: 53; OBJECTIVE: 1; TYPE: concept

78. The reason for writing a message is its _____.

ANSWER: Purpose
DIFFICULTY: moderate; PAGE: 54; OBJECTIVE: 1; TYPE: concept

79. You must tailor your message to the needs and expectations of your _____.

ANSWER: Audience
DIFFICULTY: easy; PAGE: 54; OBJECTIVE: 1; TYPE: concept

80. To help you define the _____ purpose of your message, ask yourself what you hope to accomplish with your message and what your audience should do or think after receiving your message.

ANSWER: Specific
DIFFICULTY: difficult; PAGE: 54; OBJECTIVE: 1; TYPE: concept

81. Before writing any message, it is helpful to develop a profile of your _____.

ANSWER: Audience
DIFFICULTY: moderate; PAGE: 54; OBJECTIVE: 1; TYPE: concept

82. _____ media include face-to-face conversation, telephone calls, speeches, presentations, and meetings.

ANSWER: Oral
DIFFICULTY: moderate; PAGE: 57; OBJECTIVE: 1; TYPE: concept

83. _____ media range from notes to formal reports, letters, and memos.

ANSWER: Written
DIFFICULTY: easy; PAGE: 57; OBJECTIVE: 4; TYPE: concept

84. 'PDF' stands for _____.

ANSWER: Portable Document Format.
DIFFICULTY: moderate; PAGE: 58; OBJECTIVE: 5; TYPE: concept

85. Faxes have been replaced by e-mail and _____ files (which are less vulnerable to viruses than word processor files).

ANSWER: PDF
DIFFICULTY: moderate; PAGE: 58; OBJECTIVE: 3; TYPE: concept

86. _____ media include voice mail, DVD, e-mail, websites, and instant messaging.

ANSWER: Electronic
DIFFICULTY: moderate: PAGE: 58-59; OBJECTIVE 4; TYPE: concept

87. When you need speed and are physically separated from your audience, you should select a(n) ____ medium.

ANSWER: Electronic
DIFFICULTY: moderate; PAGE 59; OBJECTIVE 4; TYPE: concept

88. The richest communication medium is _____.

ANSWER: Face-to-face conversation
DIFFICULTY: moderate; PAGE: 60; OBJECTIVE: 4; TYPE: concept

89. Media _____ depends in part on the medium's ability to facilitate feedback.

ANSWER: Richness
DIFFICULTY: moderate; PAGE: 60; OBJECTIVE: 5; TYPE: concept

90. The _____ _____ of your message is a specific statement about its more general topic.

ANSWER: Main idea
DIFFICULTY: moderate; PAGE: 61; OBJECTIVE: 7; TYPE: concept

91. In addition to brainstorming, another method for generating ideas is the _____ approach, which asks *who, what, when, where, why,* and *how.*

ANSWER: Journalistic
DIFFICULTY: moderate; PAGE: 63; OBJECTIVE: 5; TYPE: concept

92. The _____ of your message is the range of information you present, the overall length, and the level of detail in your message.

ANSWER: Scope
DIFFICULTY: moderate; PAGE: 63; OBJECTIVE: 7; TYPE: concept

Short Answer/Essay

93. Describe the three-step writing process.

ANSWER: The three-step writing process includes planning, writing, and completing the business message. Planning includes clarifying the purpose, analyzing the audience, and adapting your message. Writing the message includes organizing your ideas and composing your first draft. Completing the business message involves reviewing the content and organization for overall style, structure, and readability.
DIFFICULTY: moderate; PAGE: 52-53; OBJECTIVE: 1; TYPE: concept

94. Briefly explain the activities involved in the planning step of the writing process.

ANSWER: The planning step involves analyzing the situation, gathering information, selecting the right medium for the message, and organizing the information.
DIFFICULTY: moderate; PAGE: 53; OBJECTIVE: 1; TYPE: concept

95. Briefly explain the activities involved in the writing step of the writing process.

ANSWER: In the writing step, you adapt to your audience with sensitivity, relationship skills, and style, and then you compose your message by choosing strong words, creating effective sentences, and developing coherent paragraphs.
DIFFICULTY: moderate; PAGE: 53; OBJECTIVE: 1; TYPE: concept

96. Describe the activities involved in the final step of the writing process.

ANSWER: In the completing step, you revise your message, produce the message, proofread it to eliminate typos, spelling errors and other mechanical problems, and then you distribute the message using a combination of personal and technological tools.
DIFFICULTY: moderate; PAGE: 53; OBJECTIVE: 1; TYPE: concept

97. List four questions that can help you test the purpose of your message.

ANSWER: 1) Will anything change as a result of my message? 2) Is my purpose realistic? 3) Is this the right time? 4) Is my purpose acceptable to the organization?
DIFFICULTY: difficult; PAGE: 54; OBJECTIVE: 2; TYPE: concept

98.   Discuss two ways to satisfy your audience's information needs.

ANSWER: In many situations your audience's information needs are readily apparent, but sometimes your audience might be unable to articulate exactly what is needed. If you are responding to a broad request, ask questions to narrow the focus. Also, try to think of information needs that your audience may not even be aware of. In some cases, you may be able to tell your audience something they consider important but wouldn't have thought to ask.
DIFFICULTY: difficult; PAGE: 56; OBJECTIVE: 3; TYPE: concept

99.   Briefly describe at least four factors to consider in choosing a medium for your message.

ANSWER: In considering which medium to use for your message, it is important to consider: 1) Media richness—the medium's ability to utilize more than one informational cue, facilitate feedback, and establish personal focus; 2) Message formality, including your audience's expectations for style and tone; 3) Media limitations; 4) Sender intentions—your choice of medium will influence how the audience perceives your intentions; 5) Audience preferences, paying close attention to any cultural variations; and 6) Urgency and cost.
DIFFICULTY: difficult; PAGE: 60-61; OBJECTIVE: 5; TYPE: concept

100.   List three ways that effective organization can help your audience.

ANSWER: Good organization aids your audience in a variety of ways, including 1) helping them to understand your message, 2) helping them to accept your message, and 3) saving them time.
DIFFICULTY: moderate; PAGE: 61; OBJECTIVE: 6; TYPE: concept

CHAPTER 4
WRITING BUSINESS MESSAGES

Multiple Choice

1. Select the sentence with the best "you" attitude.
    a. Your letter claims that you sent your check last week, but we have not received it.
    b. Once we receive your check for $190.98, your order will be shipped within three working days.
    c. You cannot receive your order until you send us a check for $190.98.
    d. You continue to owe us $190.98. When we receive that check, we will ship your order within three working days.

ANSWER: b. Only "b" gives the necessary information in a positive "you" attitude.
DIFFICULTY: difficult; PAGE: 77; OBJECTIVE: 2; TYPE: application

2. A "you" attitude
    a. emphasizes an audience-centered approach.
    b. focuses on your audience's wishes, interests, and preferences.
    c. replaces terms that refer to your company with terms that refer to your audience.
    d. all of the above

ANSWER: d. All of these are characteristics of a "you" attitude.
DIFFICULTY: moderate; PAGE: 77-78; OBJECTIVE: 2; TYPE: application

3. Select the sentence with the best "you" attitude.
    a. Because your report was poorly written, we cannot accept it.
    b. Your report failed to meet company requirements.
    c. When we receive a report that is professional, we can act on your recommendations.
    d. Once the report includes the necessary estimates, we can proceed with the project.

ANSWER: d. Only "d" gives specific information in a way that avoids blame and personal accusations.
DIFFICULTY: difficult; PAGE: 77-78; OBJECTIVE: 2; TYPE: application

4. Select the sentence with the best "you" attitude.
    a. Crepe's credit policy requires each holder to have steady employment for at least 18 months.
    b. Your credit rating is too poor for you to receive a Crepe's Gold card.
    c. You are not eligible for a Crepe's Gold card because you have not been at your present job for 18 months.
    d. We cannot allow your credit request.

ANSWER: a. Only "a" presents the specific information the reader needs in a non-judgmental manner.
DIFFICULTY: difficult; PAGE: 77-78; OBJECTIVE: 2; TYPE: application

5. Select the sentence with the best "you" attitude.
   a. You must get approval from the research committee before you can proceed with any test trials on human subjects.
   b. Your test trial procedures must get approval from the research committee before you can conduct them.
   c. Any research based on test trials with human subjects must be approved by the research committee.
   d. Do not proceed with research that involves test trials on human subjects until the research committee has approved your procedures.

ANSWER: c. In this instance, "you" attitude is best achieved by taking a neutral approach that does not target the reader.
DIFFICULTY: difficult; PAGE: 77-78; OBJECTIVE: 2; TYPE: application

6. In general written communication requires
   a. about the same amount of tact as oral communication.
   b. less tact than oral communication.
   c. more tact than oral communication.
   d. none of the above

ANSWER: c. Written communication cannot be softened by your tone of voice and facial expression. Therefore, it needs more tact than oral communication.
DIFFICULTY: moderate; PAGE: 78; OBJECTIVE: 2; TYPE: concept

7. Select the sentence with the best positive emphasis.
   a. We failed to complete the process audit on time.
   b. We will complete the process audit by Friday.
   c. We haven't completed the process audit.
   d. Because of Joan's inaccurate figures on the Haymen project, we are not finished with the process audit.

ANSWER: b. Only "b" avoids unnecessary negatives and gives specific information on a completion date.
DIFFICULTY: moderate; PAGE: 78-80; OBJECTIVE: 2; TYPE: application

8. Select the sentence with the best "you" attitude and positive emphasis.
   a. Crepe's will refund the purchase price of items returned within 30 days of purchase and in new condition.
   b. Because you have worn the shoes, we cannot refund your money.
   c. You returned the shoes six days after our return limit, and you had worn them.
   d. We make no refunds to customers who ignore our store policy on returns.

ANSWER: a. Only "a" accommodates the customer and avoids unnecessary negatives.
DIFFICULTY: moderate; PAGE: 78-80; OBJECTIVE: 2; TYPE: application

9. All of the following are types of biased language, *except*:
    a. gender bias
    b. racial and ethnic bias
    c. age bias
    d. social bias

ANSWER: d. Social bias is not a type of biased language.
DIFFICULTY: moderate; PAGE: 80-81; OBJECTIVE: 3; TYPE: concept

10. Select the sentence that is bias-free.
    a. All salesmen and their wives are invited to the reception.
    b. All sales representatives and their spouses are invited to the reception.
    c. All salesmen and their spouses are invited to the reception.
    d. All sales representatives and their guests are invited to the reception.

ANSWER: d. Only "d" avoids gender and marital status assumptions.
DIFFICULTY: moderate; PAGE: 80-81; OBJECTIVE: 3; TYPE: application

11. Select the sentence that is bias-free.
    a. Despite Ms. Curtis's disability, she does a good job.
    b. Ms. Curtis's disability does not prevent her from doing a good job.
    c. For a disabled person, Ms. Curtis does a good job.
    d. Ms. Curtis's employee evaluations rank among the top five in the company.

ANSWER: d. Only "d" avoids unnecessary reference to an employee's disability.
DIFFICULTY: moderate; PAGE: 81; OBJECTIVE: 3; TYPE: application

12. Using the term *chairperson* for women and *chairman* for men is an example of:
    a. racial bias
    b. ethnic bias
    c. sexual bias
    d. gender bias

ANSWER: d. Use the same label for everyone.
DIFFICULTY: moderate: PAGE 81; OBJECTIVE 3; TYPE: application

13. All of the following are ways to improve your credibility, *except*:
    a. showing that you can look at all sides of an issue
    b. showing an understanding of the audience's situation
    c. analyzing your audience's likely response
    d. explaining your credentials

ANSWER: c. Analyzing your audience's likely response is part of planning your message; it doesn't necessarily improve your credibility.
DIFFICULTY: difficult; PAGE: 82; OBJECTIVE: 3; TYPE: application

14. Select the sentence that expresses the most confidence and professionalism.
    a. We hope you are happy with your new Nature's End camping gear.
    b. If you have any problems with your Nature's End camping gear, call me at the number listed above.
    c. Every Nature's End product comes with a one-year replacement guarantee.
    d. We trust that you will be happy with your Nature's End purchase.

ANSWER: c. Only "c" expresses confidence and enhances credibility.
DIFFICULTY: moderate; PAGE: 82; OBJECTIVE: 6; TYPE: application

15. For most business messages you should use a _____ tone.
    a. formal
    b. conversational
    c. legalistic
    d. confidential

ANSWER: b. Most business messages aim for a conversational tone with plain language that sounds businesslike without being stuffy or full of jargon.
DIFFICULTY: moderate; PAGE: 83; OBJECTIVE: 5; TYPE: concept

16. If you begin a message with the following: "Hi Susan: How is it going? I am just sending along the information you asked for", you are using
    a. a formal tone.
    b. an informal tone.
    c. a conversational tone.
    d. A direct tone.

ANSWER: b. This is an example of informal tone.
DIFFICULTY: moderate; PAGE: 83; OBJECTIVE 5; TYPE: application

17. Which of the following phrases no longer belongs in business messages?
    a. attached please find
    b. please be advised that
    c. none of the above
    d. all of the above

ANSWER: d. Both a and b are obsolete and should be avoided in business prose.
DIFFICULTY: moderate; PAGE: 83; OBJECTIVE: 5; TYPE: application

18. Which of the following is *not* a recommended strategy for creating an effective business writing style?
    a. avoid obsolete language
    b. use an elevated and formal tone
    c. avoid preaching and bragging
    d. use plain English

ANSWER: b. Good business writing uses a tone that is conversational while being effective for business.
DIFFICULTY: moderate; PAGE: 83; OBJECTIVE: 5; TYPE: concept

19. To create an effective business writing style, it is a good idea to
    a. use humor.
    b. adapt a personal and familiar tone—like you are old friends.
    c. simplify your language by using plain English.
    d. all of the above

ANSWER: c. Business writing should be simple and unambiguous. Avoid using humor or adopting an overly friendly or personal tone.
DIFFICULTY: difficult; PAGE: 83-84; OBJECTIVE: 5; TYPE: concept

20. All of the following are techniques for selecting the best words *except*:
    a. choose formal and unfamiliar words
    b. blend abstract and concrete words
    c. avoid jargon
    d. avoid clichés

ANSWER: a. Avoid formal or unfamiliar words.
DIFFICULTY: moderate; PAGE: 83-84; OBJECTIVE: 6; TYPE: application

21. Which voice will allow you to be diplomatic about pointing out a problem or error?
    a. active
    b. passive
    c. imperative or vocative
    d. state of being

ANSWER: b. A passive voice seems less like an accusation.
DIFFICULTY: moderate; PAGE: 84; OBJECTIVE: 7; TYPE: application

22. Which voice makes your writing more direct, livelier, and easier to read?
    a. active
    b. passive
    c. imperative or vocative
    d. state of being

ANSWER: a. Using active voice produces these results.
DIFFICULTY: moderate; PAGE: 84; OBJECTIVE: 7; TYPE: application

23. Which voice would you use if you wanted to avoid sounding accusatory?
    a. active
    b. passive
    c. imperative or vocative
    d. state of being

ANSWER: b. Passive voice allows you to sound less accusatory.
DIFFICULTY: moderate; PAGE: 84-85; OBJECTIVE: 7; TYPE: application

24. Which voice can allow you to leave the actor completely out of the sentence?
    a. active
    b. passive
    c. imperative or vocative
    d. state of being

ANSWER: b. Passive voice can leave the actor completely out of the sentence.
DIFFICULTY: moderate; PAGE: 84-85; OBJECTIVE: 7; TYPE: application

25. Identify the voice in the following sentence: "Mary wrote the report."
    a. active
    b. passive
    c. imperative or vocative
    d. state of being

ANSWER: a. The sentence is active.
DIFFICULTY: moderate; PAGE: 84-85; OBJECTIVE: 7; TYPE: application

26. Identify the voice in the following sentence: "The bridge was faultily designed."
    a. active
    b. passive
    c. imperative or vocative
    d. state of being

ANSWER: b. The sentence is passive.
DIFFICULTY: moderate; PAGE: 84-85; OBJECTIVE: 7; TYPE: application

27. Identify the voice in the following sentence: "The national anthem was sung by Mark."
    a. active
    b. passive
    c. imperative or vocative
    d. state of being

ANSWER: b. The sentence is passive.
DIFFICULTY: moderate; PAGE: 84-85; OBJECTIVE: 7; TYPE: application

28. Identify the voice in the following sentence: "When the committee hired Jane, it followed correct procedures."
    a. active
    b. passive
    c. imperative or vocative
    d. state of being

ANSWER: a. Both clauses in this sentence are active.
DIFFICULTY: moderate; PAGE: 84-85; OBJECTIVE: 7; TYPE: application

29.   Identify the voice in the following sentence: "Ben is filling in each item on the form."
        a.   active
        b.   passive
        c.   imperative or vocative
        d.   state of being

ANSWER: a. This sentence is written in the active voice.
DIFFICULTY: moderate; PAGE: 84-85; OBJECTIVE: 7; TYPE: application

30.   In business writing, grammatical correctness is very important because errors can
        a.   damage your credibility.
        b.   distract the reader.
        c.   confuse the reader.
        d.   all of the above

ANSWER: d. All of these are reasons why grammatical correctness is so important in business writing.
DIFFICULTY: easy; PAGE: 85; OBJECTIVE: 4; TYPE: concept

31.   Words such as liberty, love, motivation, or happiness are examples of
        a.   strong words.
        b.   clichés.
        c.   concrete words.
        d.   abstract words.

ANSWER: d. These are abstract words because they express concepts, qualities, or characteristics.
DIFFICULTY: difficult; PAGE 86; OBJECTIVE: 6; TYPE: application

32.   To choose strong words,
        a.   use nouns.
        b.   use action verbs.
        c.   avoid adjectives and adverbs.
        d.   all of the above

ANSWER: d. Nouns and verbs are strong words; adjectives and adverbs are not.
DIFFICULTY: difficult; PAGE: 86; OBJECTIVE: 6; TYPE: application

33.   To minimize problems of a message being subject to multiple interpretations or being boring, you should
        a.   use only strong words and verbs that are powerful in your message.
        b.   use jargon that is familiar to your audience.
        c.   blend abstract terms with concrete terms.
        d.   minimize the use of adjectives and adverbs.

ANSWER: c. Blending abstract and concrete words minimizes the 'fuzziness' of abstract terms.
DIFFICULTY: moderate; PAGE: 86; OBJECTIVE 6; TYPE: concept

34. The words "business prosperity" used in a message would be considered
    a. a cliché.
    b. a strong term.
    c. a weak phrase.
    d. plain language.

ANSWER: c. This is an example of a weak phrase.
DIFFICULTY: moderate; PAGE: 86; OBJECTIVE 6; TYPE: application

35. The term "costs an arm and a leg" is an example of
    a. a weak phrase.
    b. plain language.
    c. jargon.
    d. a cliché.

ANSWER: d. This is an example of a cliché.
DIFFICULTY: moderate; PAGE: 86; OBJECTIVE 6; TYPE: application

36. A sentence that expresses one main thought and one or more subordinate thoughts related
    to it is called a
    a. simple sentence.
    b. compound sentence.
    c. complex sentence.
    d. compound-complex sentence.

ANSWER: c. The complex sentence expresses one main thought and one or more subordinate thoughts.
DIFFICULTY: difficult; PAGE: 87; OBECTIVE: 7; TYPE: concept

37. A sentence that has a single subject and a single predicate is called a
    a. simple sentence.
    b. compound sentence.
    c. complex sentence.
    d. compound-complex sentence.

ANSWER: a. A simple sentence has one main clause.
DIFFICULTY: moderate; PAGE: 87; OBJECTIVE: 7; TYPE: concept

38. A sentence that expresses two or more independent but related thoughts of equal
    importance, usually joined by *and, but, or*, is called a
    a. simple sentence.
    b. compound sentence.
    c. complex sentence.
    d. compound-complex sentence.

ANSWER: b. The compound sentence is a merger of two or more simple sentences that are related.
DIFFICULTY: difficult; PAGE: 87; OBJECTIVE: 7; TYPE: concept

39.   A sentence that has two main clauses, at least one of which contains a subordinate clause, is called a
    a.   simple sentence.
    b.   compound sentence.
    c.   complex sentence.
    d.   compound-complex sentence.

ANSWER: d. A compound-complex sentence has two main clauses, at least one of which contains a subordinate clause.
DIFFICULTY: difficult; PAGE: 87; OBJECTIVE: 7; TYPE: concept

40.   Identify this sentence: "While you may disagree with Joan's recommendations, you must admit that her suggestions would save the company money."
    a.   simple sentence
    b.   compound sentence
    c.   complex sentence
    d.   compound-complex sentence

ANSWER: c. The complex sentence expresses one main thought and one or more subordinate thoughts.
DIFFICULTY: difficult; PAGE: 87; OBJECTIVE: 7; TYPE: application

41.   Identify this sentence: "Stock prices have fallen at an unprecedented rate, and foreign investments are far below normal levels."
    a.   simple sentence
    b.   compound sentence
    c.   complex sentence
    d.   compound-complex sentence

ANSWER: b. The compound sentence merges two or more simple sentences that are related.
DIFFICULTY: difficult; PAGE: 87; OBJECTIVE: 7; TYPE: application

42.   Identify this sentence: "Management is hiring a new head of personnel."
    a.   simple sentence
    b.   compound sentence
    c.   complex sentence
    d.   compound-complex sentence

ANSWER: a. A simple sentence has one main clause.
DIFFICULTY: difficult; PAGE: 87; OBJECTIVE: 7; TYPE: application

43. Identify this sentence: "Management is hiring a new head of personnel, and while we may not agree with their move, we know the reasons for their action."
    a. simple sentence
    b. compound sentence
    c. complex sentence
    d. compound-complex sentence

ANSWER: d. A compound-complex sentence has two main clauses, at least one of which contains a subordinate clause.
DIFFICULTY: difficult; PAGE: 87; OBJECTIVE: 7; TYPE: application

44. You can give emphasis to key points by
    a. giving more space to important ideas.
    b. making important ideas the subject.
    c. using effective phrasing or sentence style.
    d. all of the above

ANSWER: d. All of the elements listed will give emphasis to key points.
DIFFICULTY: moderate; PAGE: 88; OBJECTIVE: 7; TYPE: concept

45. Words or phrases that tie ideas together and show how one thought is related to another are called
    a. clichés.
    b. jargon.
    c. transitions.
    d. coherent.

ANSWER: c. Transitions are words or phrases that tie ideas together and show how one thought is related to another.
DIFFICULTY: easy; PAGE: 89; OBJECTIVE: 8; TYPE: concept

46. All of the following methods can be used to establish transitions *except*:
    a. echoing a word/phrase from the previous sentence
    b. using a pronoun that refers to a previously used noun
    c. using clichés
    d. using words that are frequently or commonly paired

ANSWER: c. In addition to the 3 methods above, using connecting words can establish a transition.
DIFFICULTY: difficult; PAGE: 89; OBJECTIVE: 8; TYPE: concept

47. When you want to use similarities or differences to develop the main idea in a paragraph, which of these methods would you use?
    a. illustration
    b. comparison or contrast
    c. cause and effect
    d. classification

ANSWER: b. Comparison or contrast uses similarities or differences to develop a topic.
DIFFICULTY: difficult; PAGE: 91; OBJECTIVE: 7; TYPE: concept

48. When you want to develop a paragraph by showing how a general idea is broken into specific categories, which of these methods would you use?
   a. illustration
   b. comparison or contrast
   c. cause and effect
   d. classification

ANSWER: d. Classification shows how a general idea is broken into specific categories.
DIFFICULTY: moderate; PAGE: 91; OBJECTIVE: 7; TYPE: concept

49. A paragraph that focuses on the reasons for something is developed according to which method?
   a. illustration
   b. comparison or contrast
   c. cause and effect
   d. problem and solution

ANSWER: d. The paragraph developed according to the problem/solution pattern focuses on the reasons for something.
DIFFICULTY: difficult; PAGE: 91; OBJECTIVE: 7; TYPE: concept

True/False

50. _____ Using the "you" attitude means putting the sender's priorities first.

ANSWER: False. "You" attitude emphasizes an audience-centered approach.
DIFFICULTY: moderate; PAGE: 77; OBJECTIVE: 2; TYPE: concept

51. _____ The "you" attitude is not intended to be manipulative or insincere.

ANSWER: True. "You" attitude acknowledges your audience's concerns and your appreciation for their concerns.
DIFFICULTY: easy; PAGE: 78; OBJECTIVE: 2; TYPE: concept

52. _____ To emphasize the positive side of your messages, focus on the solution rather than the problem.

ANSWER: True. Emphasize the positive side of your messages.
DIFFICULTY: moderate; PAGE: 78-80; OBJECTIVE: 2; TYPE: concept

53. _____ If you must refer to someone's disability, avoid terms like handicapped; put the person first and the disability second.

ANSWER: True. Avoid mentioning a disability unless it is pertinent.
DIFFICULTY: moderate; PAGE: 80; OBJECTIVE: 6; TYPE: application

54. _____ The main types of language bias include: gender, racial, ethnicity, age, and disability.

ANSWER: True. Languages bias includes: gender, racial, ethnicity, age, and disability.
DIFFICULTY: moderate; PAGE: 80; OBJECTIVE: 3; TYPE: concept

55. _____ Good business writing is very formal in tone.

ANSWER: False. Good business writing is conversational and appropriate for conducting business.
DIFFICULTY: moderate; PAGE: 83; OBJECTIVE: 5; TYPE: concept

56. _____ Most business messages aim for a conversational tone, using plain language that sounds businesslike without being stuffy, stiff, wordy, or full of jargon.

ANSWER: True. Effective business messages aim to accommodate the reader's needs in every way possible.
DIFFICULTY: easy; PAGE: 83-84; OBJECTIVE: 4; TYPE: concept

57. _____ To attain a conversational tone in a message, you should use humorous and more intimate language.

ANSWER: False. One should avoid obsolete language, intimacy, humor, and preaching/bragging.
DIFFICULTY: difficult; PAGE 83-84; OBJECTIVE: 5; TYPE: concept.

58. _____ When communicating across cultures it is important to include humor in order to put your audience at ease.

ANSWER: False. One should generally avoid humor in business messages.
DIFFICULTY: moderate; PAGE: 84; OBJECTIVE: 5; TYPE: concept

59. _____ It's a good rule when writing business messages to avoid being too intimate and casual.

ANSWER: True. Such a familiar tone may be seen as an attempt to seem like an old friend when, in fact, you're not.
DIFFICULTY: easy; PAGE: 84; OBJECTIVE: 5; TYPE: concept

60. _____ It's always appropriate to use humor in business prose.

ANSWER: False. Using humor can backfire, can be misunderstood when you're communicating across cultures, and can be out-of-date within a week or month.
DIFFICULTY: moderate; PAGE: 84; OBJECTIVE: 5; TYPE: concept

61. _____ Plain English enables your audience to grasp the meaning of your message without reading it over and over.

ANSWER: True. By choosing words that have only one interpretation, you will surely communicate more clearly with your audience.
DIFFICULTY: easy; PAGE: 84; OBJECTIVE: 5; TYPE: concept

62. _____ Passive voice creates more direct, shorter sentences and makes your writing more vigorous, concise, and easier to understand.

ANSWER: False. Active voice creates more direct, shorter sentences and makes your writing more lively and easier to understand.
DIFFICULTY: moderate; PAGE: 84; OBJECTIVE: 7; TYPE: concept

63. _____ Using passive voice makes sense in some situations when it allows you to focus on your audience and demonstrate the "you" attitude.

ANSWER: True. Passive voice can allow you to focus on "you" attitude.
DIFFICULTY: moderate; PAGE: 84-85; OBJECTIVE: 2; TYPE: concept

64. _____ When you want to point out what has happened without placing blame, it's best to use the passive voice.

ANSWER: True. The passive voice allows you to avoid mentioning the subject of the action.
DIFFICULTY: moderate; PAGE: 84-85; OBJECTIVE: 7; TYPE: application

65. _____ Grammatical or usage errors detract from your credibility with your audience.

ANSWER: True. If you make grammatical or usage errors, you lose credibility with your audience.
DIFFICULTY: easy; PAGE: 85; OBJECTIVE: 5; TYPE: concept

66. _____ An abstract word stands for something you can touch, see, or visualize.

ANSWER: False. An abstract word expresses a concept, quality, or characteristic.
DIFFICULTY: easy; PAGE: 86; OBJECTIVE: 86; TYPE: concept

67. _____ Concrete words are far more specific than abstractions.

ANSWER: True. Concrete words allow you to give data your business reader needs in order to be clear and to conduct business effectively.
DIFFICULTY: easy; PAGE: 86; OBJECTIVE: 6; TYPE: concept

68. _____ Abstract words should be avoided in all business writing; they are too unclear.

ANSWER: False. Don't assume that concrete words are better than abstract words. Abstractions permit us to rise above the common and tangible.
DIFFICULTY: difficult; PAGE: 86; OBJECTIVE: 6; TYPE: concept

69. _____ The words "kick," "increase," "dog," and "desk" are examples of abstract words.

ANSWER: False. These are concrete words.
DIFFICULTY: moderate; PAGE: 86; OBJECTIVE: 6; TYPE: application

70. _____ Nouns and verbs are the most concrete kinds of words.

ANSWER: True. Nouns and verbs are the most concrete kinds of words.
DIFFICULTY: moderate; PAGE: 86; OBJECTIVE: 6; TYPE: concept

71. _____ The words "take by storm" is an example of plain language.

ANSWER: False. This is a cliché.
DIFFICULTY: moderate; PAGE: 86; OBJECTIVE: 6; TYPE: application

72. _____ To write clear and direct business messages, it's important to avoid clichés.

ANSWER: True. Due to overuse, clichés have lost their meaning.
DIFFICULTY: easy; PAGE: 87; OBJECTIVE: 6; TYPE: application

73. _____ It's important to use technical jargon in business messages to build your credibility with the reader.

ANSWER: False. Handle technical or professional terms with care and let your audience's knowledge guide you.
DIFFICULTY: moderate; PAGE: 87; OBJECTIVE: 6; TYPE: concept

74. _____ Using big words is an effective technique in business writing. It makes the writer sound more credible.

ANSWER: False. Choose familiar words to communicate more effectively.
DIFFICULTY: moderate; PAGE: 87; OBJECTIVE: 7; TYPE: concept

75. _____ Placement of ideas is one way to emphasize key points in your sentences.

ANSWER: True. To give emphasis to key ideas, place them first or last.
DIFFICULTY: moderate; PAGE: 88; OBJECTIVE: 7; TYPE: concept

76. _____ To draw attention to important ideas in a sentence, either put them first or last.

ANSWER: True. Putting an idea at the beginning or at the end will draw attention to it.
DIFFICULTY: moderate; PAGE: 88; OBJECTIVE: 7; TYPE: concept

77. _____ You achieve coherence by using active or passive voice to show the relationship between paragraphs and among sentences within paragraphs.

ANSWER: False. Transitions show the relationship between paragraphs and among sentences within paragraphs.
DIFFICULTY: moderate; PAGE: 89; OBJECTIVE: 8; TYPE: concept

78. _____ You should consider using a transition device whenever it might help the reader understand your ideas and follow you from point to point.

ANSWER: True. Transitional elements help the reader understand your ideas and follow you from point to point.
DIFFICULTY: easy; PAGE: 89; OBJECTIVE: 8; TYPE: application

79. _____ Your choice of how to develop an effective paragraph depends on your subject, your intended audience, and your purpose.

ANSWER: True. Criteria to use when determining which method of development to use in a paragraph depends upon your subject, your intended audience, and your purpose.
DIFFICULTY: moderate; PAGE: 90; OBJECTIVE: 8; TYPE: concept

Fill-in the blank

80. Speaking and writing in terms of your audience's wishes and preferences is known as adopting the "_____ attitude."

ANSWER: You
DIFFICULTY: easy; PAGE: 77; OBJECTIVE: 6; TYPE: concept

81. Language that is _____ avoids unethical, embarrassing blunders in language related to gender, race, ethnicity, age, and disability.

ANSWER: Bias-free
DIFFICULTY: moderate; PAGE: 80; OBJECTIVE: 3; TYPE: concept

82. Mild terms used for words with unpleasant connotations are called _____.

ANSWER: Euphemisms
DIFFICULTY: moderate; PAGE: 80; OBJECTIVE: 5; TYPE: concept

83. Your_____ is based upon how reliable you are and how much trust you evoke in others.

ANSWER: Credibility
DIFFICULTY: moderate; PAGE: 81; OBJECTIVE: 5; TYPE: concept

84. _____ is the way you use words to achieve a certain tone or overall impression.

ANSWER: Style
DIFFICULTY: difficult; PAGE: 83; OBJECTIVE: 5; TYPE: concept

85. A/An _____ sentence has two main clauses that express two or more independent but related thoughts of equal importance.

ANSWER: Compound
DIFFICULTY: difficult; PAGE: 87; OBJECTIVE: 5; TYPE: concept

86. _____ _____ is a way of writing and arranging technical materials so that your audience can understand your meaning.

ANSWER: Plain English
DIFFICULTY: moderate; PAGE: 84; OBJECTIVE: 5; TYPE: concept

87. Words that describe a concept, quality, or characteristic are called _____.

ANSWER: Abstract
DIFFICULTY: moderate; PAGE: 86; OBJECTIVE: 6; TYPE: concept

88. Terms and phrases so common that they have become virtually meaningless and cloud clear meaning are called _____.

ANSWER: Clichés
DIFFICULTY: moderate; PAGE: 87; OBJECTIVE: 7; TYPE: concept

89. A/An _____ sentence expresses one main thought and one or more subordinate thoughts related to it.

ANSWER: Complex
DIFFICULTY: difficult; PAGE: 87; OBJECTIVE: 7; TYPE: concept

90. A/An _____ sentence has two main clauses, at least one of which contains a subordinate clause.

ANSWER: Compound-complex
DIFFICULTY: difficult; PAGE: 87; OBJECTIVE: 7; TYPE: concept

91. A/An _____ sentence has one main clause.

ANSWER: Simple
DIFFICULTY: difficult; PAGE: 87; OBJECTIVE: 7; TYPE: concept

Short Answer/Essay

92. List four things to avoid to achieve a conversational tone in business messages.

ANSWER: 1) Avoid obsolete language like "attached please find" or "please be advised that." 2) Avoid preaching and bragging. 3) Be careful with intimacy. 4) Be careful with humor, avoiding it altogether in formal business messages.
DIFFICULTY: difficult; PAGE: 83-84; OBJECTIVE: 5; TYPE: concept

93. You're using the _____ voice when the subject performs an action.

ANSWER: Active
DIFFICULTY: moderate; PAGE: 84; OBJECTIVE: 7; TYPE: concept

94. You're using a/an _____ voice when the subject receives the action.

ANSWER: Passive
DIFFICULTY: moderate; PAGE: 84; OBJECTIVE: 7; TYPE: concept

95. _____ sentences generally sound less formal and usually make it easier for the reader to figure out who performed the action.

ANSWER: Active
DIFFICULTY: moderate; PAGE: 84; OBJECTIVE: 7; TYPE: concept

96. _____ sentences de-emphasize the subject and imply action done by something or someone.

ANSWER: Passive
DIFFICULTY: moderate; PAGE: 84-85; OBJECTIVE: 7; TYPE: concept

97. "The Customer Service Department is being analyzed to determine the problem," is an example of a/an _____ voice.

ANSWER: Passive
DIFFICULTY: moderate; PAGE: 84-85; OBJECTIVE: 7; TYPE: application

98. While you need to use active voice in general, discuss when and how passive voice is effective.

ANSWER: Use passive voice 1) when you want to be diplomatic about pointing out a problem or error of some kind, 2) when you want to point out what's being done without taking or attributing either the credit or the blame, and 3) when you want to avoid personal pronouns in order to create an objective tone.
DIFFICULTY: difficult; PAGE: 84-85; OBJECTIVE: 7; TYPE: application

99. List four techniques for selecting the best words when writing business messages.

ANSWER: 1) Choose powerful words—verbs and nouns are better than adjectives and adverbs. 3) Choose words that are familiar to you and your audience. 4) Avoid clichés and buzzwords. 5) Use jargon carefully.
DIFFICULTY: difficult; PAGE: 86-87; OBJECTIVE: 6; TYPE: application

100.   List two steps you can take to help you create more effective sentences.

ANSWER: 1) Strive for variety and balance using all four types of sentences. 2) Use sentence style to emphasize key thoughts.
DIFFICULTY: moderate; PAGE: 87; OBJECTIVE: 7; TYPE: application

101.   List four ways you can emphasize key ideas in your paragraphs.

ANSWER: 1) Reflect relationships with sentence type. Less important ideas go in dependent clauses. 2) Devote more space to the important ideas. 3) Make important ideas the subject of your sentences. 4) Place more important ideas first or last.
DIFFICULTY: difficult; PAGE: 88; OBJECTIVE: 7; TYPE: application

102.   List four methods of establishing transitions to make paragraphs coherent.

**ANSWER: 1) Use connecting words—and, but, or, nevertheless, however, in addition.
2) Echo a word or phrase from a previous paragraph or sentence. 3) Use a pronoun that
refers to a noun previously used. 4) Use words that are frequently paired.**
DIFFICULTY: difficult; PAGE: 89; OBJECTIVE: 8; TYPE: application

CHAPTER 5
COMPLETING BUSINESS MESSAGES

Multiple Choice

1. The main tasks in completing a business message consist of all the following *except*:
   a. proofreading
   b. revising
   c. forecasting
   d. producing

ANSWER: c. Forecasting is not one of the tasks needed to write a business message.
DIFFICULTY: easy; PAGE: 103; OBJECTIVE: 1; TYPE: concept

2. The opening statement of a document should
   a. summarize the main idea.
   b. list all of the points and ideas that are in the documents.
   c. be short and to the point.
   d. be relevant and interesting.

ANSWER: d. Opening statements need to have an impact on the audience by being relevant and interesting.
DIFFICULTY: moderate; PAGE 103; OBJECTIVE: 1; TYPE: concept

3. When revising a document,
   a. first read through it quickly to evaluate overall effectiveness.
   b. first look carefully for grammatical errors.
   c. read just one time to finish quickly.
   d. pay closest attention to the document's spelling.

ANSWER: a. Look first at broader general issues before moving to smaller points and grammatical issues.
DIFFICULTY: moderate; PAGE: 103; OBJECTIVE: 1; TYPE: concept

4. A conclusion should
   a. summarize the main points.
   b. bring up any additional point that you forgot to include in the message.
   c. leave a positive impression.
   d. all of the above
   e. only a and c

ANSWER: e. Conclusions should not bring up points that were not addressed in the document.
DIFFICULTY: moderate; PAGE: 103; OBJECTIVE: 1; TYPE: concept

5. To shorten sentences,
    a. avoid putting dissimilar thoughts into the same sentence.
    b. avoid using commas.
    c. use passive voice.
    d. all of the above

ANSWER: a. Expressing two dissimilar thoughts in a single sentence can make it difficult for the audience to understand.
DIFFICULTY: moderate; PAGE: 104; OBJECTIVE: 2; TYPE: concept

6. Which of the following is an example of a hedging sentence?
    a. The deadline is next Tuesday.
    b. The report seems to be incomplete.
    c. The financial statement needs to have two sections.
    d. none of the above

ANSWER: b. Hedging sentences usually include words like *seems* or *may*.
DIFFICULTY: moderate; PAGE: 105; OBJECTIVE: 2; TYPE: application

7. Key words that indicate a hedging sentence would include
    a. 'and' or 'also'.
    b. 'may' or 'seems'.
    c. 'yes' or 'no'.
    d. 'I will consider . . .'

ANSWER: b. Using may or seems avoids making a statement of fact.
DIFFICULTY: moderate; PAGE 105; OBJECTIVE: 2; TYPE: concept

8. Which of the following sentences is *not* written in parallel construction?
    a. She enjoys singing, dancing, and reading.
    b. He needed to format the report, bind the document, and turn it in to his supervisor.
    c. He opened the office, checked the mail, and was turning on the computers.
    d. After completing the survey and finishing the exam, he went home.

ANSWER: c. *Was turning* is not parallel with *opened* and *checked*.
DIFFICULTY: moderate; PAGE: 105-06; OBJECTIVE: 2; TYPE: application

9. When revising for clarity it is important to do all of the following *except*:
    a. try not to display too much enthusiasm
    b. use parallel construction for similar ideas
    c. avoid stringing several nouns together
    d. avoid writing in the first person

ANSWER: d. Writing in the first person generally will improve the clarity rather than detract from it.
DIFFICULTY: moderate; PAGE: 105-07; OBJECTIVE: 2; TYPE: concept

10. Which of the following includes a dangling modifier?
   a. Situated in the break room, employees will find the vending machines.
   b. The vending machines are situated in the break room.
   c. Employees will find the vending machines situated in the break room.
   d. The break room has several vending machines for employees to use.

ANSWER: a. Situated in the break room is a dangling modifier because the word that it modifies in sentence "a" is employees. But, the sentence is not saying that the employees are situated in the break room, the vending machines are.
DIFFICULTY: moderate; PAGE: 106; OBJECTIVE: 2; TYPE: application

11. When revising for clarity, it is important to
   a. keep the subject and predicate as close to each other as possible.
   b. always write in the third person.
   c. avoid using an active voice.
   d. all of the above

ANSWER: a. When you separate the subject and the predicate with other phrases and words, the sentence becomes more confusing.
DIFFICULTY: moderate; PAGE: 106; OBJECTIVE: 2; TYPE: concept

12. Which of the following suggestions will *not* make your message more concise?
   a. shorten long words and phrases
   b. eliminate redundancies
   c. begin sentences with short phrases like *it is* or *there are*
   d. delete unnecessary words

ANSWER: c. Phrases like *it is* or *there are* at the beginning of a sentence generally are not needed and make the sentence longer.
DIFFICULTY: moderate; PAGE: 109; OBJECTIVE: 3; TYPE: concept

13. To help make your writing more concise, do all of the following *except*:
   a. eliminate redundancies
   b. avoid using wordy phrases
   c. avoid using "you" statements
   d. avoid the clutter of too many relative pronouns like *who, that,* or *which*

ANSWER: c. "You" statements rarely increase the length of a document; redundancies, wordy phrases, and relative pronouns do add to length.
DIFFICULTY: moderate; PAGE: 107; OBJECTIVE: 3; TYPE: concept

14. Use the word 'can' instead of the phrase 'you have the capability of' to avoid
   a. redundancy.
   b. 'you' statements.
   c. wordy phrases.
   d. using too many pronouns.

ANSWER: c. Use one word equivalents of wordy phrases when possible.
DIFFICULTY: moderate; PAGE: 107; OBJECTIVE: 3; TYPE: application

15. When trying to make a message more concise,
   a. examine every word.
   b. replace long words with shorter ones.
   c. remove adverbs that don't add to the meaning.
   d. all of the above

ANSWER: d. All choices are methods for making messages more concise.
DIFFICULTY: moderate; PAGE: 107-09; OBJECTIVE: 3; TYPE: concept

16. All of the following phrases are redundant *except*:
   a. round in shape
   b. free gift
   c. return home
   d. follows after

ANSWER: c. Return home is not redundant because return does not necessarily mean to go home; you can return to many places. In the other choices, round is always a shape (can something be round in smell?), gifts are always free (if you have to pay for it, it is not a gift), and if you are following something you must be coming after it.
DIFFICULTY: moderate; PAGE: 109; OBJECTIVE: 3; TYPE: concept

17. The four design elements include all of the following *except*:
   a. white space
   b. page size
   c. justification
   d. typestyles

ANSWER: b. Page size is not something that most business writers need to consider when designing their document. Nearly all written documents use standard paper.
DIFFICULTY: moderate; PAGE: 112; OBJECTIVE: 4; TYPE: concept

18. When designing a business document, a writer should
   a. try to balance graphics and text on the page.
   b. always center all headings and subheadings.
   c. use at least three different typestyles to add visual appeal.
   d. all of the above

ANSWER: a. Text and graphics should be balanced to make the page easier to read and more visually appealing.
DIFFICULTY: moderate; PAGE: 112; OBJECTIVE: 4; TYPE: concept

19. All of the following are points to consider in making the design elements effective, *except:*
    a. Strive for a number of decorative touches.
    b. Be consistent throughout the message regarding margins, type size, and typeface.
    c. Balance all of the visual elements.
    d. Pay attention to design details such as headings, column width, etc.

ANSWER: a. See Table 5.2. Pointers include: be consistent, balance visual elements, use technology, strive for simplicity, pay attention to design.
DIFFICULTY: difficult; PAGE: 112; OBJECTIVE: 4; TYPE: concept

20. White space is important in a document because it
    a. allows writers to get more text on one page.
    b. provides visual contrast for readers.
    c. gives readers' eyes a resting point.
    d. a and b
    e. b and c

ANSWER: e. White space provides visual contrast and allows readers' eyes to briefly rest. A document without enough white space will appear cluttered and unappealing.
DIFFICULTY: moderate; PAGE: 114; OBJECTIVE: 4; TYPE: concept

21. All of the following are ways of making your document design more effective *except*:
    a. being consistent
    b. maintaining balance
    c. using spell check
    d. being detail oriented

ANSWER: c. Although it is important to check for spelling errors, using spell check is not a method of improving the design of your documents.
DIFFICULTY: moderate; PAGE: 112; OBJECTIVE: 4; TYPE: concept

22. Justified margins are not preferred for business documents because
    a. they make the document harder to read.
    b. there is less white space, darkening the message's appearance.
    c. they often cause excessive hyphenation.
    d. all of the above

ANSWER: d. All of the choices are problems caused by justified margins.
DIFFICULTY: moderate; PAGE: 114; OBJECTIVE: 4; TYPE: concept

23. The advantages of a flush-left, ragged-right margin includes all of the following *except*:
    a. It makes the document more informal.
    b. It tends to "lighten" the appearance of the message.
    c. It provides a feeling of openness.
    d. It allows the writer to include more text on a page.

ANSWER: d. Justified margins allow more text.
DIFFICULTY: difficult; PAGE: 114; OBJECTIVE: 4; TYPE: concept

24. Centered type should be avoided for business documents because
    a. it makes the message look too informal.
    b. it slows the reader down.
    c. it creates word spacing problems.
    d. all of the above

ANSWER: b. Centered type slows reading because the reader has to search for the beginning of each line.
DIFFICULTY: moderate; PAGE: 114; OBJECTIVE: 4; TYPE: concept

25. Typeface refers to
    a. the physical design of letters, numbers, and other text characters.
    b. the size of the letters, numbers, and other text characters.
    c. underlining, boldface, italics, and other modifications made to the letters, numbers, and other text characters.
    d. a and b
    e. all of the above

ANSWER: a. Typeface is the physical design of the characters; not the size or modifications made to them.
DIFFICULTY: moderate; PAGE: 114; OBJECTIVE: 4; TYPE: concept

26. A kind of sans serif typeface is
    a. Helvetica.
    b. Times Roman.
    c. Wingdings.
    d. all of the above

ANSWER: a. Helvetica is a kind of sans serif typeface.
DIFFICULTY: moderate; PAGE: 114; OBJECTIVE: 4; TYPE: concept

27. Type style refers to
    a. the physical design of letters, numbers, and other text characters.
    b. any modification that lends contrast or emphasis to type.
    c. serif and sans serif styles.
    d. all of the above

ANSWER: b. Type style refers to contrast or emphasis in the typeface. Choices "a" and "c" refer to elements of typeface.
DIFFICULTY: moderate; PAGE: 115; OBJECTIVE: 4; TYPE: concept

28. Boldface and italics
    a. should be used for key words only.
    b. can slow readers down if overused.
    c. can draw attention to specific points.
    d. all of the above

ANSWER: d. All of these are features of italics and boldface.
DIFFICULTY: moderate; PAGE: 115; OBJECTIVE: 4; TYPE: concept

29. The best font size to use for the text in most business documents is
    a. 7-9.
    b. 10-12.
    c. 13-15.
    d. 16-18.

ANSWER: b. Most business documents are written using a type size of 10-12.
DIFFICULTY: moderate; PAGE: 115; OBJECTIVE: 4; TYPE: concept

30. All of the following are ways to improve proofreading *except*:
    a. Have a friend or colleague do the proofreading for you.
    b. Proofread 1-2 days after writing the document.
    c. Read the document out loud.
    d. Proofread quickly, looking at the document in large chunks rather than at individual words to speed up the process.

ANSWER: d. Good proofreaders go slowly and look carefully at every word.
DIFFICULTY: moderate; PAGE: 116; OBJECTIVE: 6; TYPE: application

31. Proofreading is important because it
    a. ensures that your document is the correct length.
    b. adds credibility to your document.
    c. prevents other writers from stealing your ideas.
    d. all of the above

ANSWER: b. A carefully proofread document is more credible and professional than a document that is poorly designed or filled with errors.
DIFFICULTY: moderate; PAGE: 116; OBJECTIVE: 5; TYPE: concept

32. When you proofread a document you should check
    a. the format.
    b. the spelling.
    c. the grammar.
    d. b and c
    e. all of the above

ANSWER: e. Format, spelling, and grammar are things that all good proofreaders will examine.
DIFFICULTY: moderate; PAGE: 116; OBJECTIVE: 5; TYPE: concept

True/False

33. _____ Revision should only occur after you have completed the entire first draft of your message.

ANSWER: False. Revision occurs throughout the writing process.
DIFFICULTY: easy; PAGE: 102; OBJECTIVE: 1; TYPE: concept

34. _____ If possible, it is better to revise a few days after completing a rough draft rather than right away.

ANSWER: True. This lets you approach the material with a fresh eye.
DIFFICULTY: easy; PAGE: 102; OBJECTIVE: 1; TYPE: concept

35. _____The beginning and end of a message are the parts that have the most impact on an audience.

ANSWER: True. These sections are read first and make the most impact on the audience.
DIFFICULTY: moderate; PAGE: 102; OBJECTIVE: 1; TYPE: concept

36. _____ Hedging statements are used when the writer wants to avoid stating a judgment as fact.

ANSWER: True. Hedging statements are used when the writer wants to avoid stating a judgment as fact.
DIFFICULTY: moderate; PAGE: 105; OBJECTIVE: 2; TYPE: concept

37. _____ Parallel construction occurs when a writer uses the same grammatical pattern to express similar ideas.

ANSWER: True. Parallel construction occurs when a writer uses the same grammatical pattern to express similar ideas.
DIFFICULTY: easy; PAGE: 105; OBJECTIVE: 2; TYPE: concept

38. _____ Avoiding dangling modifiers is one way to improve the clarity of your document.

ANSWER: True. Dangling modifiers often make the focus of a sentence unclear.
DIFFICULTY: easy; PAGE: 106; OBJECTIVE: 2; TYPE: concept

39. _____ One good way to shorten your sentences and improve clarity is to string many nouns together as modifiers.

ANSWER: False. Stringing many nouns together makes the sentence longer and more difficult to understand.
DIFFICULTY: moderate; PAGE: 106; OBJECTIVE: 2; TYPE: concept

40. _____ Change verbs to nouns whenever it is possible in order to make your writing sound more formal. For example, use the word "implementation" rather than "implement."

ANSWER: False. Avoid making nouns out of verbs; this makes writing longer and less clear.
DIFFICULTY: moderate; PAGE: 106; OBJECTIVE: 2; TYPE: concept

41. _____ Avoid using phrases like "the aforementioned," "the former," and "the latter," because they make readers jump from point to point.

ANSWER: True. Using these phrases forces the reader to jump from point to point.
DIFFICULTY: moderate; PAGE: 107; OBJECTIVE: 2; TYPE: concept

42. _____ An occasional adjective or adverb can intensify and emphasize your meaning.

ANSWER: True. However, too many of these types of phrases can ruin writing by making you sound insincere.
DIFFICULTY: moderate; PAGE: 107; OBJECTIVE: 2; TYPE: concept

43. _____ In business communication it is important to always be as enthusiastic as possible in order to appear professional.

ANSWER: False. Overly enthusiastic writing may be perceived as unprofessional and juvenile.
DIFFICULTY: moderate; PAGE: 107; OBJECTIVE: 2; TYPE: concept

44. _____ In business writing, longer, more formal words will make you sound more professional.

ANSWER: False. Short words are generally more vivid and easier to read than long ones.
DIFFICULTY: moderate; PAGE: 108; OBJECTIVE: 3; TYPE: concept

45. _____ Using infinitives in place of some phrases can shorten sentences and make them clearer.

ANSWER: True. Infinitives can often effectively take the place of wordy phrases.
DIFFICULTY: moderate; PAGE: 108; OBJECTIVE: 3; TYPE: concept

46. _____ Often the best way to deal with a troublesome element in a sentence is to remove it rather than trying to rewrite it.

ANSWER: True. Troublesome elements are often trying to do an unnecessary job. It is often more efficient to remove them rather than trying to rewrite them.
DIFFICULTY: moderate; PAGE: 109; OBJECTIVE: 1; TYPE: concept

47. _____ Using the word 'outcome' instead of the phrase 'final outcome' is an example of avoiding wordy phrases.

ANSWER: False. This is an example of a redundancy.
DIFFICULTY: moderate; PAGE: 109; OBJECTIVE: 3; TYPE: application

48. _____ A sentence that begins with an indefinite pronoun such as "it" or "there," is probably longer than it needs to be.

ANSWER True. "It is/There" are starters usually add length rather than meaning to a sentence.
DIFFICULTY: moderate; PAGE: 109; OBJECTIVE: 3; TYPE: concept

49. _____ The way you package your ideas in a written document influences how successful your communication will be.

ANSWER: True. The way you package your ideas in a written document influences how successful your communication will be.
DIFFICULTY: moderate; PAGE: 111; OBJECTIVE: 4; TYPE: concept

50. _____ When creating a document, the only thing that really matters is the quality of the writing. The appearance of the document is unimportant.

ANSWER: False. Although the quality of the writing is important, the look and design of the document are also very important. Good looks can help get your message across.
DIFFICULTY: moderate; PAGE: 111; OBJECTIVE: 4; TYPE: concept

51. _____ You do not need to proofread for spelling errors if you use the spell check feature on your computer.

ANSWER: False. Spell check misses many errors.
DIFFICULTY: easy; PAGE: 111; OBJECTIVE: 4; TYPE: concept

52. _____ You should not rely on your grammar checker. It will often miss errors.

ANSWER: True. Grammar checkers are a good start, but they are not sophisticated enough to catch all errors.
DIFFICULTY: easy; PAGE: 111; OBJECTIVE: 4; TYPE: concept

53. _____ Graphics software helps you create overhead transparencies and computerized slide shows.

ANSWER: False. Presentation software does this.
DIFFICULTY: moderate; PAGE: 112; OBJECTIVE: 4; TYPE: concept

54. _____ It is acceptable to leave a heading hanging at the bottom of a page if the text that follows it on the next page is preceded with the word "continued"

ANSWER: False. A heading should never appear at the bottom of a page without any text.
DIFFICULTY: moderate; PAGE: 112; OBJECTIVE: 5; TYPE: concept

55. _____ Business writers should try to incorporate as many design elements as possible into their documents in order to make them more visually appealing and interesting to readers.

ANSWER: False. Too many design elements will confuse the audience. Instead, use just enough design elements to help make the document look inviting and professional.
DIFFICULTY: moderate; PAGE: 112; OBJECTIVE: 4; TYPE: concept

56. _____ All business documents should have justified margins because it makes the document look more professional.

ANSWER: False. Justified text tends to make your message look more like a form letter and is more difficult to read.
DIFFICULTY: moderate; PAGE: 114; OBJECTIVE: 4; TYPE: concept

57. _____ To add a formal tone to the message, use centered type.

ANSWER: True. To add a formal tone to the message, use centered type.
DIFFICULTY: moderate; PAGE: 114; OBJECTIVE 4; TYPE: concept

58. _____ The typeface you choose can affect the tone of your message.

ANSWER: True. The typeface that you select can make the message look friendly, classy, casual, etc.
DIFFICULTY: moderate; PAGE: 114; OBJECTIVE: 4; TYPE: concept

59. _____ Serif typefaces like this one, (Times New Roman), have small cross lines at the ends of each letter stroke.

ANSWER: True. Serif typefaces like this one, (Times New Roman), have small cross lines at the ends of each letter stroke.
DIFFICULTY: moderate; PAGE: 114; OBJECTIVE: 4; TYPE: application

60. _____ Serif Typefaces are best for text rather than for large-sized headings or titles.

ANSWER: True. Serif typefaces often look cluttered when used for larger text like headings. Sans serif is better for headings, while serif works well for text.
DIFFICULTY: moderate; PAGE: 114; OBJECTIVE: 4; TYPE: concept

61. _____ It is a good idea to reduce your type size and decrease your margins to keep documents to as few pages as possible.

ANSWER: False. Small type and crowded margins make a document unappealing and difficult to read.
DIFFICULTY: moderate; PAGE: 114-15; OBJECTIVE: 4; TYPE: application

62. One of the best ways to make your document more visually appealing and interesting is to use a wide variety of typefaces. Three to five per page is ideal.

ANSWER: False. Two different typefaces, one for headings and one for text, is all that is recommended for most business documents.
DIFFICULTY: moderate; PAGE: 114-15; OBJECTIVE: 4; TYPE: application

63. _____ Using all uppercase letters is a good idea when you want to draw readers' attention to a specific paragraph.

ANSWER: False. Use all uppercase very sparingly. It will slow readers down because it interferes with readers' ability to recognize the shapes of words.
DIFFICULTY: moderate; PAGE: 115; OBJECTIVE: 4; TYPE: concept

64. _____ In business writing it is a good idea to minimize the use of underlining, boldface, italics, shadow, all caps, and other typestyles that will slow your reader down.

ANSWER: True. Changing typestyles slows down your readers.
DIFFICULTY: easy; PAGE: 115; OBJECTIVE: 4; TYPE: concept

65. _____ Proofreading quickly is important. Therefore, you should try to complete your proofreading in just one read through of the document to save time.

ANSWER: False. Good proofreading requires multiple reads.
DIFFICULTY: moderate; PAGE: 116; OBJECTIVE: 5; TYPE: concept

66. _____ One proofreading method is to read the page backwards to help you focus on every single word.

ANSWER: True. Our brain has been trained to read quickly and skip over errors. Therefore, anything you can do that will slow you down, like reading the page backwards, is a good idea.
DIFFICULTY: moderate; PAGE: 116; OBJECTIVE: 6; TYPE: application

67. _____ Always try to proofread the entire document in one sitting, even if it is lengthy. This will prevent interference from other work and writing.

ANSWER: False. It is easy to get burned-out and miss errors when proofreading one document. Avoid reading large amounts of text in one sitting.
DIFFICULTY: moderate; PAGE: 116; OBJECTIVE: 6; TYPE: application

Fill-in the blank

68. The _____ of a document should summarize the main idea and leave the audience with a positive impression.

ANSWER: Conclusion
DIFFICULTY: moderate; PAGE: 103; OBJECTIVE: 1; TYPE: concept

69. To eliminate _____ sentences, you should avoid words such as "may" or "seems."

ANSWER: Hedging
DIFFICULTY: moderate; PAGE: 105; OBJECTIVE 3; TYPE: concept

70. Sentences that include words such as "may" or "seems" and don't really say anything are called _____ _____.

ANSWER: Hedging Sentences
DIFFICULTY: difficult; PAGE: 105; OBJECTIVE: 2; TYPE: concept

71. When you revise for _____, you should do things like break up long sentences, rewrite hedging sentences, impose parallelism, correct dangling modifiers, and replace camouflaged verbs.

ANSWER: Clarity
DIFFICULTY: easy; PAGE: 105-07; OBJECTIVE: 2; TYPE: concept

72. Modifiers that have no logical connection to the subject of the sentence are known as _____ modifiers.

ANSWER: Dangling
DIFFICULTY: moderate: PAGE: 106; OBJECTIVE 2; TYPE: concept

73. When you revise for _____, you should do things like delete long words and phrases, eliminate redundancies, and avoid excessive enthusiasm.

ANSWER: Conciseness
DIFFICULTY: easy; PAGE: 107-09; OBJECTIVE: 3; TYPE: concept

74. To delete unnecessary words, it would be appropriate to replace the phrase "at this point in time" with the word _____.

ANSWER: Now
DIFFICULTY: moderate; PAGE: 108; OBJECTIVE: 3; TYPE: application

75. Using the same grammatical pattern to express two or more similar ideas is called _____ construction.

ANSWER: Parallel
DIFFICULTY: moderate; PAGE: 109; OBJECTIVE: 2; TYPE: concept

76. Word combinations that say the same thing twice, such as "round in shape," are known as _____.

ANSWER: Redundancies
DIFFICULTY: moderate; PAGE: 109; OBJECTIVE: 3; TYPE: concept

77. Software for creating business visuals falls into two groups: _____ and _____.

ANSWER: Presentation (slides, PowerPoint); Graphics (diagrams, charts, tables, art)
DIFFICULTY: moderate; PAGE: 112; OBJECTIVE: 4; TYPE: concept

78. White space, margins, line justification, and typeface are examples of _____ _____.

ANSWER: Design Elements
DIFFICULTY: moderate; PAGE: 114-15; OBJECTIVE 4; TYPE: concept

79. To give readers' eyes a resting point, be sure to include _____ _____ in the document.

ANSWER: White Space
DIFFICULTY: moderate; PAGE: 114; OBJECTIVE: 4; TYPE: concept.

80. Margins that are _____ have both left and right margins lining up in a solid block of text.

ANSWER: Justified
DIFFICULTY: moderate; PAGE: 114; OBJECTIVE: 4; TYPE: concept

81. The two main categories of typefaces are _____ and _____.

ANSWER: Serif; Sans Serif
DIFFICULTY: moderate; PAGE: 114; OBJECTIVE: 4; TYPE: concept

82. In business writing you should limit the number of typefaces on a page. In general, use no more than _____ typefaces on a page.

ANSWER: Two
DIFFICULTY: difficult; PAGE: 114; OBJECTIVE: 4; TYPE: application

83. Two kinds of type style include _____ and _____.

ANSWER: Choices here include: underlining, boldface, italics, or other highlighting or decorative styles.
DIFFICULTY: moderate; PAGE: 115; OBJECTIVE: 4; TYPE: concept

84. In order to check a document for grammar, usage, punctuation, spelling errors, special elements, use of heading or source notes, you must _____ the document.

ANSWER: Proofread
DIFFICULTY: moderate; PAGE: 119; OBJECTIVE: 5; TYPE: concept

Short Answer/Essay

85. List the characteristics and functions of the beginning of a business document.

ANSWER: The opening of a shorter document should be relevant, interesting and geared to the reader's probable reaction. For longer messages the opening should establish the subject, purpose, and organization of the material.
DIFFICULTY: difficult; PAGE: 103; OBJECTIVE: 1; TYPE: concept

86. Conclusions should accomplish what two tasks in business documents?

ANSWER: 1) Summarize the main idea. 2) Leave the audience with a positive impression.
DIFFICULTY: difficult; PAGE: 103; OBJECTIVE: 1; TYPE: concept

87. Rewrite the following sentence to improve clarity and to avoid the long noun sequence: The financial estimates and accounting consulting firm will be closed next week.

ANSWER: The consulting firm that does financial estimates and accounting will be closed next week.
DIFFICULTY: moderate; PAGE: 105; OBJECTIVE: 2; TYPE: application

88. Correct the parallelism problems in the following paragraph:
In order to graduate on time, he will have to take courses in finance, marketing, and how to do account management. But in order to pass them, he will have to study hard, go to class, and will probably have to be working fewer hours at his campus job.

ANSWER: To graduate on time, he will have to take courses in finance, marketing, and account management. But, to pass them he will have to study hard, go to class and work fewer hours at his campus job.
DIFFICULTY: difficult; PAGE: 105-06; OBJECTIVE: 2; TYPE: application

89. List and describe the nine techniques for revising for clarity.

ANSWER: The nine techniques are:
- **Break up overly long sentences—don't connect too many clauses with "and."**
- **Rewrite hedging sentences—avoid using "may" or "seems."**
- **Impose parallelism—use the same grammatical pattern to express two or more similar ideas.**
- **Correct dangling modifiers—delete phrases with no connection to the subject of the sentence or those that are placed too closely to the wrong noun or verb.**
- **Reword long noun sequences—avoid stringing many nouns together as modifiers.**
- **Replace camouflaged verbs—watch for verbs that have been turned into nouns.**
- **Clarify sentence structure—keep the subject and predicate of a sentence as close together as possible.**
- **Clarify awkward references—avoid words and phrases which cause readers to jump from point to point.**
- **Moderate your enthusiasm—don't overuse adjectives and adverbs to sound falsely positive.**

DIFFICULTY: difficult; PAGE: 105-07; OBJECTIVE: 2; TYPE: application

90. Rewrite the sentence to avoid camouflaged verbs:
The manager will make a determination about when to issue the refund.

ANSWER: **The manager will determine when to issue the refund.**
DIFFICULTY: moderate; PAGE: 106; OBJECTIVE: 2; TYPE: application

91. Rewrite the sentence to keep the subject and predicate close together and improve clarity:
This report will help our employees with an easy to read format and organization.

ANSWER: **The report with its easy to read format and organization will help our employees. [or] The easy to read format and organization of this report will help our employees.**
DIFFICULTY: moderate; PAGE: 106; OBJECTIVE: 2; TYPE: application

92. Rewrite the following sentence to remove the dangling modifier:
Lying next to the filing cabinet, the office manager found the financial report.

ANSWER: **The office manager found the financial report next to the filing cabinet.**
DIFFICULTY: moderate; PAGE: 106; OBJECTIVE: 2; TYPE: application

93. Remove the awkward references to improve clarity:
Of the inventory and marketing departments, we announced that only the former will undergo a review this year, while the latter will undergo a review next spring.

ANSWER: **We will review the marketing department this year and the inventory department next spring.**
DIFFICULTY: difficult; PAGE: 107; OBJECTIVE: 2; TYPE: application

94. Rewrite the following sentence to avoid excessive enthusiasm:
We are thrilled to announce the very important merger of our extraordinarily effective accounting department with our very highly efficient finance department.

ANSWER: We are pleased to announce the merger of our finance and accounting departments. [or] The finance and accounting departments will merge.
DIFFICULTY: moderate; PAGE: 107; OBJECTIVE: 2; TYPE: concept

95. Rewrite the following sentence in a more concise way by eliminating the wordy phrases:
In view of the fact that the customer service department is closed, we do not have the capability of offering refunds until such a time as they reopen.

ANSWER: We cannot offer refunds until the customer service department opens.
DIFFICULTY: moderate; PAGE: 107-08; OBJECTIVE: 3; TYPE: application

96. Rewrite the following sentence in a more concise way by eliminating the wordy phrases:
Due to the fact that there has been a decline in revenues, layoffs of employees are likely to occur until such a time as the economy improves.

ANSWER: Because revenues have declined, layoffs are likely until the economy improves.
DIFFICULTY: moderate; PAGE: 107-08; OBJECTIVE: 3; TYPE: application

97. List and explain the four techniques for making documents more concise.

ANSWER: The four techniques are:
- **Delete unnecessary words and phrases—frequently you can say something more efficiently with one word than you can with a longer phrase.**
- **Shorten long words and phrases—short words are generally more vivid and easier to read than long ones are.**
- **Eliminate redundancies—avoid word combinations that say the same thing.**
- **Rewrite "it is/there are" starters—you can usually shorten sentences that start with these phrases.**

DIFFICULTY: difficult; PAGE: 107-09; OBJECTIVE: 3; TYPE: application

98. Rewrite the following sentence in a more concise way by eliminating excessive relative pronouns and articles:
If the system is not shut down correctly, it may accidentally delete the documents that have not been saved.

ANSWER: If the system is not shut down correctly, it may accidentally delete unsaved documents.
DIFFICULTY: moderate; PAGE: 108; OBJECTIVE: 3; TYPE: application

99. Rewrite the following sentence in a more concise way using infinitive phrases:
If you want clarity in your writing, you must revise carefully.

ANSWER: To write clearly, revise carefully.
DIFFICULTY: moderate; PAGE: 108; OBJECTIVE: 3; TYPE: application

100. Rewrite the following sentence in a more concise way by using short, simple words: During the preceding month, company managers became cognizant of the fact that an increase in low employee morale was a direct causation of the decrease in sales.

ANSWER: Last month, managers realized that low employee morale was causing a decrease in sales.
DIFFICULTY: moderate; PAGE: 108; OBJECTIVE: 3; TYPE: application

101. Rewrite the following sentence in a more concise way by using short, simple words: Effective immediately, all employees need to terminate their excessive utilization of the office duplication machine for personal endeavors.

ANSWER: The office copier is not for personal use. [or] Please do not make personal copies.
DIFFICULTY: moderate; PAGE: 108; OBJECTIVE: 3; TYPE: application

102. Rewrite the following sentence in a more concise way by eliminating redundancies: The engineers collaborated together in order to produce the uniquely original final outcomes of their research.

ANSWER: The engineers collaborated to produce their original research outcomes.
DIFFICULTY: moderate; PAGE: 109; OBJECTIVE: 3; TYPE: application

103. Rewrite the following sentence in a more concise way by eliminating the indefinite pronouns in the opening:
There are three new tenants who are moving in today.

ANSWER: Three new tenants are moving in today.
DIFFICULTY: moderate; PAGE: 109; OBJECTIVE: 3; TYPE: application

104. Discuss the dangers and benefits of using technology when writing, designing, and proofreading a document.

ANSWER: Word processors, computer software, graphics programs, etc. are all excellent tools for business writers. They can save time, create a more professional, visually appealing product, and improve the credibility of the document. However, they will not create the document for you, and they do not take the place of good writing, clear design, and careful proofreading.
DIFFICULTY: difficult; PAGE: 111; OBJECTIVE: 2-5; TYPE: application

105. Explain how the 4 design elements work together to create an effective message.

ANSWER: The four design techniques are consistency, balance, restraint, and detail. Especially in business settings, writers should be consistent in their use of margins, typeface, type size, spacing, color, and position. They should balance the space devoted to text, visuals, and white space. They should strive for simplicity and avoid clutter, and pay close attention to detail.
DIFFICULTY: difficult; PAGE: 112-15; OBJECTIVE: 4; TYPE: concept

106. Explain the importance and process of proofreading. Why does it matter and what should you look for?

ANSWER: This essay should mention that proofreading is important because errors will make the document harder to read and understand and will detract from the writer's credibility. When proofreading, you should look at every word and punctuation point as well as at the overall format and design of the document. This includes a wide range of things such as page layout, margins, consistency, headings, type size, typeface, grammar, usage, punctuation, spelling, columns, graphics, etc.
DIFFICULTY: difficult; PAGE: 116; OBJECTIVE: 5; TYPE: concept

107. List at least three tips for effective proofreading.

ANSWER: This essay should address the following points:
- **Read a document several times when proofreading. Focus on different aspects each time.**
- **Use tactics to avoid the errors and typos that your brain has been trained to ignore. They include reading the page backwards, reading aloud, and reading each word or sentence alone.**
- **Focus on high-priority items such as names, dates, and addresses.**
- **Try to wait a day or two after you have written the document before you proofread it.**
- **Avoid proofreading large amounts of text in one sitting.**
- **Take your time; don't rush proofreading.**

DIFFICULTY: difficult; PAGE: 116; OBJECTIVE: 5; TYPE: application

CHAPTER 6
CHOOSING AND USING MEDIA FOR BRIEF MESSAGES

Multiple choice

1. For routine, internal communication you should use
   a. memos.
   b. e-mail.
   c. letters.
   d. all of the above
   e. a and b only
   f. b and c only

ANSWER: e. For routine, internal communication use memos and e-mail. Letters are for more formal, external communication.
DIFFICULTY: moderate; PAGE: 130-31; OBJECTIVE: 1; TYPE: application

2. Many businesses are now using podcasts to replace or supplement
   a. letters.
   b. memos.
   c. conference calls.
   d. none of the above

ANSWER: c. Podcasts often replace or supplement conference calls.
DIFFICULTY: easy; PAGE: 131; OBJECTIVE: 1; TYPE: concept

3. When it comes to writing messages in today's business environment,
   a. old-fashioned printed letters are virtually extinct.
   b. you'll probably still find it necessary to send printed letters.
   c. e-mail has replaced printed letters for all domestic external communication.
   d. all of the above

ANSWER: b. Printed letters are still necessary, for the sake of formality and other reasons.
DIFFICULTY: easy; PAGE: 131; OBJECTIVE: 1; TYPE: concept

4. When you want your message to stand out amidst the flood of e-mail your audience receives, you should
   a. consider sending a printed letter.
   b. flag your e-mail messages as 'high priority' or 'urgent.'
   c. send multiple copies of the same e-mail message.
   d. none of the above.

ANSWER: a. A printed message can stand out and get noticed in this case.
DIFFICULTY: moderate; PAGE: 131; OBJECTIVE: 1; TYPE: concept

5. E-mail can be used for external communication
   a. in response to e-mail messages that you receive.
   b. only for formal documents that you need to keep a record of.
   c. in response to letters your customers have sent.
   d. all of the above

ANSWER: a. It is acceptable to use e-mail to respond to an external e-mail, but do not use it for formal documents.
DIFFICULTY: moderate; PAGE: 131; OBJECTIVE: 1; TYPE: application

6. The most formal type of written communication is:
   a. instant messaging
   b. e-mail
   c. memo
   d. letter

ANSWER: d. The letter is most formal.
DIFFICULTY: easy; PAGE: 131; OBJECTIVE: 2; TYPE: concept

7. In a business letter the inside address
   a. appears at the top of the page as part of the letterhead.
   b. identifies the person receiving the letter.
   c. contains the sender's address.
   d. all of the above

ANSWER: b. The inside address gives the receiver's address. The sender's address should be in the letterhead.
DIFFICULTY: easy; PAGE: 131-32; OBJECTIVE: 2; TYPE: application

8. What is the correct order of elements to include in a business letter?
   a. inside address, date, salutation, signature, complimentary close
   b. date, inside address, salutation, signature, complimentary close
   c. inside address, date, salutation, complimentary close, signature
   d. date, inside address, salutation, complimentary close, signature

ANSWER: d. This is the correct order.
DIFFICULTY: moderate; PAGE: 132; OBJECTIVE: 2; TYPE: application

9. Memos should include all of the following sections *except*:
   a. to
   b. from
   c. subject
   d. salutation

ANSWER: d. Memos open with to, from, subject. They do not have salutations.
DIFFICULTY: moderate; PAGE: 132; OBJECTIVE: 2; TYPE: application

10. Memos should *not* include
    a. a signature.
    b. a salutation.
    c. multiple topics.
    d. all of the above

ANSWER: d. Signatures and salutations are for letters and e-mails; multiple topics are better addressed in separate memos or in reports.
DIFFICULTY: moderate; PAGE: 132; OBJECTIVE: 2; TYPE: concept

11. Generally speaking, memos are _____ most other message formats.
    a. less private than
    b. more private than
    c. as private as
    d. none of the above

ANSWER: a. Because they are often distributed without sealed envelopes, memos are generally less private than most other formats.
DIFFICULTY: moderate; PAGE: 132; OBJECTIVE: 2; TYPE: concept

12. E-mail
    a. should follow the convention of other business writing in formal situations.
    b. should never be longer than one screen.
    c. does not need to be proofread.
    d. all of the above

ANSWER: a. The nature of e-mail in the workplace is very different from that of personal e-mail.
DIFFICULTY: moderate; PAGE: 133; OBJECTIVE: 3; TYPE: concept

13. E-mails should include all of the following *except*:
    a. information about attachments
    b. inside address
    c. e-mail addresses of sender and receiver
    d. contact information

ANSWER: b. An inside address is used for letters, not emails.
DIFFICULTY: moderate; PAGE: 133-34; OBJECTIVE: 2; TYPE: concept

14. Using e-mail in the workplace
    a. requires no more formality than using it for personal correspondence.
    b. is frowned upon by most executives.
    c. has dramatically different demands than using it for personal messages.
    d. is a good idea only in technological fields.

ANSWER: c. The nature of business e-mail is very different from that of personal e-mail.
DIFFICULTY: moderate; PAGE: 133-34; OBJECTIVE: 3; TYPE: concept

15.   When it comes to legal issues,
       a.   e-mails mean nothing—only printed documents can be used in court.
       b.   e-mail and other electronic documents have the same weight as printed ones.
       c.   your e-mail messages are off limits—using them in court would violate your privacy.
       d.   none of the above

ANSWER: b. In recent years, e-mail and other electronic messages have been used as evidence in numerous lawsuits.
DIFFICULTY: moderate; PAGE: 134-35; OBJECTIVE: 3; TYPE: concept

16.   What percentage of companies now monitor incoming and outgoing e-mail?
       a.   5%
       b.   25%
       c.   50%
       d.   75%

ANSWER: c. Half of employers monitor the e-mail messages their employees send to and receive from individuals outside the company.
DIFFICULTY: moderate; PAGE: 135; OBJECTIVE: 3; TYPE: concept

17.   The subject line of an e-mail message
       a.   is one of the most important parts.
       b.   helps recipients decide whether or not to read the message.
       c.   should do more than simply describe the general topic of the message.
       d.   all of the above

ANSWER: d. All of these are characteristics of e-mail subject lines.
DIFFICULTY: moderate; PAGE: 135; OBJECTIVE: 3; TYPE: concept

18.   Which of the following is an example of an effective e-mail subject line?
       a.   Website redesign is on schedule
       b.   Status Report
       c.   Employee Parking
       d.   all of the above

ANSWER: a. Only 'A' is both informative and compelling.
DIFFICULTY: moderate; PAGE: 135; OJBECTIVE: 3; TYPE: application

19.   When exchanging multiple e-mails with someone on the same topic,
       a.   use the same subject line to avoid confusion.
       b.   write a descriptive kind of subject line.
       c.   modify the subject line with each response.
       d.   change the topic whenever the date changes but not before.

ANSWER: c. E-mails should use informative subject lines. You should change the subject line with each new response to prevent reader confusion and make it easier to locate the message at a later date.
DIFFICULTY: difficult; PAGE: 135; OBJECTIVE: 3; TYPE: application

20. To make e-mail more readable do all of the following *except*:
    a. limit subject lines to describing the general topic of your message
    b. make your message easy to follow
    c. personalize your message
    d. observe e-mail etiquette

ANSWER: a. You should make your subject lines informative, not simply descriptive of the general topic.
DIFFICULTY: moderate; PAGE: 135; OBJECTIVE: 3; TYPE: concept

21. Which of the following is an example of an effective subject line for an e-mail requesting information about the August inventory for bananas?
    a. information needed
    b. banana inventories
    c. banana information needed
    d. please send August banana inventory

ANSWER: d. This gives a good overview of the message.
DIFFICULTY: moderate; PAGE: 135; OBJECTIVE: 3; TYPE: application

22. One important element of basic e-mail etiquette includes
    a. proofreading your message before sending it out.
    b. using bullets and lists.
    c. including headings on all e-mails.
    d. capturing your readers' attention.

ANSWER: a. Proofreading shows that you care enough to avoid careless errors. Although using bullets, lists, and headings are all good ideas, they are not part of e-mail etiquette.
DIFFICULTY: difficult; PAGE: 135; OBJECTIVE: 3; TYPE: concept

23. E-mail etiquette requires that writers be all of the following *except*:
    a. sure every e-mail they send is absolutely necessary
    b. respectful of the chain of command
    c. careful to keep their emotions in check when composing messages
    d. all of the above

ANSWER: d. All of these are important aspects of e-mail etiquette.
DIFFICULTY: difficult; PAGE: 135-36; OBJECTIVE: 3; TYPE: concept

24. All of the following are benefits of instant messaging *except*:
    a. It allows a rapid response to urgent messages.
    b. It is private.
    c. It costs less than phone calls or e-mail.
    d. It can mimic a conversation more closely than e-mail.

ANSWER: b. Privacy is not a stated benefit of instant messaging.
DIFFICULTY: difficult; PAGE: 136; OBJECTIVE: 2; TYPE: concept

25. Advantages of using IM rather than e-mail include
    a. lower cost.
    b. less vulnerability to viruses.
    c. its ability to mimic conversation more closely.
    d. all of the above

ANSWER: d. These are all factors that separate IM from e-mail.
DIFFICULTY: moderate; PAGE: 136; OBJECTIVE: 4; TYPE: concept

26. Drawbacks of IM include
    a. the challenge of logging messages for later review and archiving.
    b. the need for users to learn complicated software.
    c. the ability to use it only on expensive, highly specialized devices.
    d. none of the above

ANSWER: a. None of the other statements are true of IM.
DIFFICULTY: moderate; PAGE: 136; OBJECTIVE: 4; TYPE: application

27. In e-mail "bcc" stands for
    a. blanket carbon copy.
    b. blind courtesy copy.
    c. blanket computer calibration.
    d. blind copy combination.

ANSWER: b. In an e-mail, "bcc" stands for blind courtesy copy.
DIFFICULTY: easy; PAGE: 136; OBJECTIVE: 3; TYPE: application

28. A "flame" is
    a. a negative e-mail message containing insulting, critical comments.
    b. an appropriate way to express displeasure via e-mail.
    c. an e-mail message that goes out rapidly—like flames—to multiple audiences at once.
    d. none of the above

ANSWER: a. A flame is a negative, critical e-mail message. They are never appropriate in a business setting.
DIFFICULTY: easy; PAGE: 136; OBJECTIVE: 5; TYPE: concept

29. In e-mail messages, the difference between the "cc" and "bcc" features is
    a. nothing—they're just different designations of the same thing.
    b. one prints the message in regular type while the other prints it in boldface.
    c. all recipients can see who is on the "cc" line, but not who is included on the "bcc" line.
    d. none of the above

ANSWER: c. Use "bcc" when you do not want all recipients to know who is receiving a copy of the message.
DIFFICULTY: easy; PAGE: 136; OBJECTIVE: 3; TYPE: concept

30. 'Spim' refers to
    a. unwanted e-mail from unknown sources.
    b. e-mail that contains computer viruses.
    c. the IM version of e-mail spam.
    d. none of the above

ANSWER: c. This is the correct definition.
DIFFICULTY: moderate; PAGE: 138; OBJECTIVE: 4; TYPE: application

31. Many businesses now use blogs to
    a. keep project teams up to date.
    b. replace conventional intranet sites.
    c. inform employees about general business matters.
    d. all of the above

ANSWER: d. Companies use blogs for all of these purposes.
DIFFICULTY: moderate; PAGE: 139-40; OBJECTIVE: 5; TYPE: concept

32. 'Viral marketing' is
    a. the unethical practice of marketing products through computer viruses.
    b. advertising products and services related to the health-care industry.
    c. spreading the word about your company and products in much the same way that biological viruses are spread from person to person.
    d. none of the above

ANSWER: c. Many companies use blogs to engage in viral marketing of their products and services.
DIFFICULTY: moderate; PAGE: 140; OBJECTIVE: 5; TYPE: concept

33. When it comes to blogging for business,
    a. don't worry about proofreading—your audience doesn't expect it.
    b. you should apply the three-step writing process as you would for any other business message.
    c. don't spend a lot of time trying to define your audience: you're writing for everyone.
    d. all of the above

ANSWER: b. Business blogs require careful planning and preparation, just as other business messages do.
DIFFICULTY: moderate; PAGE: 141; OBJECTIVE: 5; TYPE: concept

34. If you do not have a constant supply of new information to post on a business blog,
    a. your readers will appreciate not having to process information that changes constantly.
    b. re-post old material so your audience will not lose interest.
    c. create a traditional website instead of a blog.
    d. none of the above

ANSWER: c. A traditional website would be more appropriate in this situation.
DIFFICULTY: difficult; PAGE: 142; OBJECTIVE: 5; TYPE: application

35. If you receive criticism based on a business blog,
    a. you should respond to it promptly and honestly.
    b. ignore it unless the critic is incorrect.
    c. post it, and follow with a blog entry to show your audience that it will not be tolerated.
    d. none of the above

ANSWER: a. Hiding sends the message that you don't have a valid response, and attacking your audience will not preserve your company's image.
DIFFICULTY: moderate; PAGE: 142; OBJECTIVE: 5; TYPE: concept

36. Podcasts are
    a. great for entertainment, but not useful in business.
    b. helpful for training in business, but not much else.
    c. too technical to be practical for business use.
    d. none of the above

ANSWER: d. None of these statements are accurate.
DIFFICULTY: moderate; PAGE: 142-43; OBJECTIVE: 6; TYPE: application

37. Compared to blogging, podcasting is
    a. much easier and simpler.
    b. not quite as simple.
    c. less professional.
    d. none of the above

ANSWER: b. Podcasting is not quite as simple as blogging.
DIFFICULTY: moderate; PAGE: 143; OBJECTIVE: 5-6; TYPE: concept

38. One of the greatest drawbacks to using podcasts in business is the
    a. costly, specialized equipment you'll need to purchase regardless of the production quality you want.
    b. increased difficulty of editing your material.
    c. challenge of scanning back and forth to find specific parts of the message.
    d. all of the above

ANSWER: c. It is much easier for your audience to scan back and forth in other message formats.
DIFFICULTY: moderate; PAGE: 143; OBJECTIVE: 6; TYPE: concept

True/False

39. _____ You should use memos and e-mails for written, internal communication.

ANSWER: True. E-mail and memos are the most efficient ways to communicate in writing with others members of your organization.
DIFFICULTY: easy; PAGE: 130-31; OBJECTIVE: 2; TYPE: application

40. _____ Printed letters are the still the most common form of formal internal business communication.

ANSWER: False. Printed letters are still popular for formal external communication.
DIFFICULTY: easy; PAGE: 131; OBJECTIVE: 2; TYPE: concept

41. _____ E-mail should never be used for external communication.

ANSWER: False. E-mail is appropriate for external communication in some situations.
DIFFICULTY: moderate; PAGE: 131; OBJECTIVE: 1; TYPE: application

42. _____ E-mail is now a primary communication medium for most companies.

ANSWER: True. E-mail is now a primary communication medium for most companies.
DIFFICULTY: moderate: PAGE: 131; OBJECTIVE: 2; TYPE: concept

43. _____ Of letters, memos, and e-mails, memos are the most formal.

ANSWER: False. Letters are the most formal form of business correspondence.
DIFFICULTY: easy; PAGE: 131; OBJECTIVE: 2; TYPE: concept

44. _____ Memos should always open with a salutation.

ANSWER: False. Letters and e-mails open with a salutation; memos do not.
DIFFICULTY: moderate; PAGE: 132; OBJECTIVE: 2; TYPE: application

45. _____ Memos are generally more private than most other message formats.

ANSWER: False. Because they are often distributed without sealed envelopes, memos are generally less private.
DIFFICULTY: moderate; PAGE: 132; OBJECTIVE: 2; TYPE: concept

46. _____ In many companies, it is common practice to sign your initials next to your name in the *From* line of a memo.

ANSWER: True. This is common practice in many companies.
DIFFICULTY: moderate; PAGE: 132; OBJECTIVE: 2; TYPE: concept

47. _____ When it comes to e-mail, some seasoned businesspeople advocate a general disregard for punctuation, grammar, spelling and other conventions.

ANSWER: True. Even some seasoned employees believe addressing these issues in e-mail messages takes too much time.
DIFFICULTY: moderate; PAGE: 134; OBJECTIVE: 3; TYPE: concept

48. _____ In a court of law, e-mail messages can have the same weight as more traditional printed documents.

ANSWER: True. In recent years, e-mail and other electronic message forms have been used in numerous lawsuits.
DIFFICULTY: moderate; PAGE: 134; OBJECTIVE: 3; TYPE: concept

49. _____ Spelling, punctuation, and grammar do not matter in e-mail; getting your message out quickly should be your only concern.

ANSWER: False. You should always proofread your e-mails. Mistakes in spelling, punctuation, and grammar will make you look careless.
DIFFICULTY: easy; PAGE: 134; OBJECTIVE: 3; TYPE: concept

50. _____ Only about 10% of all employers monitor incoming and outgoing e-mail.

ANSWER: False. About half of all employers now monitor incoming and outgoing e-mail.
DIFFICULTY: moderate; PAGE: 135; OBJECTIVE: 3; TYPE: concept

51. _____ It is illegal for your company to open and read e-mail you send and receive at work.

ANSWER: False. About 25% of employers monitor internal e-mail, and 50% monitor incoming and outgoing e-mail.
DIFFICULTY: moderate; PAGE: 135; OBJECTIVE: 3; TYPE: concept

52. _____ You should modify your subject line with each new e-mail response.

ANSWER: True. This will help prevent reader confusion and can make it easier to locate messages later.
DIFFICULTY: moderate; PAGE: 135; OBJECTIVE: 3; TYPE: concept

53. _____ E-mail subject lines should capture your audience's attention and be informative.

ANSWER: True. Subject lines should do more than just describe or classify message content.
DIFFICULTY: moderate; PAGE: 135; OBJECTIVE: 3; TYPE: concept

54. _____ An effective e-mail subject line is very short and describes only the general topic of the message.

ANSWER: False. An effective subject line does more than just describe or classify message content—it builds interest with key words, quotations, directions, or questions.
DIFFICULTY: moderate; PAGE: 135; OBJECTIVE: 3; TYPE: concept

55. _____ E-mail etiquette requires that you respect the chain of command.

ANSWER: True. Do not abuse your ability to e-mail the CEO directly.
DIFFICULTY: easy; PAGE: 135-36; OBJECTIVE: 3; TYPE: concept

56. _____ In e-mail, "bcc" stands for "blind courtesy copy."

ANSWER: True. This is what "bcc" denotes.
DIFFICULTY: moderate; PAGE: 136; OBJECTIVE: 3; TYPE: concept

57. _____ Instant messaging is a faster communication tool than e-mail.

ANSWER: True. Instant messaging is a faster communication tool than e-mail.
DIFFICULTY: moderate; PAGE: 136; OBJECTIVE: 4; TYPE: concept

58. _____ Compared to e-mails and phone calls, IM is less costly.

ANSWER: True. This is one advantage of instant messaging.
DIFFICULTY: moderate; PAGE: 136; OBJECTIVE: 3; TYPE: concept

59. _____ If you write an emotionally charged e-mail message, let it sit for at least one day before sending it.

ANSWER: True. This is an important technique to avoid sending 'flames.'
DIFFICULTY: moderate; PAGE: 136; OBJECTIVE: 3; TYPE: concept

60. _____ In e-mails it is a good idea to make frequent use of background colors and colored type in order to add visual appeal to the text.

ANSWER: False. Avoid overformatting your messages: it makes them difficult and annoying to read on screen.
DIFFICULTY: moderate; PAGE: 137; OBJECTIVE: 3; TYPE: concept

61. _____ Request return receipts for all the e-mails you send—it is the only way to know who is reading them and who is not.

ANSWER: False. Use this feature only for the most critical messages.
DIFFICULTY: easy; PAGE: 137; OBJECTIVE: 3; TYPE: concept

62. _____ 'Spim' is the term used to describe the IM version of e-mail spam.

ANSWER: True. This is the correct definition.
DIFFICULTY: moderate; PAGE: 138; OBJECTIVE: 4; TYPE: concept

63. _____ Traditional intranets are much easier to set up and maintain than blogs.

ANSWER: False. It is easier to set up and maintain a blog than an intranet.
DIFFICULTY: moderate; PAGE: 139; OBJECTIVE: 5; TYPE: concept

64. _____ Blogs are useful in business for communicating in the midst of a company crisis.

ANSWER: True. Blogs enable companies to distribute information instantly during a crisis.
DIFFICULTY: moderate; PAGE: 140; OBJECTIVE: 5; TYPE: concept

65. _____ Blogging is a great way to promote your company's products, so you should take advantage of the chance to tell readers about what's new.

ANSWER: False. Readers who think they're being advertised to will stop reading.
DIFFICULTY: moderate; PAGE: 142; OBJECTIVE: 5; TYPE: concept

66.	_____ If you do not frequently have new information to post, a traditional website will be more effective than a blog for your business.

ANSWER: True. Readers expect blogs to be updated frequently.
DIFFICULTY: moderate; PAGE: 142; OBJECTIVE: 3; TYPE: concept

67.	_____ To avoid mistakes, it is best to read a script when creating podcasts for business.

ANSWER: False. This eliminates the conversational feel of a podcast, which is one of the medium's most attractive features.
DIFFICULTY: moderate; PAGE: 143; OBJECTIVE: 6; TYPE: concept

68.	_____ To create the most basic podcasts, inexpensive equipment is all you'll need.

ANSWER: True. More expensive equipment and software are unnecessary unless you need higher production quality.
DIFFICULTY: moderate; PAGE: 143; OBJECTIVE: 6; TYPE: concept

Fill-in the Blank

69.	For many companies, e-mail has replaced the more traditional _____ as the primary means of internal communication.

ANSWER: Memo
DIFFICULTY: easy; PAGE: 131; OBJECTIVE: 1; TYPE: concept

70.	A video podcast is often called a _____ or _____.

ANSWER: Vidcast; Vodcast
DIFFICULTY: moderate; PAGE: 131; OBJECTIVE: 1; TYPE: concept

71.	A _____ is the online equivalent of recorded audio or video broadcasts.

ANSWER: Podcast
DIFFICULTY: moderate: PAGE: 131; OBJECTIVE: 1; TYPE: concept

72.	In a business letter, the _____ usually appears in the form of *Dear Mr.* or *Ms. Last Name*.

ANSWER: Salutation
DIFFICULTY: moderate; PAGE: 132; OBJECTIVE: 2; TYPE: concept

73.	*Sincerely* and *Cordially* are both examples of the _____ close in a business letter.

ANSWER: Complimentary
DIFFICULTY: moderate: PAGE: 132; OBJECTIVE: 2; TYPE: concept

74. Unlike business letters, memos generally do not include a _____ (such as *Dear Mr. Smith*) before the text of the message.

ANSWER: Salutation
DIFFICULTY: moderate: PAGE: 132; OBJECTIVE: 2; TYPE: concept

75. Memos are generally _____ private than other message forms because they are distributed without sealed envelopes.

ANSWER: Less
DIFFICULTY: moderate; PAGE: 132; OBJECTIVE: 2; TYPE: concept

76. E-mail _____ refers to all the efforts companies are making to keep e-mail clean and safe –from spam blocking and virus protection to content filtering.

ANSWER: Hygiene
DIFFICULTY: moderate; PAGE: 135; OBJECTIVE: 3; TYPE: concept

77. The _____ _____ of an e-mail is important because it helps readers decide whether to read the message or delete it.

ANSWER: Subject Line
DIFFICULTY: moderate; PAGE: 135; OBJECTIVE: 3; TYPE: concept

78. In an e-mail message, "cc" refers to _____ _____.

ANSWER: Courtesy Copy
DIFFICULTY: moderate; PAGE: 135; OBJECTIVE: 3; TYPE: concept

79. An e-mail message that contains insensitive, insulting, or critical comments is called a(n) _____.

ANSWER: Flame
DIFFICULTY: moderate; PAGE: 136; OBJECTIVE: 3; TYPE: concept

80. One feature of instant messaging software is _____ *awareness*, which enables users to see which people are at their desks and available to IM.

ANSWER: Presence
DIFFICULTY: difficult; PAGE: 136; OBJECTIVE: 4; TYPE: concept

81. Benefits of IM include is rapid response to urgent messages and its _____ cost when compared to phone calls and e-mail.

ANSWER: Lower
DIFFICULTY: moderate; PAGE: 136; OBJECTIVE: 4; TYPE: concept

82. The IM version of e-mail spam is known as _____.

ANSWER: Spim
DIFFICULTY: moderate; PAGE: 138; OBJECTIVE: 4; TYPE: concept

83.   Another term for a video blog is _____.

ANSWER: Vlog
DIFFICULTY: moderate; PAGE: 139; OBJECTIVE: 5; TYPE: concept

84.   Since blogs are easier to set up and maintain, many companies are using them to replace conventional _____ sites as a way for employees to communicate internally.

ANSWER: Intranet
DIFFICULTY: difficult; PAGE: 139; OBJECTIVE: 5; TYPE: concept

85.   Blogs have also become a popular medium for _____ support—enabling employees to answer questions and offer tips and advice.

ANSWER: Customer or Client
DIFFICULTY: moderate: PAGE: 139; OBJECTIVE: 5; TYPE: concept

86.   Viral _____ refers to spreading the word about your company and its products in much the same way that biological viruses are transmitted from person to person.

ANSWER: Marketing
DIFFICULTY: easy; PAGE: 140; OBJECTIVE: 5; TYPE: concept

87.   The _____ feature enables readers of your blog to receive headlines of new posts.

ANSWER: Newsfeed
DIFFICULTY: difficult; PAGE: 141; OBJECTIVE: 5; TYPE: concept

88.   When creating a _____ for clients to download and listen to, an inexpensive microphone and free recording software are all you need.

ANSWER: Podcast
DIFFICULTY: moderate; PAGE: 143; OBJECTIVE: 7; TYPE: concept

Short Answer/ Essay

89.   List at least five media that are popular for sending short business messages.

ANSWER: Popular media for sending short business messages include: 1) Memos and letters, 2) E-mail, 3) Instant messaging (IM), 4) Blogs, and 5) Podcasts.
DIFFICULTY: moderate PAGE: 130-31; OBJECTIVE: 1; TYPE: concept

90.   Give at least three reasons to send a hard copy of a business message instead of using an electronic medium.

ANSWER: Reasons for sending a printed message include: 1) When you want to make a formal impression, 2) When you need to accompany products with other physical materials, 3) When you want to stand out from the flood of electronic messages your audience receives, and 4) When you are legally required to provide information in printed form.
DIFFICULTY: moderate; PAGE: 131; OBJECTIVE: 1; TYPE: concept

91. Briefly explain why it is important to pay attention to issues such as spelling, punctuation, and grammar when composing e-mail messages in business.

ANSWER: As a general rule, the time you save with careless e-mail writing won't make up for the damage it can do to your career. First, sloppy writing may require less time for writers, but it usually demands more time from readers who are forced to dig the meaning out of poorly written messages. Second, people who care about effective communication often judge the quality of your work by the quality of your writing. Third, it is easy for e-mail messages to end up in places you never expected, so it is important for them to make a good impression.
DIFFICULTY: difficult; PAGE: 134; OBJECTIVE: 3; TYPE: concept

92. Define 'e-mail hygiene.'

ANSWER: E-mail hygiene refers to all the efforts companies are making to keep e-mail clean and safe—from spam blocking and virus protection to content filtering.
DIFFICULTY: easy; PAGE: 135; OBJECTIVE: 3; TYPE: concept

93. Briefly describe the characteristics of an effective e-mail subject line.

ANSWER: An effective subject line is both informative and compelling, and captures the audience's attention. It does more than just describe or classify message content, and builds interest with key words, quotations, directions, or questions.
DIFFICULTY: moderate; PAGE: 135; OBJECTIVE: 3; TYPE: concept

94. Write an informative subject line for the following e-mail.

From July 6-9 the employee cafeteria will be closed in order to update the electrical system in the kitchen. Employees may bring their own food and eat in the cafeteria, but no food will be served on those dates.

ANSWER: Cafeteria kitchen closed July 6-9 (or something similar)
DIFFICULTY: difficult; PAGE: 135; OBJECTIVE: 3; TYPE: application

95. Define 'flames' and explain how to avoid them in business.

ANSWER: Flames are e-mail messages that contain insensitive, insulting, or critical comments. To avoid sending them, do not allow your emotions to dictate what you include in e-mail messages. If you do write an emotionally-charged message, let it sit for at least a day and ask yourself, "Would I say this to my audience face to face?"
DIFFICULTY: moderate; PAGE: 136; OBJECTIVE: 3; TYPE: concept

96. List at least three drawbacks of using instant messaging in business.

ANSWER: Potential disadvantages of using IM in business include: 1) security problems such as computer viruses and intercepted messages, 2) the need for user authentication, 3) the challenge of logging messages for later review and archiving, and 4) incompatibility between competing IM systems.
DIFFICULTY: difficult; PAGE: 136; OBJECTIVE: 4; TYPE: application

97.	List at least three advantages of using blogs in business.

ANSWER: **Effective blogs enable companies to 1) communicate with personal style and an authentic voice (rather than an impersonal "corporate voice,") 2) deliver new information quickly during crises and at other times, 3) Choose topics of peak interest to audiences, and 4) encourage audiences to join the conversation (which can provide companies with important news, information, and insights).**
DIFFICULTY: difficult; PAGE: 138-39; OBJECTIVE: 5; TYPE: concept

98.	Give at least three examples of how podcasts could replace more traditional message formats in business.

ANSWER: **(Answers may vary.) Real estate agents could record audio podcasts that potential homebuyers could listen to while walking through homes. Marketing departments could replace expensive printed brochures with video podcasts that demonstrate new products in action. Human resource departments could use podcasts to offer video tours of their companies to entice new recruits.**
DIFFICULTY: difficult; PAGE: 142-43; OBJECTIVE: 6; TYPE: application

CHAPTER 7
WRITING ROUTINE AND POSITIVE MESSAGES

Multiple Choice

1.   The three-step writing process includes all of the following steps *except*:
    a. planning
    b. writing
    c. completing
    d. sending

ANSWER: d. The three-step process includes planning, writing, and completing.
DIFFICULTY: easy; PAGE: 160-61; OBJECTIVE: 1; TYPE: concept

2.   In the planning stage of the three-step process, it is important that you
    a. analyze your purpose.
    b. gather relevant information.
    c. organize your information effectively.
    d. all of the above

ANSWER: d. You may do all these things quickly with routine messages, but it is important to analyze purpose and audience and to adapt your message.
DIFFICULTY: moderate; PAGE: 160-61; OBJECTIVE: 1; TYPE: concept

3.   Finding out what readers need to know and having all of the relevant information is part of the _____ step of the writing process.
    a. completing
    b. organizing
    c. writing
    d. planning

ANSWER: d. These actions are part of investigating the topic in the planning step. See Figure 7.1
DIFFICULTY: difficulty; PAGE: 160-61; OBJECTIVE: 1; TYPE: concept

4.   The completing step includes
    a. organizing your message.
    b. revising your message.
    c. considering the customs of an international audience.
    d. all of the above

ANSWER: b. Proofreading is part of the completing step. The other two are part of the writing step.
DIFFICULTY: moderate; PAGE: 161; OBJECTIVE: 1; TYPE: concept

5. The strategy for making routine requests includes all of the following *except*:
   a. state your request up front
   b. explain and justify your request
   c. adapt your request after receiving reader feedback
   d. request specific action

ANSWER: c. Adapting your request based on reader feedback is not part of the routine requests writing strategy. Routine requests should state the request, explain it, and ask for action to achieve that goal.
DIFFICULTY: moderate; PAGE: 161; OBJECTIVE: 2; TYPE: concept

6. When stating your request it is important to pay attention to
   a. tone.
   b. asking relevant questions.
   c. providing contact information.
   d. organizing your questions.

ANSWER: a. Even though you expect a favorable response, instead of demanding an action, soften your request with words such as "please." Open with a favorable tone.
DIFFICULTY: moderate; PAGE: 161; OBJECTIVE: 2; TYPE: concept

7. When stating your request in a routine request, you should do all of the following *except*:
   a. assume your audience will comply with the request
   b. begin the communication with a personal introduction
   c. state precisely what you want
   d. use the word "please" to soften your request

ANSWER: b. Personal introductions are not needed here.
DIFFICULTY: difficulty; PAGE: 161; OBJECTIVE: 2; TYPE: concept

8. When stating your request you should
   a. use words such as *Please* and *I would appreciate*.
   b. assume your audience will comply.
   c. state precisely what you want.
   d. all of the above

ANSWER: d. When stating a request you should follow all of these guidelines.
DIFFICULTY: moderate; PAGE: 161; OBJECTIVE: 3; TYPE: concept

9. In the body of your request you should
   a. use an indirect approach.
   b. explain and justify your request.
   c. provide contact information.
   d. all of the above

ANSWER: b. After you have stated your request in the opening, you should then explain and justify your request in the body of the message.
DIFFICULTY: difficult; PAGE: 161; OBJECTIVE: 2; TYPE: concept

10. When listing a series of questions, you should
    a. ask the most important questions last.
    b. ask only relevant questions.
    c. ask as many questions as possible to avoid having to send another message.
    d. all of the above

ANSWER: b. You should put important questions first, ask only relevant questions and don't overwhelm your reader with extra questions. Deal with one topic at a time.
DIFFICULTY: moderate; PAGE: 161-62; OBJECTIVE: 2; TYPE: concept

11. A simple request says all of the following *except*:
    a. This is what I want to know.
    b. This is why I'm making the request.
    c. This is why it may be in your interest to help me.
    d. This is why I demand immediate action from you.

ANSWER: d. It is preferable to soften your request with words such as *please* and *I would appreciate*.
DIFFICULTY: moderate; PAGE: 161; OBJECTIVE: 2; TYPE: concept

12. The body of a simple request should
    a. give a clear statement of your reason for writing.
    b. provide an explanation to justify your request.
    c. include a deadline for when you need the request completed.
    d. catch your reader's attention.

ANSWER: b. The body should provide whatever explanation is needed to justify your request. A deadline goes in the closing; the other two go in the opening.
DIFFICULTY: moderate; PAGE: 161; OBJECTIVE: 2; TYPE: concept

13. Routine, positive messages should do all of the following *except*:
    a. leave your reader with a good impression
    b. use an indirect approach
    c. provide all required detail
    d. communicate the information or good news

ANSWER: b. You should use a direct approach for positive messages, requests, and routine replies.
DIFFICULTY: moderate; PAGE: 161; OBJECTIVE: 2; TYPE: concept

14. When requesting information and action, all of the following are correct *except*:
    a. Use a direct approach.
    b. Provide an explanation to justify your request in the opening statement.
    c. Internal requests to fellow employees may be oral and are casual.
    d. The closing statement should include a specific account of what you expect and a deadline, if appropriate.

ANSWER: b. The explanation should be in the body of the message.
DIFFICULTY: difficult; PAGE: 161; OBJECTIVE: 3; TYPE: concept

15. The closing of a request should
    a. give a date or time for completion of the request.
    b. provide contact information.
    c. express appreciation or goodwill.
    d. all of the above

ANSWER: d. An effective closing needs to provide a date or time for the response, help your readers contact you if they have questions, and should express goodwill.
DIFFICULTY: moderate; PAGE: 162; OBJECTIVE: 2; TYPE: concept

16. Types of routine requests include all of the following *except*:
    a. asking for action
    b. requesting information
    c. making claims
    d. delivering bad news

ANSWER: d. Delivering bad news is not a type of routine request. The format and tone for this kind of communication are very different from a routine request.
DIFFICULTY: moderate; PAGE: 162; OBJECTIVE: 2; TYPE: concept

17. The opening of a request for a recommendation should include
    a. a request for a recommendation.
    b. a reminder of who you are.
    c. the dates of your association with your reader.
    d. all of the above

ANSWER: d. The opening should remind your reader about who you are and ask for a recommendation.
DIFFICULTY: moderate; PAGE: 162; OBJECTIVE: 4; TYPE: concept

18. When requesting a recommendation you should include
    a. information about yourself that the reader might use to support a recommendation.
    b. a copy of your résumé.
    c. the name and address of the person who should receive the recommendation.
    d. all of the above

ANSWER: d. All of these should be part of your request for a recommendation. They will help the writer produce a better account of your skills and abilities.
DIFFICULTY: moderate; PAGE: 162-64; OBJECTIVE: 3; TYPE: concept

19. When making a claim or requesting an adjustment, your closing should
    a. clearly state how angry and disappointed you are.
    b. explain the specific details of the problem.
    c. request a specific action to resolve the situation.
    d. all of the above

ANSWER: c. The tone should be professional rather than angry and the details go in the body, not in the closing.
DIFFICULTY: difficult; PAGE: 164; OBJECTIVE: 3; TYPE: concept

20. The body of a claim or a request for an adjustment should include
   a. all information needed to verify your claim.
   b. a request for a specific action.
   c. a suggestion that the relationship will continue only if the problem is solved satisfactorily.
   d. all of the above

ANSWER: a. The body should include a complete, specific explanation of the details with all information an adjuster would need to verify your claim.
DIFFICULTY: difficult; PAGE: 164; OBJECTIVE: 2; TYPE: concept

21. When requesting an immediate recommendation, you should include
   a. a copy of your résumé.
   b. a stamped, preaddressed envelope.
   c. the deadline for submitting it.
   d. all of the above

ANSWER: d. All of these things will make it more likely that your writer will be able to produce an effective letter.
DIFFICULTY: moderate; PAGE: 164; OBJECTIVE: 2; TYPE: application

22. When writing a positive message, open with
   a. a review of the events that led up to the situation you will be discussing.
   b. a direct statement of the good news.
   c. an explanation of how the decision was reached.
   d. all of the above

ANSWER: b. Start good news messages by directly and clearly delivering the good news.
DIFFICULTY: difficult; PAGE: 164; OBJECTIVE: 4; TYPE: concept

23. Which of the following is the best opening for a good-news letter offering a job to a potential employee?
   a. Congratulations, we would like to offer you a position at our company.
   b. As you know, much deliberation and debate has gone into interviewing and selecting only the very best candidates for this position.
   c. Thank you for meeting with us last week to discuss employment possibilities.
   d. any of the above

ANSWER: a. When delivering good news, open directly with the good news.
DIFFICULTY: moderate; PAGE: 164; OBJECTIVE: 4; TYPE: application

24. The body of a positive message should
   a. explain your point completely.
   b. help the audience avoid any confusion or lingering doubt.
   c. maintain a supportive tone.
   d. all of the above

ANSWER: d. The body of a positive message should be positive and provide enough details to prevent your audience from experiencing any confusion or doubt.
DIFFICULTY: moderate; PAGE: 167; OBJECTIVE: 4; TYPE: concept

25. If you have mildly disappointing information to deliver as part of a positive message you should
   a. put the negative information in a favorable context.
   b. put the negative information in a separate message; never combine positive and negative information.
   c. put the negative information first.
   d. put the negative information last.

ANSWER: a. You should put the negative information in a favorable context by emphasizing how the change or the news might actually benefit the reader.
DIFFICULTY: moderate; PAGE: 167; OBJECTIVE: 4; TYPE: concept

26. If you have strongly negative information to deliver as part of a positive message you should
   a. open with the negative information.
   b. use an indirect approach.
   c. put the negative information in a separate message; never combine positive and negative information.
   d. explain how the negative information will impact the positive information.

ANSWER: b. If you are delivering a negative message along with the good news or as part of a routine reply, avoid using the routine messages and good-news strategy. Instead use an indirect approach.
DIFFICULTY: difficult; PAGE: 167; OBJECTIVE: 4; TYPE: concept

27. The closing of a routine reply or positive message should
   a. clearly state who will do what next.
   b. explain the reasons for any negative news that you have mentioned.
   c. offer an explanation for why this decision was made.
   d. all of the above

ANSWER: a. Close on a positive note, highlight a benefit to the audience, express goodwill, and clearly state who will do what next.
DIFFICULTY: difficult; PAGE: 167; OBJECTIVE: 4; TYPE: concept

28. The four types of routine replies and positive messages include all of the following *except*:
   a. granting requests for information and action
   b. granting claims and adjustments
   c. refusing requests
   d. sending goodwill messages

ANSWER: c. The fourth type of positive message is providing recommendations and references. Refusing a request would not use a positive message strategy.
DIFFICULTY: moderate; PAGE: 167; OBJECTIVE: 4; TYPE: concept

29. Use the direct approach when
    a. your answer to a request is yes.
    b. you are providing straightforward information.
    c. you are delivering good news.
    d. all of the above

ANSWER: d. A direct approach for these kinds of communication is the most effective.
DIFFICULTY: easy; PAGE: 168; OBJECTIVE: 4; TYPE: concept

30. Form responses to handle routine requests
    a. should never be used.
    b. can be effective if your organization receives numerous routine requests.
    c. are cold, impersonal, and unprofessional.
    d. all of the above

ANSWER: b. A form response to frequent routine requests allows you to handle these requests quickly and consistently.
DIFFICULTY: moderate; PAGE: 169; OBJECTIVE: 4; TYPE: concept

31. When granting a claim or an adjustment it is important to
    a. use an indirect approach.
    b. remember that customers frequently make up problems to try to win adjustments.
    c. treat them as opportunities for building customer loyalty.
    d. all of the above

ANSWER: c. Angry customers will hurt your business and create poor public relations. Handling claims and adjustments well will build customer loyalty.
DIFFICULTY: moderate; PAGE: 169-70; OBJECTIVE: 5; TYPE: concept

32. The most sensible reaction to a routine claim is to
    a. assume that the customer is not telling the whole truth.
    b. assume that the customer's version of events is an honest statement.
    c. avoid granting the customer's request to prevent fraud.
    d. avoid acknowledging any fault on the part of your company.

ANSWER: b. Few people go to the trouble of requesting an adjustment unless they actually have a problem. So, you should assume that the claimant's account of the transaction is an honest statement of what happened.
DIFFICULTY: difficult; PAGE: 170; OBJECTIVE: 4; TYPE: concept

33. When granting a claim or making an adjustment you should do all of the following
    except:
    a. promise that the problem will not happen again
    b. explain how you have resolved (or plan to resolve) the situation
    c. imply that the problem was an unusual incident
    d. avoid blaming any specific individual by name

ANSWER: a. You cannot be sure that the problem will never happen again. Don't make unrealistic promises about situations that may be beyond your control.
DIFFICULTY: moderate; PAGE: 170; OBJECTIVE: 4; TYPE: concept

34.   If the customer is at fault your response can
       a.   reject the claim and justify your refusal.
       b.   weigh the cost of making the adjustment against the cost of losing future business
             from one or more customers.
       c.   help the customers understand what they did wrong.
       d.   all of the above

**ANSWER: d. You want to carefully consider the best response. You may want to simply
reject the claim, but you will lose the customer if you do so. You may want to grant the
claim while educating the customer about how to not repeat the mistake.**
DIFFICULTY: moderate; PAGE: 170; OBJECTIVE: 5; TYPE: concept

35.   If you choose to grant a claim even though your customer is at fault, you should
       a.   educate the customer about what went wrong.
       b.   try to prevent a reoccurrence of this complaint.
       c.   open with the good news.
       d.   all of the above

**ANSWER: d. You want to open with the good news and then tactfully explain what the
customer did to cause the problem. You need to educate the customer to prevent a repeat of
this claim.**
DIFFICULTY: difficult; PAGE: 170; OBJECTIVE: 5; TYPE: concept

36.   When writing a letter of recommendation you should
       a.   explain the nature of your relationship with the candidate.
       b.   give facts relevant to the position being sought.
       c.   state your overall evaluation of the candidate's suitability for the job.
       d.   all of the above

**ANSWER: d. Your letter should contain all the relevant data that will help convince
readers that the person being recommended has the characteristics necessary for the job or
benefit being sought.**
DIFFICULTY: easy; PAGE: 172; OBJECTIVE: 4; TYPE: concept

37.   If you have negative or critical things to say about a person for whom you are writing a
       letter of recommendation, you should
       a.   omit the negatives from your letter.
       b.   list them as areas for improvement.
       c.   use vague wording and unclear statements to suggest a negative evaluation
             without coming right out and saying it.
       d.   all of the above

**ANSWER: b. It is unethical to omit the negatives. Instead you should stick to the facts,
avoid value judgments, and place your criticism in the context of a generally favorable
recommendation.**
DIFFICULTY: difficult; PAGE: 172; OBJECTIVE: 4; TYPE: application

38. All of the following are good ideas for writing letters of recommendation *except*:
    a. illustrate your general points with specific examples
    b. explain the nature of your relationship with the candidate
    c. indicate whether you're answering a request from the candidate or taking the initiative to write
    d. omit information about the candidate's obvious shortcomings

ANSWER: d. List shortcomings as areas for future improvement.
DIFFICULTY: moderate; PAGE: 172; OBJECTIVE: 4; TYPE: concept

39. Unlike responses to requests for information, informative messages
    a. are not solicited by the reader.
    b. do not require an explanation of why you are writing.
    c. are usually written in the indirect format.
    d. all of the above

ANSWER: a. Since an informative message is not solicited by the reader, it is important to explain why the reader is receiving it.
DIFFICULTY: moderate; PAGE: 172; OBJECTIVE: 6; TYPE: concept

40. Sincere, honest goodwill messages
    a. can enhance your relationship with customers, colleagues, and other businesspeople.
    b. should always be sent confidentially.
    c. should use an indirect approach.
    d. all of the above

ANSWER: a. Effective goodwill messages help to improve your business relationships.
DIFFICULTY: moderate; PAGE: 172; OBJECTIVE: 7; TYPE: concept

41. When writing a goodwill message it is important to
    a. avoid exaggeration.
    b. come across as sincere and honest.
    c. back up compliments with specific examples.
    d. all of the above

ANSWER: d. Be sincere and honest and avoid exaggeration. Readers often regard more restrained praise as being more sincere. Avoid looking like you are writing to achieve personal gain rather than to convey goodwill.
DIFFICULTY: easy; PAGE: 173-74; OBJECTIVE: 7; TYPE: concept

42. Goodwill messages include all of the following *except*:
    a. congratulations
    b. messages of appreciation
    c. recommendations
    d. condolences

ANSWER: c. Recommendations are not a kind of goodwill message.
DIFFICULTY: moderate; PAGE: 174; OBJECTIVE: 7; TYPE: concept

43.   Appreciation messages are very important because they
    a. make people feel good.
    b. encourage further excellence.
    c. can become part of a person's personnel file.
    d. all of the above

ANSWER: d. All of these are important reasons to write appreciation messages. They improve your business relationships and encourage further excellence.
DIFFICULTY: moderate; PAGE: 174; OBJECTIVE: 7; TYPE: concept

44.   A condolence message should *not*
    a. be sent as promptly as possible.
    b. open with a brief statement of sympathy.
    c. focus on how difficult and painful things will now be for the reader.
    d. all of the above

ANSWER: c. Write a condolence letter promptly, open with an expression of sympathy and avoid dwelling on the details of the loss or adding to the reader's anguish.
DIFFICULTY: moderate; PAGE: 174-76; OBJECTIVE: 7; TYPE: application

45.   In writing a condolence letter, all of the following are correct suggestions *except*:
    a. end the message with a statement of sympathy
    b. write about special qualities of the deceased
    c. write in your own words
    d. recount a memory or anecdote of the deceased

ANSWER: a. A statement of sympathy is in the opening statement of the letter.
DIFFICULTY: difficult; PAGE: 174-76; OBJECTIVE: 7; TYPE: concept

True/False

46.   _____ Planning your message includes analyzing your purpose and selecting an appropriate medium.

ANSWER: True. These are important parts of the planning step.
DIFFICULTY: easy; PAGE: 160-61; OBJECTIVE: 1; TYPE: concept

47.   _____When you make a routine request, you anticipate that your audience will comply.

ANSWER: True. This is communication that is part of the normal course of business.
DIFFICULTY: moderate; PAGE: 161; OBJECTIVE: 2; TYPE: concept

48.   _____ For routine requests you should use an indirect approach.

ANSWER: False. Use a direct approach for routine requests.
DIFFICULTY: moderate; PAGE: 161; OBJECTIVE: 2; TYPE: concept

49. _____ When writing routine requests, your message should be forceful and demand that your audience comply with your request.

ANSWER: False. Instead of demanding action you should soften your request with words such as "please".
DIFFICULTY: easy; PAGE: 161; OBJECTIVE: 2; TYPE: application

50. _____ When listing a series of questions, you should save the most important ones for last.

ANSWER: False. The most important questions go first. Then the reader is more likely to see them.
DIFFICULTY: moderate; PAGE: 161; OBJECTIVE: 2; TYPE: application

51. _____ Your closing should always include a specific request for action.

ANSWER: True. Restate your request and ask that readers respond by a specific time or date.
DIFFICULTY: moderate; PAGE: 162; OBJECTIVE: 2; TYPE: application

52. _____ Before giving someone's name as a reference, ask the person's permission.

ANSWER: True. Some people are not comfortable writing recommendation letters, and some organizations have policies that prohibit employees from endorsing former colleagues or suppliers.
DIFFICULTY: moderate; PAGE: 162; OBJECTIVE: 3; TYPE: concept

53. _____ Always include a "thank you in advance" as part of your goodwill closing.

ANSWER: False. If a reader's response warrants a thank you, send it after you've received the reply.
DIFFICULTY: difficult; PAGE: 162; OBJECTIVE: 2; TYPE: application

54. _____ Two of the three types of routine requests include making claims and requesting adjustments and asking for recommendations.

ANSWER: True. The other category is asking for information and action.
DIFFICULTY: moderate; PAGE: 162-64; OBJECTIVE: 2; TYPE: concept

55. _____ When writing a claim letter, your tone should be angry and upset; otherwise the letter may be ignored.

ANSWER: False. You should use an objective, courteous tone to create a more favorable impression.
DIFFICULTY: easy; PAGE: 164; OBJECTIVE: 3; TYPE: concept

56. _____ A claim is a formal complaint that you make when you are dissatisfied with a company's product or service.

ANSWER: True. A claim may also include a request for an adjustment or a settlement.
DIFFICULTY: easy; PAGE: 164; OBJECTIVE: 2; TYPE: concept

57. _____ The opening of a claim should include a request for a specific action or solution to the problem.

ANSWER: False. The opening should state the problem. Save the request for action for the close.
DIFFICULTY: difficult; PAGE: 164; OBJECTIVE: 2; TYPE: application

58. _____ When making a routine reply or sending a positive message it is important to use an indirect approach to make sure that the audience reads your entire message.

ANSWER: False. Use a direct approach to save time for positive messages and routine replies.
DIFFICULTY: moderate; PAGE: 164; OBJECTIVE: 4; TYPE: concept

59. _____ One of the main goals when sending routine replies and positive messages is to leave your reader with a good impression of your company.

ANSWER: True. You should deliver positive messages in a courteous, up-beat way that will create a good impression of you and your company.
DIFFICULTY: moderate; PAGE: 164; OBJECTIVE: 4; TYPE: concept

60. _____ When using the strategy for sending routine replies and positive messages it is acceptable to include negative information only if you are reasonably sure that the audience will still respond positively.

ANSWER: True. If the message is too negative for a positive response, you should use an indirect approach instead of the direct approach recommended for routine replies and positive messages.
DIFFICULTY: moderate; PAGE: 167; OBJECTIVE: 4; TYPE: concept

61. _____ When making a request it is important to explain how the request will benefit the readers.

ANSWER: True. Tell the readers how fulfilling your request is in their best interests.
DIFFICULTY: moderate; PAGE: 167; OBJECTIVE: 3; TYPE: concept

62. _____ The closing of a positive message should express appreciation or goodwill.

ANSWER: True. End positive messages with a courteous close.
DIFFICULTY: easy; PAGE: 167; OBJECTIVE: 4; TYPE: application

63. _____ A form message is a viable way to handle routine requests quickly and consistently.

ANSWER: True. Form messages that have been designed for replies to frequent routine requests can be carefully written and designed ahead of time.
DIFFICULTY: moderate; PAGE: 169; OBJECTIVE: 4; TYPE: concept

64. _____ People frequently make up claims in an attempt to win an adjustment from a company. You should always assume that claimants are not telling you the whole truth.

ANSWER: False. Few people go to the trouble of requesting an adjustment unless they actually have a problem. Unless the same customer repeatedly submits dubious claims or the dollar amount is very large, assume the claimant's account is honest.
DIFFICULTY: difficult; PAGE: 170; OBJECTIVE: 4; TYPE: concept

65. _____ You should respond to a claim differently depending on who is at fault.

ANSWER: True. Although you should always be courteous, you will respond differently depending on who caused the problem.
DIFFICULTY: easy; PAGE: 170; OBJECTIVE: 4; TYPE: concept

66. _____ When your company is at fault you should imply that the customer deserves at least some of the blame.

ANSWER: False. In this case it is important to take responsibility for setting matters straight.
DIFFICULTY: moderate; PAGE: 170; OBJECTIVE: 5; TYPE: application

67. _____ When your company is at fault you should respond to the request for an adjustment by carefully explaining who caused the problem.

ANSWER: False. Avoid blaming individuals or departments.
DIFFICULTY: difficult; PAGE: 170; OBJECTIVE: 5; TYPE: application

68. _____ If the customer is at fault, you should never grant the requested adjustment. If you do, this will make it seem as if you are acknowledging that your company was at fault when it was not.

ANSWER: False. Sometimes when the customer is at fault you should still do what is requested. If not, you will lose the customer. You must balance the cost of making the claim against the cost of losing future business from one or more customers.
DIFFICULTY: difficult; PAGE: 170; OBJECTIVE: 5; TYPE: application

69. _____ If you choose to grant a claim even though the customer is wrong, you should open the letter by acknowledging that the customer caused the problem—bring attention to the fact that your company is not at fault.

ANSWER: False. You should open with the good news that your company is granting the claim. Keep the focus positive.
DIFFICULTY: moderate; PAGE: 170; OBJECTIVE: 5; TYPE: application

70. _____ Form letters for responding to complaints are never appropriate and should not be used.

ANSWER: False. Companies often receive many claims that are quite similar. In this case, companies can create a form letter that can be customized through word processing and then individually signed.
DIFFICULTY: difficult; PAGE: 169; OBJECTIVE: 5; TYPE: concept

71.	_____ You should never honor a claim if a third party is at fault. It makes your company look bad.

ANSWER: False. Your best response is to honor the claim even if a third party is at fault. This will maintain your company's reputation for fairness. You can recoup the cost of the claim from the third party.
DIFFICULTY: difficult; PAGE: 170-72; OBJECTIVE: 5; TYPE: application

72.	_____ When writing a recommendation letter, you have an obligation to mention any shortcomings that are serious and related to job performance.

ANSWER: True. It is unethical to omit negative job related information from a recommendation.
DIFFICULTY: moderate; PAGE: 172; OBJECTIVE: 4; TYPE: concept

73.	_____ There are no significant differences between informative messages and responses to requests for information.

ANSWER: False. Unlike responses to requests for information, an informative message is not solicited by the reader and must include an explanation of why the reader is receiving it.
DIFFICULTY: moderate; PAGE: 172; OBJECTIVE: 6; TYPE: concept

74.	_____ When writing a letter of recommendation, the candidate's full name and your relationship with the candidate should be included.

ANSWER: True. This information makes it easier for the recipient to match your letter with the candidate's other application materials.
DIFFICULTY: moderate; PAGE: 172; OBJECTIVE: 4; TYPE: concept

75.	_____ When writing a goodwill message you should be extravagant and even exaggerated in your praise; people like to hear good things about themselves.

ANSWER: False. To come across as sincere, avoid exaggeration and illustrate your general points with specific examples.
DIFFICULTY: moderate; PAGE: 173; OBJECTIVE: 4; TYPE: concept

Fill-in the Blank

76.	The three-step writing process for routine messages includes _____, _____, and _____.

ANSWER: Planning; writing; completing
DIFFICULTY: moderate; PAGE: 160-61; OBJECTIVE: 1; TYPE: concept

77.	Adapting to your audience and maintaining a "you" attitude is part of the _____ step of the writing process for routine messages.

ANSWER: Writing
DIFFICULTY: moderate; PAGE: 161; OBJECTIVE: 1; TYPE: concept

78. When making a routine request, you should use a/an _____ approach and open with a statement of your request.

ANSWER: Direct
DIFFICULTY: easy; PAGE: 161; OBJECTIVE: 2; TYPE: concept

79. When making a routine request pay particular attention to the sound and feel or the _____ of your sentences. For example, instead of demanding action, soften your requests with words like "please" and "thank you".

ANSWER: Tone
DIFFICULTY: moderate; PAGE: 161; OBJECTIVE: 2; TYPE: concept

80. The closing of a routine request should include a specific request for _____.

ANSWER: Action
DIFFICULTY: moderate; PAGE: 162; OBJECTIVE: 2; TYPE: concept

81. When asking an employer to vouch for your ability, skills, character, and integrity you are requesting a _____.

ANSWER: Recommendation
DIFFICULTY: moderate; PAGE: 162; OBJECTIVE: 4; TYPE: concept

82. When you are dissatisfied with a company's product or service you make a formal complaint called a _____.

ANSWER: Claim
DIFFICULTY: moderate; PAGE: 164; OBJECTIVE: 4; TYPE: concept

83. When you make a complaint against a company because of poor service or a defective product, the settling of that complaint (either monetarily or otherwise) is called a/an_____.

ANSWER: Adjustment
DIFFICULTY: difficult; PAGE: 164; OBJECTIVE: 4; TYPE: concept

84. List two of the four types of routine replies and positive messages:
_____ and _____.

ANSWER: Choices here include: 1) granting requests for information and action 2) granting claims and requests for adjustments 3) providing recommendations and references 4) sending goodwill messages
DIFFICULTY: difficult; PAGE: 167; OBJECTIVE: 4; TYPE: concept

85. To handle numerous, routine inquiries, companies usually develop standard _____ messages that can be personalized for each recipient.

ANSWER: Form
DIFFICULTY: moderate; PAGE: 169; OBJECTIVE: 4; TYPE: concept

86. Unlike responses to requests for information, _____ messages require that you explain why the reader is receiving the message.

ANSWER: Informative
DIFFICULTY: moderate; PAGE: 172; OBJECTIVE: 6; TYPE: concept

87. Two of the three kinds of goodwill messages include _____ and _____.

ANSWER: Choices here include: 1) congratulations 2) messages of appreciation 3) condolences
DIFFICULTY: moderate; PAGE: 174; OBJECTIVE: 7; TYPE: concept

88. Written expressions of sympathy are called _____.

ANSWER: Condolences
DIFFICULTY: moderate; PAGE: 174; OBJECTIVE: 6; TYPE: concept

Short Answer/Essay

89. List the guidelines to follow for the opening of a routine request.

ANSWER:
- **place your request first**
- **pay attention to tone**
- **assume your audience will comply**
- **be specific**

DIFFICULTY: moderate; PAGE: 161; OBJECTIVE: 2; TYPE: concept

90. List the guidelines to follow in the body of a routine request.

ANSWER:
- **explain and justify your request**
- **show how fulfilling the request will benefit the readers**
- **ask the most important questions first**
- **ask only relevant questions**
- **deal with only one topic per question**

DIFFICULTY: difficult; PAGE: 161-62; OBJECTIVE: 2; TYPE: concept

91. List the elements that should be included in an effective closing for a routine request.

ANSWER:
- **request a specific action**
- **provide contact information**
- **express appreciation or goodwill**

DIFFICULTY: difficult; PAGE: 162; OBJECTIVE: 2; TYPE: concept

92. Describe the three-step strategy for sending routine replies and positive messages.

ANSWER: 1) Use a direct approach. Open with your main idea, which includes the positive reply or the good news. 2) Then use the body to explain all the relevant details. 3) Finally, close cordially, perhaps highlighting a benefit to your reader.
DIFFICULTY: moderate; PAGE: 164-67; OBJECTIVE: 4; TYPE: concept

93. Explain what you should do when replying to a claim when the customer is at fault.

ANSWER: First you must decide whether the cost of making the adjustment outweighs the cost of losing this customer's future business. You can refuse the claim and explain your refusal, but remember that refusal will most likely cost you this customer's future business and perhaps the business of many of the customer's friends. If you grant the claim, be sure to tactfully try to educate the customer on how to prevent this situation from occurring again. Be careful not to offend the person by being condescending or preachy.
DIFFICULTY: moderate; PAGE: 169-70; OBJECTIVE: 5; TYPE: application

94. Explain some general guidelines to keep in mind when responding to a request for adjustment when a third party is at fault.

ANSWER: No general scheme applies to every case involving a third party, but if customers contact you, you need to respond with messages that explain how the problem will be solved. Pointing fingers is both unproductive and unprofessional; resolving the situation is the only issue customers care about.
DIFFICULTY: moderate; PAGE: 169-72; OBJECTIVE: 5; TYPE: application

95. Explain what you should include in a good recommendation letter.

ANSWER: You should include: the candidate's name, the job or objective being sought, the nature of your relationship with the candidate, whether you're answering a request or taking the initiative, facts relevant to the position sought, and your overall evaluation of the candidate's suitability for the job or benefit. You should illustrate your general points with specific examples that show the person's abilities.
DIFFICULTY: difficult; PAGE: 172; OBJECTIVE: 4; TYPE: concept

96. How should you deal with a candidate's shortcomings when writing a recommendation?

ANSWER: You have an obligation to mention any shortcomings that are serious and related to job performance. The best option is to present the shortcomings as areas for future improvement.
DIFFICULTY: moderate; PAGE: 172; OBJECTIVE: 4; TYPE: application

97. Briefly explain how creating informative messages differs from responding to information requests.

ANSWER: When you respond to a request for information, the reader already knows why he or she is receiving your message. Informative messages, on the other hand, are not solicited by the reader so they must include an explanation of why they are being sent.
DIFFICULTY: moderate; PAGE: 172; OBJECTIVE: 6; TYPE: concept

98.   Explain why goodwill messages are important.

ANSWER: Goodwill messages can improve your relationships with customers, colleagues, and other businesspeople. They should be sincere and honest, otherwise the writer appears interested only in personal gain. Avoid exaggeration, back up compliments with specific points, and be restrained but sincere in your praise.
DIFFICULTY: moderate; PAGE: 172-73; OBJECTIVE: 7; TYPE: concept

99.   Briefly explain why appreciation messages are important and what they should include.

ANSWER: It is important to recognize the contributions of employees, colleagues, suppliers, and other associates. Your praise will make the person feel good and encourage further good work. It also can become part of a person's personnel file. The message should specifically mention the person or persons you want to praise.
DIFFICULTY: difficult; PAGE: 174; OBJECTIVE: 7; TYPE: concept

100.   Describe the contents and characteristics of a well-written condolence letter.

ANSWER: Condolence letters should open with a brief statement of sympathy. In the body, mention the good qualities or the positive contributions made by the deceased. State what the person or business meant to you. In closing, you can offer your condolences and your best wishes. Be sure to keep reminiscences brief, write in your own words, be tactful, take special care to avoid misspellings and mistakes, write about special qualities of the deceased and those of the bereaved person who will receive the letter.
DIFFICULTY: difficult; PAGE: 174-76; OBJECTIVE: 7; TYPE: application

CHAPTER 8
WRITING NEGATIVE MESSAGES

Multiple Choice

1. If you have to say "no," you should always
    a. try to gain the audience's acceptance of your decision.
    b. deliver it directly.
    c. pull back from communicating.
    d. all of the above

ANSWER: a. This is an important goal in negative messages.
DIFFICULTY: moderate; PAGE: 196-97; OBJECTIVE: 1; TYPE: concept

2. When planning your bad-news message you should
    a. adapt your medium and tone to your audience.
    b. analyze how your readers will receive your message.
    c. determine whether or not to send the message in the first place.
    d. all of the above

ANSWER: d. When planning your message carefully analyze the situation; determine how to best approach your audience. How will the audience be likely to respond?
DIFFICULTY: moderate; PAGE: 197; OBJECTIVE: 1; TYPE: concept

3. When delivering bad news, you want to accomplish all of the following goals *except*:
    a. to convey the bad news
    b. to encourage questions and correspondence from the reader
    c. to gain acceptance for the bad news
    d. to maintain a good image for your organization

ANSWER: b. You want to reduce or eliminate the need for further correspondence on the matter.
DIFFICULTY: moderate; PAGE: 197; OBJECTIVE: 1; TYPE: concept

4. When conveying negative news it is important to always
    a. maintain goodwill with your audience.
    b. use an indirect approach.
    c. convey the bad news directly.
    d. avoid acknowledging any emotional issues.

ANSWER: a. Your tone helps your readers accept that your bad news represents a firm and fair decision. It also helps the readers preserve their pride.
DIFFICULTY: moderate; PAGE: 197; OBJECTIVE: 1; TYPE: concept

5. The tone you use in a bad news letter should do all of the following *except*:
    a. show the readers that your focus is on what is best for your business
    b. let the readers know that your bad news represents a firm decision
    c. help your readers preserve their pride
    d. retain the readers' goodwill toward your business

ANSWER: a. Your tone should show them that your decision is firm in a way that lets them retain their pride and preserves their goodwill.
DIFFICULTY: moderate; PAGE: 197; OBJECTIVE: 1; TYPE: concept

6. To create an audience-centered tone in negative messages, you should do all of the following *except*:
    a. avoid accusing your audience
    b. choose positive words
    c. hide the bad news
    d. use respectful language

ANSWER: c. You do not want to hide the bad news. Make sure the message is clear, but deliver it with positive and respectful language while keeping the reader's concerns and feelings in mind.
DIFFICULTY: moderate; PAGE: 197; OBJECTIVE: 1; TYPE: concept

7. Which of the following statements is the correct use of a positive tone for bad news messages?
    a. There will be a delay in fulfilling your request.
    b. Sorry for your inconvenience.
    c. Please recheck the enclosed statement.
    d. I was shocked to learn you are unhappy.

ANSWER: c. Statements a, b, & d are negative tone statements.
DIFFICULTY: moderate; PAGE: 197;   OBJECTIVE: 1; TYPE: application

8. Which of the following statements illustrates a positive tone appropriate for bad news messages?
    a. We are sorry for any inconvenience you may encounter.
    b. We will ship your order as soon as possible.
    c. The enclosed statement is wrong.
    d. The error was not our fault.

ANSWER: b. This statement uses positive wording.
DIFFICULTY: moderate; PAGE: 197; OBJECTIVE: 1; TYPE: application

9. When using respectful language you
    a. avoid an accusing tone.
    b. help your audience accept your decision.
    c. protect your audience's pride.
    d. all of the above

ANSWER: d. All of these are characteristics of respectful language.
DIFFICULTY: easy; PAGE: 197; OBJECTIVE: 1; TYPE: application

10. When delivering bad news, use the direct approach if
   a. your audience prefers the bad news first.
   b. the situation is minor.
   c. the news will cause your audience little disappointment.
   d. all of the above

ANSWER: d. The direct approach should be used for bad news if the news is not too bad or if you know that your reader prefers hearing the bad news first.
DIFFICULTY: moderate; PAGE: 197; OBJECTIVE: 2; TYPE: concept

 11. Because your main idea in a bad-news message is negative, it is important to
   a. always use a direct approach.
   b. always use an indirect approach.
   c. carefully choose whether an indirect or a direct approach is best.
   d. use both a direct and an indirect approach in each letter.

ANSWER: c. Choosing between the direct and indirect approaches takes on added importance in bad-news messages. You need to decide whether to open with the bad news or to prepare your readers with an explanation before giving them the negative information.
DIFFICULTY: moderate; PAGE: 198; OBJECTIVE: 2; TYPE: concept

12. Routine external messages that relay decisions that have little or no personal impact should use
   a. an indirect approach.
   b. a direct approach.
   c. an informal approach.
   d. a formal approach.

ANSWER: b. A direct approach is appropriate for news that has little personal impact.
DIFFICULTY: moderate; PAGE: 198; OBJECTIVE: 2; TYPE: concept

13. The direct approach for delivering bad-news messages is appropriate for all of the following *except* when
   a. the news will likely come as a shock to your readers.
   b. the reader has little emotional investment in the situation.
   c. you need to get the reader's attention.
   d. your audience prefers messages that get straight to the point.

ANSWER: a. Use an indirect approach if the news is likely to shock the audience.
DIFFICULTY: moderate; PAGE: 198; OBJECTIVE: 2; TYPE: concept

14. When using the direct approach to deliver bad news, the opening of your message should
    a. include a goodwill statement aimed at maintaining a good relationship with the reader.
    b. give a clear statement of the bad news.
    c. offer explanations for the bad news.
    d. provide an apology.

ANSWER: b. When using the direct approach, you should open with a clear statement of the bad news.
DIFFICULTY: moderate; PAGE: 198; OBJECTIVE: 2; TYPE: application

15. The advantages of a direct approach with bad news include
    a. delivering the message more gently.
    b. making the message shorter.
    c. providing more detail.
    d. all of the above

ANSWER: b. A direct approach makes the message shorter and allows the audience to get to the main point more quickly.
DIFFICULTY: difficult; PAGE: 198; OBJECTIVE: 2; TYPE: concept

16. The direct approach for delivering bad news is best for people who
    a. you do not know well.
    b. prefer straightforward messages.
    c. are unfamiliar with your company.
    d. all of the above

ANSWER: b. The direct approach is usually best for audiences who prefer messages that get right to the point.
DIFFICULTY: moderate; PAGE: 198; OBJECTIVE: 2; TYPE: concept

17. An indirect approach for delivering bad news is best when
    a. you need to maintain a close working relationship with the reader.
    b. the news will come as a surprise to your audience.
    c. your organization prefers a less blunt communication style.
    d. all of the above

ANSWER: d. An indirect approach would be best in all of these situations.
DIFFICULTY: easy; PAGE: 198; OBJECTIVE: 2; TYPE: concept

18. When using the direct approach to deliver bad news, the body of your message should include
    a. a clear statement of the bad news.
    b. reasons for the decision.
    c. an action step for ways to change or lessen the bad news.
    d. all of the above

ANSWER: b. The body should include the reasons for the decision.
DIFFICULTY: moderate; PAGE: 199; OBJECTIVE: 2; TYPE: application

19. When using the direct approach to deliver bad news, the closing should include
    a. an explanation for the bad news.
    b. an action step for those who want to appeal or contest the bad news.
    c. an apology.
    d. a positive statement aimed at maintaining a good relationship with the reader.

ANSWER: d. The closing should end with a positive statement that helps to maintain the relationship.
DIFFICULTY: moderate; PAGE: 200; OBJECTIVE: 2; TYPE: application

20. When using an indirect approach to deliver bad news, the opening should
    a. include a buffer.
    b. clearly state the bad news.
    c. give the reasons for the bad news.
    d. all of the above

ANSWER: a. An indirect approach should begin with a buffer.
DIFFICULTY: moderate; PAGE: 200; OBJECTIVE: 2; TYPE: application

21. When using an indirect approach to deliver bad news, the body should
    a. include a buffer.
    b. offer an explanation of the reasons for the bad news.
    c. imply the bad news without ever actually stating it.
    d. all of the above

ANSWER: b. The body should give explanations for the bad news and provide a clear but diplomatic statement of the bad news.
DIFFICULTY: moderate; PAGE: 201-02; OBJECTIVE: 2; TYPE: application

22. A good buffer should be
    a. noncontroversial.
    b. relevant.
    c. neutral.
    d. all of the above

ANSWER: d. A buffer should have all of these characteristics.
DIFFICULTY: moderate; PAGE: 200-01; OBJECTIVE: 2; TYPE: concept

23. When using the indirect approach to deliver bad news, the reasons you provide should
    a. explain why you reached your decision before you explain what that decision is.
    b. be brief.
    c. convince the audience that the decision is justified.
    d. all of the above

ANSWER: d. Briefly convince the audience that you have carefully considered the situation. Show them that your reasons are fair.
DIFFICULTY: moderate; PAGE: 202; OBJECTIVE: 2; TYPE: application

24. When explaining the reasons for the bad news, it is a good idea to
    a. point out that you are following company policy.
    b. apologize for unfavorable news.
    c. start with the most positive points first.
    d. all of the above

ANSWER: c. Guide readers' responses by starting with the positive points and moving forward to increasingly negative ones.
DIFFICULTY: difficult; PAGE: 202; OBJECTIVE: 3; TYPE: application

25. To clearly and kindly say no, you should do all of the following *except*:
    a. imply that the bad news is not very important to you
    b. de-emphasize the bad news
    c. imply that the audience might someday receive a favorable answer
    d. tell the audience what you can or will do rather than what you cannot or will not do

ANSWER: a. All of the other strategies enhance the effectiveness of negative messages.
DIFFICULTY: difficult; PAGE: 202-03; OBJECTIVE: 4; TYPE: concept

26. All of the following are methods to de-emphasize bad news *except*:
    a. state the bad news in the closing statement
    b. state the bad news in a complex or compound sentence
    c. minimize the space devoted to the bad news
    d. embed the bad news in the middle of a paragraph

ANSWER: a. All answers are methods to de-emphasize bad news except "a".
DIFFICULTY: difficult; PAGE: 202; OBJECTIVE: 4; TYPE: concept

27. Which of the following statements does the best job of delivering the bad news clearly and kindly?
    a. I am sorry to have to tell you that you were not selected for the position.
    b. Because you do not have the experience we clearly listed in the job posting, we cannot offer you the position.
    c. Although you currently do not have the master's degree that we require for this position, we would be happy to reconsider your application once you have completed your degree.
    d. Several other applicants were far more qualified for the position than you were, so we cannot offer you the job.

ANSWER: c. This version focuses on what the company can do and implies that the reader might receive a favorable response in the future.
DIFFICULTY: difficult; PAGE: 202-03; OBJECTIVE: 4; TYPE: application

28. When closing a negative message, you should
   a. restate the bad news.
   b. offer to answer further questions.
   c. refrain from expressing doubt that the reader will accept your explanation.
   d. all of the above

ANSWER: c. Do not dwell on the bad news by restating it. Do not encourage further correspondence. Do be sincere and confident of retaining the reader as a customer.
DIFFICULTY: moderate; PAGE: 203; OBJECTIVE: 4; TYPE: concept

29. In general, the closing of a bad-news message should *not*
   a. anticipate further problems.
   b. restate the bad news.
   c. encourage further correspondence.
   d. all of the above

ANSWER: d. A positive and confident close should not anticipate additional problems, restate the bad news, or encourage further correspondence.
DIFFICULTY: moderate; PAGE: 203; OBJECTIVE: 4; TYPE: concept

30. When refusing a request for information, you should
   a. use a direct approach.
   b. use an indirect approach.
   c. use either a direct or indirect approach.
   d. use neither the direct nor indirect approach.

ANSWER: c. You may use either the direct or the indirect approach depending on the audience and the situation.
DIFFICULTY: moderate; PAGE: 204; OBJECTIVE: 4; TYPE: application

31. When refusing an invitation or a request for a favor, your use of the direct or indirect approach will depend on
   a. your relationship with the reader.
   b. how many readers you are addressing.
   c. how often the request has been made in the past.
   d. all of the above

ANSWER: a. Using the direct or indirect approach depends on your relationship with the reader.
DIFFICULTY: difficult; PAGE: 204; OBJECTIVE: 4; TYPE: concept

32. Letters declining a routine request should do all of the following *except*:
   a. use the direct approach in some cases
   b. imply that you might change your mind, even if you will not
   c. offer an alternative suggestion
   d. avoid encouraging further correspondence on the matter

ANSWER: b. This is unethical and would frustrate the audience.
DIFFICULTY: difficult; PAGE: 204; OBJECTIVE: 4; TYPE: concept

33. When you are refusing a request that you may have said yes to in the past, it is best to use the
    a. direct approach.
    b. indirect approach.
    c. combination approach.
    d. formal approach.

ANSWER: b. in this case, you should use the indirect approach.
DIFFICULTY: moderate; PAGE: 204; OBJECTIVE: 4; TYPE: application

34. When delivering bad news to a customer about an order, you should do all of the following *except*:
    a. work toward repairing the relationship with the customer
    b. encourage the customer to cancel the order
    c. encourage future business with your company
    d. inform the customer of when to expect the order

ANSWER: b. Your goal is to emphasize the positive by focusing on when the order will be filled.
DIFFICULTY: difficult; PAGE: 206; OBJECTIVE: 4; TYPE: application

35. When refusing a claim you should be sure to
    a. apologize to the customer.
    b. explain that the customer is clearly at fault.
    c. show that you understand the complaint.
    d. all of the above

ANSWER: c. Do not accept responsibility for the situation or blame the customer. Instead, show that you understand and have considered the claim.
DIFFICULTY: difficult; PAGE: 206-07; OBJECTIVE: 4; TYPE: concept

36. To avoid defamation you should do all of the following *except*:
    a. avoid using abusive language
    b. express your personal opinions
    c. consult your company's legal department
    d. provide accurate information

ANSWER: b. Do not express your personal opinions about the claim or the reader.
DIFFICULTY: moderate; PAGE: 206; OBJECTIVE: 5; TYPE: application

37. When writing a rejection letter to a job applicant,
    a. the direct approach may be best.
    b. the indirect approach is sometimes appropriate.
    c. clearly state why the applicant was not selected.
    d. all of the above

ANSWER: d. All of these strategies are effective.
DIFFICULTY: difficult; PAGE: 211; OBJECTIVE: 7; TYPE: application

38. When writing a rejection letter to a job applicant, it is best to close with
    a. a buffer.
    b. the reasons why you did not select the applicant.
    c. some alternative suggestions they might consider.
    d. an apology.

ANSWER: c. Close by mentioning some alternatives such as other openings at your company or the fact that you will keep their résumé on file for future positions.
DIFFICULTY: moderate; PAGE: 211; OBJECTIVE: 7; TYPE: application

39. Which of the following is the most effective close for a letter rejecting a job applicant?
    a. If you have any questions about our decision, don't hesitate to contact us.
    b. We hope that despite this rejection you will continue to frequent our establishments.
    c. Again, we are sorry that we cannot offer you a position at this time.
    d. I wish you the best of luck in your job search. I am sure that you will find a match for your skills and interests.

ANSWER: d. Offer a positive and encouraging statement in the close. Don't encourage further correspondence; don't sound unsure of your decision; don't offer an apology or repeat the bad news.
DIFFICULTY: moderate; PAGE: 211-12; OBJECTIVE: 4; TYPE: application

40. Performance reviews should do all of the following *except*:
    a. establish an unbiased and objective tone
    b. compare an employee's performance to other employees' work
    c. emphasize and clarify job requirements
    d. focus on resolving problems

ANSWER: b. Do not compare one employee to other employees. Instead compare the employee's performance to the company expectations or the job requirements.
DIFFICULTY: difficult; PAGE: 211-13; OBJECTIVE: 7; TYPE: concept

41. Positive and negative performance reviews share all of the following characteristics *except*:
    a. the language is nonjudgmental
    b. the tone is objective
    c. they do not mix positive and negative comments
    d. the focus is on resolving problems

ANSWER: c. Even when a performance review is generally negative, it is best to include some positive comments about the employee.
DIFFICULTY: difficult; PAGE: 211-13; OBJECTIVE: 7; TYPE: concept

42. When writing a negative performance review, do all of the following *except*:
    a. wait to confront the problem until you are sure that the issue is serious
    b. plan your message
    c. deliver the message in private
    d. ask for a commitment from the employee

ANSWER: a. Do not wait to confront the problem. Avoiding performance problems only makes them worse.
DIFFICULTY: difficult; PAGE: 211-13; OBJECTIVE: 7; TYPE: application

43. A negative performance review should
    a. focus on the problems caused by the employee's behavior.
    b. compare employee behavior with what's expected or with job requirements.
    c. mention some good points about the employee's contributions.
    d. all of the above

ANSWER: d. All of these elements should be part of a performance review.
DIFFICULTY: easy; PAGE: 211-13; OBJECTIVE: 7; TYPE: application

True/False

44. _____ When delivering bad news, you want to try to get the readers to agree that the news is fair and reasonable.

ANSWER: True. You want readers to accept the news you are delivering and to feel as if they have been treated fairly.
DIFFICULTY: easy; PAGE: 196-97; OBJECTIVE: 1; TYPE: concept

45. _____ Tone and word choice are unimportant in a bad-news message. What really matters is clearly delivering the information.

ANSWER: False. Tone and word choice are especially important when delivering negative messages. You want to create sentences that are tactful and diplomatic.
DIFFICULTY: moderate; PAGE: 197; OBJECTIVE: 1; TYPE: concept

46. _____ One of the main goals when delivering bad news is to maintain a good image for your organization.

ANSWER: True. You want to maintain goodwill and not damage your company's image.
DIFFICULTY: easy; PAGE: 197; OBJECTIVE: 1; TYPE: concept

47. _____ Use positive words to try to hide the bad news.

ANSWER: False. Use positive words to ease the disappointment, but always clearly convey the bad news.
DIFFICULTY: moderate; PAGE: 197; OBJECTIVE: 2; TYPE: application

48. _____ You can ease disappointment by using positive words rather than negative ones.

ANSWER: True. The words you choose can make a letter either offensive or acceptable.
DIFFICULTY: easy; PAGE: 197; OBJECTIVE: 2; TYPE: concept

49. _____ When planning your bad-news message, determine whether your readers would prefer a direct or an indirect approach.

ANSWER: True. Analyze the audience and determine which approach will be more effective before you begin to write your message.
DIFFICULTY: easy; PAGE: 198; OBJECTIVE: 1; TYPE: concept

50. _____ You should use the direct approach for a bad-news method only for particularly negative or difficult news.

ANSWER: False. You should use the direct approach mostly when the news is not too negative and the audience will likely not be overly upset by it.
DIFFICULTY: moderate; PAGE: 198; OBJECTIVE: 2; TYPE: application

51. _____ When the opening of a negative message includes a clear statement of the bad news, you are using the direct approach.

ANSWER: True. The direct approach opens with the bad news.
DIFFICULTY: moderate; PAGE: 198; OBJECTIVE: 2; TYPE: concept

52. _____ In some bad-news situations, a direct approach would be inappropriate.

ANSWER: True. The direct approach is usually used for readers who see bad news frequently; the indirect approach is better for readers who would like an explanation first.
DIFFICULTY: moderate; PAGE: 198; OBJECTIVE: 2; TYPE: concept

53. _____ The two advantages of a direct approach are: the message can be shorter and the audience needs less time to reach the main idea of the message.

ANSWER: True. There are two advantages to a direct approach.
DIFFICULTY: difficult; PAGE: 198; OBJECTIVE: 2; TYPE: concept

54. _____ The closing of a bad-news message should provide the reader with an explanation and a rationale for the negative message.

ANSWER: False. The explanation goes in the body; the closing should include just a final goodwill statement.
DIFFICULTY: moderate; PAGE: 199; OBJECTIVE: 2; TYPE: application

55. _____ Some critics believe that it is unethical to use buffers in negative messages.

ANSWER: True. However, buffers are unethical only if they're insincere or deceptive.
DIFFICULTY: moderate; PAGE: 200; OBJECTIVE: 2; TYPE: application

56. _____ A buffer should get the readers in a positive frame of mind by letting them think they will be pleased with the news they are about to hear.

ANSWER: False. A buffer should not be misleading. Avoid implying that good news will follow. Building up expectations at the beginning only makes the bad news even more surprising.
DIFFICULTY: moderate; PAGE: 200-01; OBJECTIVE: 2; TYPE: concept

57. _____ In an indirect approach to delivering bad news, the body provides explanations for the bad news before delivering the negative message.

ANSWER: True. First explain the reasons for the bad news, then follow with a clear statement of the bad news.
DIFFICULTY: moderate; PAGE: 200-02; OBJECTIVE: 2; TYPE: application

58. _____ A direct approach in sending bad-news messages has a four-part sequence: buffer, reasons, bad news, and a positive close.

ANSWER: False. The indirect approach has a four-part sequence.
DIFFICULTY: difficult; PAGE: 200-03; OBJECTIVE: 2; TYPE: concept

59. _____ A bad-news message should always provide a lengthy explanation of the reasons for the bad news.

ANSWER: False. Provide enough detail for the audience to understand your reasons, but be concise.
DIFFICULTY: moderate; PAGE: 202; OBJECTIVE: 2; TYPE: concept

60. _____ One way to de-emphasize bad news is to put it in the middle of a paragraph or use a parenthetical expression.

ANSWER: True. This takes the focus off the bad news and puts it on the other elements of the paragraph or sentence.
DIFFICULTY: moderate; PAGE: 202; OBJECTIVE: 4; TYPE: application

61. _____ A conditional statement is one method to clearly say no as kindly as possible.

ANSWER: True. This is an effective strategy for stating the bad news.
DIFFICULTY: moderate; PAGE: 202; OBJECTIVE: 4; TYPE: concept

62. _____ By implying the bad news, you may not actually need to state it.

ANSWER: True. It is vital, however, to make sure your audience understands the entire message—including the bad news.
DIFFICULTY: moderate; PAGE: 202-03; OBJECTIVE: 4; TYPE: concept

63. _____ The close of a bad-news message should anticipate possible future problems.

ANSWER: False. Be optimistic; avoid statements such as, "should you have further problems…"
DIFFICULTY: difficult; PAGE: 203; OBJECTIVE: 4; TYPE: application

64. _____ The close of a bad-news letter should offer to answer additional questions and provide further answers if needed.

ANSWER: False. In most cases you do not want to encourage additional communication.
DIFFICULTY: difficult; PAGE: 203; OBJECTIVE: 4; TYPE: application

65. _____ When refusing a request for information, you should always use the direct approach.

ANSWER: False. Whether you use the direct or indirect approach depends on who your audience is and what the likely response to your refusal will be.
DIFFICULTY: moderate; PAGE: 204; OBJECTIVE: 4; TYPE: application

66. _____ When conveying bad news about an order, it is best to explain exactly how you will resolve the problem.

ANSWER: True. Additionally, it is often appropriate to apologize in these cases.
DIFFICULTY: moderate; PAGE: 206; OBJECTIVE: 4; TYPE: concept

67. _____ When refusing a claim or a request for an adjustment, it is usually best to use an indirect approach.

ANSWER: True. Almost every customer who makes a claim is emotionally involved; therefore, the indirect approach is usually the best.
DIFFICULTY: moderate; PAGE: 206; OBJECTIVE: 3; TYPE: application

68. _____ Libel occurs when a spoken statement is made that damages someone's character or reputation.

ANSWER: False. Spoken defamation is called slander.
DIFFICULTY: moderate; PAGE: 207; OBJECTIVE: 5; TYPE: concept

69. _____ If you must deliver bad news about company operations, it is best to delay it as long as possible.

ANSWER: False. Don't delay the bad news just because you're not ready to face your audience.
DIFFICULTY: moderate: PAGE: 209; OBJECTIVE 5; TYPE: concept

70. _____ Employers may refuse to write recommendation letters because they fear legal reprisals.

ANSWER: True. Some states have laws to protect employers who provide job references for former employees, but legal problems can still arise.
DIFFICULTY: easy; PAGE: 209; OBJECTIVE: 4; TYPE: concept

71. _____ A good way to reject a job applicant is to stop communicating with them. If you don't respond to their inquiries, they will indirectly figure out that they did not get the job.

ANSWER: False. If at all possible, it is best to avoid rejecting an applicant with silence since it builds ill will and can harm your company's reputation.
DIFFICULTY: moderate; PAGE: 211; OBJECTIVE: 7; TYPE: concept

72. _____ Rejecting job applicants requires care, since poorly phrased rejection letters can invite legal troubles.

ANSWER: True. Rejecting job applicants requires care, since poorly phrased rejection letters can invite legal troubles.
DIFFICULTY: easy; PAGE: 211; OBJECTIVE: 7; TYPE: concept

73. _____ If you fire an employee for incompetence and the performance evaluations have all been positive, the employee can sue your company.

ANSWER: True. Legally, employees need to be told if their performance is not meeting expectations.
DIFFICULTY: moderate; PAGE: 211; OBJECTIVE: 4; TYPE: concept

74. _____ When delivering a negative performance review, it is best to mention some good points about the employee.

ANSWER: True. This opens the door to a discussion of how the employee can improve.
DIFFICULTY: moderate; PAGE: 211-13; OBJECTIVE: 7; TYPE: application

75. _____ Employee performance problems should be addressed with others present in case you need witnesses later.

ANSWER: False. Performance problems should be discussed in private.
DIFFICULTY: moderate; PAGE: 213; OBJECTIVE: 4; TYPE: concept.

76. _____ Effective performance reviews will suggest ways that employees can improve.

ANSWER: True. The goal is to help the employee succeed. Concrete suggestions will help in this process.
DIFFICULTY: easy; PAGE: 213; OBJECTIVE: 4; TYPE: concept

77. _____ To make termination letters diplomatic, it is best to use polite words such as *untidy* and *difficult* in explaining your decision.

ANSWER: False. Termination letters should avoid words like these because they are open to interpretation.
DIFFICULTY: moderate; PAGE: 213; OBJECTIVE: 7; TYPE: concept

78. _____ Effective termination letters provide specific justification for asking the employee to leave.

ANSWER: True. Doing so can help prevent legal problems based on the dismissal.
DIFFICULTY: moderate; PAGE: 213; OBJECTIVE: 7; TYPE: concept

Fill-in the Blank

79. In negative messages, it is important to maintain a good _____ for your organization.

ANSWER: Image
DIFFICULTY: moderate; PAGE: 197; OBJECTIVE: 1; TYPE: concept

80. When a negative message gives the bad news in the opening paragraph, the writer is using the _____ approach.

ANSWER: Direct
DIFFICULTY: moderate; PAGE: 198; OBJECTIVE: 2; TYPE: concept

81. When using the indirect approach to deliver bad news, you should open with a neutral, noncontroversial statement called a/an _____.

ANSWER: Buffer
DIFFICULTY: moderate; PAGE: 200; OBJECTIVE: 2; TYPE: concept

82. An effective buffer is a _____ statement—one that avoids misleading the reader into thinking the message actually contains good news.

ANSWER: Neutral
DIFFICULTY: moderate; PAGE: 200; OBJECTIVE: 2; TYPE: concept

83. The _____ approach has a four-part sequence that includes a buffer, reasons, bad news, and a positive close.

ANSWER: Indirect
DIFFICULTY: moderate: PAGE: 200-03; OBJECTIVE: 2; TYPE: concept

84. When denying a claim or request for adjustment, it is best to use a/an _____ approach.

ANSWER: Indirect
DIFFICULTY: moderate; PAGE: 206; OBJECTIVE: 2; TYPE: concept

85. A false statement that tends to damage someone's character or reputation is _____.

ANSWER: Defamation
DIFFICULTY: moderate; PAGE: 206; OBJECTIVE: 5; TYPE: concept

86.   Spoken defamation is known as _____.

ANSWER: Slander
DIFFICULTY: moderate; PAGE: 206; OBJECTIVE: 5; TYPE: concept

87.   Written defamation is called _____.

ANSWER: Libel
DIFFICULTY: moderate; PAGE: 206; OBJECTIVE: 5; TYPE: concept

88.   The goals of a(n) _____ letter are to present the reasons for having to end the individual's employment, avoid statements that might cause legal problems later, and maintain as positive a relationship as possible between the employee and your firm.

ANSWER: Termination
DIFFICULTY: moderate; PAGE: 213; OBJECTIVE: 7; TYPE: concept

Short Answer/Essay

89.   What are the five main goals when delivering bad news in business?

ANSWER: 1) to convey the bad news 2) to gain acceptance for it 3) to maintain as much goodwill as possible with your audience 4) to maintain a good image for your organization 5) if appropriate, to reduce or eliminate the need for future correspondence on the matter.
DIFFICULTY: difficult; PAGE: 196-97; OBJECTIVE: 1; TYPE: concept

90.   What are the three main steps you should take in planning a bad-news message?

ANSWER: 1) identify and gather relevant information, 2) select the appropriate medium to deliver the message, and 3) choose the direct or the indirect approach to organize your message.
DIFFICULTY: moderate; PAGE: 197; OBJECTIVE: 1; TYPE: concept

91.   Rewrite the following sentence using more positive words: "Unfortunately, we cannot ship your order today."

ANSWER: (Answers may vary.) We will ship your order tomorrow morning.
DIFFICULTY: difficult; PAGE: 197; OBJECTIVE: 1; TYPE: application

92.   Rewrite the following phrase using positive words rather than negative ones. "We have to reject your proposal."

ANSWER: (Answers may vary.) We've accepted another company's proposal.
DIFFICULTY: moderate; PAGE: 197; OBJECTIVE: 1; TYPE: application

93.   Describe the elements of a negative message that uses the direct approach.

ANSWER: The opening should start with a clear statement of the bad news. The body should give the reasons for the bad news and provide additional information. The closing should end with a positive statement aimed at maintaining a good relationship with the audience.
DIFFICULTY: difficult; PAGE: 198-200; OBJECTIVE: 2; TYPE: concept

94.   Briefly describe the eight characteristics of an effective buffer.

ANSWER: A good buffer is a neutral, noncontroversial statement that is closely related to the point of the message. It establishes common ground with the reader, and if you are writing in response to a request, the buffer validates that request. It also expresses appreciation (when appropriate), assures the reader of your attention to the request, and indicates your understanding of the reader's needs.
DIFFICULTY: difficult; PAGE: 200; OBJECTIVE: 2; TYPE: concept

95.   Describe the elements of a bad-news message that uses an indirect approach.

ANSWER: Begin with a buffer—a neutral, noncontroversial statement that is related to the point of the message. Follow with the reasons for the bad news and any additional, relevant information. Then state the bad news clearly, but as diplomatically as possible. Emphasize any good news and de-emphasize the bad. End with a positive, forward-looking statement that is helpful and friendly and tries to preserve goodwill.
DIFFICULTY: difficult; PAGE: 200-03; OBJECTIVE: 2; TYPE: concept

96.   Describe the three techniques for saying no as clearly and kindly as possible.

ANSWER: 1) De-emphasize the bad news—devote less space to it, embed it in the middle of a paragraph or in a parenthetical expression. 2) Use a conditional (if or when) statement to imply that the audience might someday receive a favorable answer. 3) Tell the audience what you did do, can do, or will do rather than what you did not do, cannot do or will not do.
DIFFICULTY: difficult; PAGE: 202-03; OBJECTIVE: 4; TYPE: application

97.   Describe the four guidelines to follow when using the indirect approach to close a negative message.

ANSWER: 1) Don't refer to, repeat, or apologize for the bad news. Don't express doubt that your reasons will be accepted. 2) Encourage additional communication *only* if you're willing to discuss your decision further. 3) Don't anticipate problems. 4) Avoid clichés that are insincere in view of the bad news.
DIFFICULTY: difficult; PAGE: 203; OBJECTIVE: 4; TYPE: concept

98.   Describe the guidelines for avoiding defamation.

ANSWER: 1) Avoid using any kind of abusive language. 2) Do not express your own personal opinions unless you do so on your own paper and don't include your job title or position. 3) Provide accurate information and stick to the facts. 4) Never let anger motivate your messages. 5) Consult your company's legal department whenever you think a message might have legal consequences. 6) Communicate honestly. 7) Emphasize a desire for a good relationship in the future.
DIFFICULTY: difficult; PAGE: 206-07; OBJECTIVE: 5; TYPE: concept

99.   Describe the three guidelines to follow when rejecting a job applicant.

ANSWER: Choose your approach carefully, keeping in mind that most candidates have a deep emotional investment in the application process. Clearly state why the applicant was not selected (this makes the rejection less personal). Finally, close by suggesting alternatives such as other openings in your company.
DIFFICULTY: difficult; PAGE: 211; OBJECTIVE: 7; TYPE: application

100.   Rewrite the following phrase using positive words rather than negative ones.
"You did not get the job because you were not qualified."

ANSWER: (Answers may vary.) Another candidate's qualifications met our needs for this position.
DIFFICULTY: moderate; PAGE: 211-12; OBJECTIVE: 1; TYPE: application

101.   List and describe the five guidelines for giving negative performance reviews.

ANSWER: 1) Confront the problem right away. Avoiding problems only makes them worse. 2) Plan your message. Be clear about your concerns and include examples of the employee's specific actions. 3) Deliver the message in private. Don't send performance reviews via e-mail. 4) Focus on the problem. Don't attack the employee. Compare employee performance with what's expected, with company goals, or with job requirements, not with the performance of other employees. 5) Ask for a commitment from the employee. Help the employee understand that planning for and making improvements are the employee's responsibility. Set a schedule for improvement.
DIFFICULTY: difficult; PAGE: 224; OBJECTIVE: 4; TYPE: application

CHAPTER 9
WRITING PERSUASIVE MESSAGES

Multiple Choice

 1. When compared to routine positive messages, persuasive messages aim to influence audiences who are likely to
    a. agree with you right away.
    b. know more than you do about the topic of your message.
    c. resist at first.
    d. be easily offended.

ANSWER: c. Persuasive messages must show the audience that the choice you present is the best among all others.
DIFFICULTY: moderate; PAGE: 228; OBJECTIVE: 1; TYPE: concept

2. When analyzing your audience for a persuasive message it is important to
    a. connect your message to your audience's existing desires and interests.
    b. consider how your audience might resist your message.
    c. examine alternative positions.
    d. all of the above

ANSWER: d. Considering your audience's current needs, how they might resist your message, and other positions are all important steps when analyzing an audience.
DIFFICULTY: moderate; PAGE: 229; OBJECTIVE: 1; TYPE: concept

 3. Demographics include all of the following about an audience *except*:
    a. age
    b. income
    c. education
    d. attitudes

ANSWER: d. Attitude is a psychographic characteristic. Demographics are quantifiable.
DIFFICULTY: moderate; PAGE: 229; OBJECTIVE: 1; TYPE: application

4. Psychographics is information about all of the following *except*:
    a. occupation
    b. attitudes
    c. lifestyle
    d. personality

ANSWER: a. Occupation is demographic information.
DIFFICULTY: moderate; PAGE: 229; OBJECTIVE: 1; TYPE: application

5.   When analyzing your audience it is important to consider
      a.   audience demographics.
      b.   audience psychographics.
      c.   audience cultural differences.
      d.   all of the above

ANSWER: d. Demographics, psychographics and cultural traits will all affect your persuasive message.
DIFFICULTY: moderate; PAGE: 229; OBJECTIVE: 1; TYPE: concept

6.   The best persuasive messages include _____ appeals.
      a.   only emotional
      b.   only logical
      c.   a combination of emotional and logical
      d.   neither emotional or logical

ANSWER: d. Positive persuasion that provides information and helps understanding allows the audience the freedom to choose.
DIFFICULTY: moderate; PAGE: 229; OBJECTIVE: 1; TYPE: concept

7.   When planning your persuasive message, it is important to do all of the following *except*:
      a.   analyze your situation
      b.   gather relevant information
      c.   write your message
      d.   select the best medium

ANSWER: c. At the planning stage, you do not yet need to start writing your message.
DIFFICULTY: moderate; PAGE: 229-30; OBJECTIVE: 1; TYPE: concept

8.   Most persuasive messages use the
      a.   direct approach.
      b.   indirect approach.
      c.   convoluted approach.
      d.   analytic approach.

ANSWER: b. Although effective persuasion may use either a direct or an indirect approach, most persuasive messages explain the reasons and build interest before revealing their purpose—an indirect approach.
DIFFICULTY: difficult; PAGE: 230; OBJECTIVE: 1; TYPE: concept

 9.   When using the direct approach to craft a persuasive message, remember to include
      a.   an emotional appeal.
      b.   a justification or explanation for your main point.
      c.   an analysis of the situation.
      d.   all of the above

ANSWER: b. Even though you are giving the audience the main point up front, you still want to provide a justification or explanation.
DIFFICULTY: moderate; PAGE: 230; OBJECTIVE: 1; TYPE: concept

10. Which of the following is an incorrect statement regarding an audience?
    a. U.S. audiences are concerned about practical matters.
    b. German audiences like to see numbers and technical information.
    c. French audiences prefer an aggressive, hard-sell technique.
    d. Swiss audiences focus on strategic implications.

ANSWER: c. French audiences do not prefer aggressive and hard-selling techniques.
DIFFICULTY: difficult; PAGE: 231; OBJECTIVE: 1; TYPE: application

11. To establish your credibility you should do all of the following *except*:
    a. use jargon and technical terms to show your audience how much you know
    b. name your sources
    c. display your good intentions
    d. establish common ground

ANSWER: a. It is important to use clear language your audience will understand.
DIFFICULTY: moderate; PAGE: 232; OBJECTIVE: 2; TYPE: concept

12. When describing the AIDA Plan, the letters A – I – D – A stand for
    a. attention, informal, definition, account.
    b. attention, interest, desire, action.
    c. audience, indirect, design, analysis.
    d. amount, insight, distinction, appeal.

ANSWER: b. The letters A – I – D – A stand for attention, interest, desire, action.

DIFFICULTY: moderate; PAGE: 233; OBJECTIVE 3; TYPE: concept

13. When using the AIDA approach to persuasion, the opening should
    a. build common ground with your audience.
    b. make your audience want to hear about your idea.
    c. catch your reader's attention.
    d. all of the above

ANSWER: d. The opening should catch your reader's attention by building common ground.
DIFFICULTY: moderate; PAGE: 233; OBJECTIVE: 3; TYPE: application

14. The "desire" step in the AIDA approach should focus on
    a. explaining how the change will benefit the audience.
    b. answering in advance any questions the audience might have.
    c. backing up your claims with evidence.
    d. all of the above

ANSWER: d. The Desire step shows the reader the benefits of the recommendation. It persuades by anticipating questions, showing how you would implement the plan, and providing evidence to support your idea.
DIFFICULTY: moderate; PAGE: 233; OBJECTIVE: 3; TYPE: application

15. When using the AIDA approach to persuasion, the closing should
    a. urge the audience to take the action you are suggesting.
    b. provide additional evidence and detail not covered in the "desire" step.
    c. explain the steps needed to implement your ideas.
    d. all of the above

ANSWER: a. The closing should be a call to action. Evidence, details, and implementation information should all come earlier.
DIFFICULTY: difficult; PAGE: 233; OBJECTIVE: 3; TYPE: application

16. The AIDA plan for persuasive messages should be used with
    a. a direct approach only.
    b. an indirect approach only.
    c. either a direct or an indirect approach.
    d. neither a direct or an indirect approach.

ANSWER: c. AIDA can use either a direct or an indirect approach. The direct approach puts your main idea in the opening. An indirect approach puts your main idea in the action step at the close.
DIFFICULTY: difficult; PAGE: 233; OBJECTIVE: 3; TYPE: concept

17. When using the AIDA plan to request an action, the opening should
    a. be brief and engaging.
    b. get your reader's attention.
    c. avoid extravagant claims.
    d. all of the above

ANSWER: d. The opening should have each of these characteristics.
DIFFICULTY: difficult; PAGE: 233; OBJECTIVE: 3; TYPE: application

 18. When requesting an action, your goals should include all of the following *except*
    a. be specific.
    b. gain credibility for you.
    c. convince readers that helping you will solve a significant problem.
    d. all of the above

ANSWER: d. All of these characterize an effective request for action.
DIFFICULTY: moderate; PAGE: 233; OBJECTIVE: 3; TYPE: concept

19. Finding the right balance between emotional and logical appeals depends on all of the following *except*:
    a. the actions you wish to motivate
    b. your reader's expectations
    c. the ethical appeals you plan to use
    d. the degree of resistance you must overcome

ANSWER: c. The right balance between emotions and logic for a persuasive message should be determined by the action you wish to motivate, your audience's expectations and resistance, and how far you can go in selling your idea.
DIFFICULTY: moderate; PAGE: 235; OBJECTIVE: 4; TYPE: concept

20. Emotional and logical appeals work together by
    a. providing rational support for an idea that an audience has already emotionally accepted.
    b. allowing the audience to choose the appeal that will be most effective.
    c. manipulating the audience into focusing on the emotional issues while ignoring the logical elements.
    d. all of the above

ANSWER: a. People who have been persuaded by compelling emotional arguments often look for rational reasons to support the idea.
DIFFICULTY: moderate; PAGE: 235; OBJECTIVE: 4; TYPE: concept

21. An analogy lets you
    a. reason from one specific evidence to another specific evidence.
    b. reason from specific evidence to a general conclusion.
    c. reason from a generalization to a specific conclusion.
    d. all of the above

ANSWER: a. Analogies reason via comparing one point to another.
DIFFICULTY: difficult; PAGE: 235; OBJECTIVE: 4; TYPE: concept

22. If you used the results of a taste test in which many individuals preferred your product over the competitor's to persuade others to buy your product, you would be using what kind of approach?
    a. analogy
    b. induction
    c. deduction
    d. a combination of all three

ANSWER: b. Induction reasons from specific evidence to a general conclusion.
DIFFICULTY: difficult; PAGE: 235; OBJECTIVE: 2; TYPE: application

23. Which of the following is an example of an analogy?
    a. The results of this survey showed that people like our product more than our competitor's product.
    b. There is a national trend toward healthier eating; as a result we should see an increase in the sales of our low-fat items.
    c. Our office operates like a wolf pack with one Alpha male on top and everyone else answering to him.
    d. All employees have health coverage. Therefore, since Tom is an employee, he must have health coverage.

ANSWER: c. An analogy makes a comparison between things that on the surface may not seem to have much in common.
DIFFICULTY: difficult; PAGE: 235; OBJECTIVE: 2; TYPE: application

24. Which of the following uses a deductive approach to persuasion?
    a. Because the stock market is expected to fall next month, shares of our company stock will probably also decline.
    b. It is important for our sales force to operate like a well-oiled machine.
    c. Our stock price is like a marathon runner, slowly making progress towards our goal.
    d. none of the above

ANSWER: a. Deductive reasoning goes from generalizations to specific conclusions.
DIFFICULTY: difficult; PAGE: 235; OBJECTIVE: 2; TYPE: application

25. When writing a claim request, you should
    a. let the company know how disappointed and upset you are.
    b. write in a calm and reasonable tone.
    c. threaten to withhold payment.
    d. convey your negative impression of the company.

ANSWER: b. When writing a claim, keep in mind that most companies respond well to calm, reasonable requests rather than emotional rants.
DIFFICULTY: moderate; PAGE: 238-39; OBJECTIVE: 3; TYPE: concept

26. A good claim letter should
    a. include a complete review of the facts.
    b. not suggest that the reader is trying to cheat you.
    c. maintain a confident and positive tone.
    d. all of the above

ANSWER: d. A claim letter should reflect your assumption that you have the right to be satisfied, but not that the reader was trying to cheat you. It should also be positive and include a specific review of the facts of the incident.
DIFFICULTY: moderate; PAGE: 238; OBJECTIVE: 3; TYPE: concept

27. In a claim letter, the opening should
    a. specify a deadline for action.
    b. give the reader a reason for granting your claim.
    c. state the problem.
    d. all of the above

ANSWER: c. The opening should contain a clear description of your reason for writing.
DIFFICULTY: difficult; PAGE: 238; OBJECTIVE: 3; TYPE: application

28. To make an effective and persuasive claim, the letter should include
    a. benefits to the company and a summary of events leading to the claim.
    b. a confident and positive tone and a complete review of the facts.
    c. problems with similar products and a critique of the company.
    d. a copy of the sales receipt and a request for reimbursement.

ANSWER: b. A review of facts and a confident, positive tone are key to a good persuasive claim.
DIFFICULTY: difficult; PAGE: 238; OBJECTIVE 3: TYPE: concept

29. For a successful sales effort, your product's distinguishing benefit must correspond to your readers'
   a. needs.
   b. social-economic demographic.
   c. attention focus.
   d. all of the above

ANSWER: a. Your product's selling points should focus on the benefits to the buyers by appealing to their primary needs and emotional concerns.
DIFFICULTY: moderate; PAGE: 239-40; OBJECTIVE: 4; TYPE: concept

30. In marketing and sales messages, what is the primary difference between selling points and benefits?
   a. Selling points are positive whereas benefits are not.
   b. Selling points focus on the user rather than the product.
   c. Selling points focus on the product rather than the user.
   d. none of the above

ANSWER: c. Unlike benefits (which are the advantages a customer will enjoy by using the product or service), selling points are the most attractive features of the product or service itself.
DIFFICULTY: moderate; PAGE: 239-40; OBJECTIVE: 6; TYPE: concept

31. All of the following are examples of selling points *except*:
   a. Get a car loan with no money down and a 0% interest rate.
   b. Your corporate sponsorship will allow your sales manager a five-minute introduction at the seminar.
   c. Our food bank provides food for 200 families daily.
   d. This digital camera can take 10 pictures per minute.

ANSWER: b. This is an example of a consumer benefit.
DIFFICULTY: difficult; PAGE: 239-40; OBJECTIVE: 6; TYPE: application

32. If the audience for your marketing or sales message promoting a new security system is made up of wealthy suburbanites, the consumer benefit you would most likely want to emphasize is
   a. the reliability of the system.
   b. the low cost.
   c. the availability of a low-interest payment plan.
   d. its easy, do-it-yourself installation.

ANSWER: a. Of these choices, this would be the best benefit based on your audience.
DIFFICULTY: moderate; PAGE: 239-40; OBJECTIVE: 6; TYPE: application

33. Strategies for writing a sales message include all of the following *except*:
a. determine selling points and benefits
b. analyze your competition
c. anticipate objections
d. all of the above

ANSWER: d. All of these strategies apply to sales messages.
DIFFICULTY: moderate; PAGE: 239-40; OBJECTIVE: 3; TYPE: concept

34. When discussing price in a sales message, you should always
a. downplay the information.
b. highlight the information.
c. prepare the readers for it, even if you do not specify the price.
d. none of the above

ANSWER: c. Whether you highlight or downplay pricing information depends on your audience and your purpose. However, whether you will downplay it or highlight it, you should prepare your audience for the pricing information.
DIFFICULTY: moderate; PAGE: 240; OBJECTIVE: 6; TYPE: concept

35. If price is not a major selling point, your sales message could
a. leave out the price.
b. discuss it after presenting selling points and benefits.
c. place the price in the middle of a paragraph.
d. all of the above

ANSWER: d. When price is not a major selling point, it is best to de-emphasize it by leaving it out, putting it in another location, or burying it mid-paragraph after you've presented the benefits and selling points.
DIFFICULTY: easy; PAGE: 240; OBJECTIVE: 6; TYPE: application

36. Which of the following is *not* an effective technique for minimizing price?
a. emphasize the cost of *not* buying your product or service
b. compare your product's price to the cost of another product
c. compare your service's price to that of a competitor's
d. all of the above are effective

ANSWER: d. All of these strategies are effective.
DIFFICULTY: moderate; PAGE: 240; OBJECTIVE: 6; TYPE: application

37. All of the following are effective ways to attract attention at the beginning of a sales letter *except*:
a. giving a sample or demonstration of your product
b. appealing to your reader's emotions and values
c. asking the readers to buy your product
d. establishing a point of common ground with the audience

ANSWER: c. Most sales letters begin by catching the readers' attention before asking them to buy the product.
DIFFICULTY: moderate; PAGE: 241; OBJECTIVE: 3; TYPE: application

38. The final section of a sales letter should
    a. persuade the readers to take the next step.
    b. pique the readers' interest in the product.
    c. explain the benefits of your product.
    d. all of the above

ANSWER: a. The closing needs to get the reader to take the next step—buy the product, meet with a sales representative, ask for further information, etc. The readers' interest should have been piqued in the opening, and they should already know the benefits of the product.
DIFFICULTY: difficult; PAGE: 242; OBJECTIVE: 3; TYPE: application

39. When writing a sales letter you are breaking the law if you
    a. misrepresent the price of a product.
    b. use a person's photograph without permission.
    c. publicize information about a person's private life.
    d. all of the above

ANSWER: a. Misrepresenting any information about your product is fraud. Publishing information or photographs without permission is invasion of privacy.
DIFFICULTY: difficult; PAGE: 242; OBJECTIVE: 7; TYPE: concept

40. All of the following may cause legal problems when writing a sales letter *except*
    a. including information about the financial condition of the company.
    b. making offers or promises that you cannot deliver.
    c. making claims without providing support.
    d. using a customer's name and picture without consent.

ANSWER: a. Financial information about a company can be included.
DIFFICULTY: easy; PAGE: 242; OBJECTIVE: 7; TYPE: application

41. In the final section of a sales letter, it is important to get the reader to act quickly because
    a. you want to overcome their natural inertia.
    b. they may forget about your offer.
    c. they are less likely to buy if they don't reply immediately.
    d. all of the above

ANSWER: d. The closing needs to persuade readers to take action right away. If not, readers are likely to forget or permanently delay purchasing.
DIFFICULTY: easy; PAGE: 242; OBJECTIVE: 3; TYPE: application

42.	A postscript is a good place to
	a.	include an additional offer.
	b.	reiterate your primary benefits.
	c.	emphasize a deadline.
	d.	all of the above

ANSWER: d. A postscript is one of the most effective ways to boost audience response; it is the place to make your final impression, include additional offers, restate your product's benefits or remind readers of dates and deadlines.
DIFFICULTY: moderate; PAGE: 242; OBJECTIVE: 3; TYPE: application

43.	Unlike electronic junk mail (spam), opt-in e-mail newsletters
	a.	reflect the "you" attitude.
	b.	are considered an unethical way to obtain personal information.
	c.	are illegal in some states.
	d.	force consumers to purchase products before being removed from the mailing list.

ANSWER: a. Opt-in newsletters are more ethical and effective than spam because they are sent only to people who have specifically requested them.
DIFFICULTY: moderate; PAGE: 244; OBJECTIVE: 3; TYPE: concept

True/False

44.	_____ Effective persuasion is the ability to present a message in a way that will lead others to support it.

ANSWER: True. Effective persuasion makes the audience choose to agree.
DIFFICULTY: easy; PAGE: 228; OBJECTIVE: 1; TYPE: concept

45.	_____ Unlike routine messages, persuasive messages present the added challenge of overcoming the audience's initial resistance to your request.

ANSWER: True. It is more difficult to write an effective persuasive message.
DIFFICULTY: moderate; PAGE: 228; OBJECTIVE 1: TYPE: concept

46.	_____ The key to an effective persuasive message is to clearly explain your company's needs to your audience.

ANSWER: False. Successful persuasive messages depend on knowing your audience and their needs.
DIFFICULTY: moderate; PAGE: 229; OBJECTIVE: 1; TYPE: concept

47.	_____ To better understand your audience, you can refer to demographic and psychological information.

ANSWER: False. Refer to demographic and psychographic information.
DIFFICULTY: moderate; PAGE: 229; OBJECTIVE: 1; TYPE: concept

48. _____ Effective persuasive techniques are generally the same from culture to culture.

ANSWER: False. When analyzing your audience for a persuasive message, take into account their cultural expectations and practices so you don't undermine your message by using an inappropriate appeal or by organizing your message in a way that seems unfamiliar or uncomfortable to your audience.
DIFFICULTY: moderate; PAGE: 229; OBJECTIVE: 1; TYPE: concept

49. _____ Psychographics looks at quantifiable audience characteristics.

ANSWER: False. Psychographics looks at *qualitative* audience characteristics like personality, attitudes, and lifestyle.
DIFFICULTY: difficult; PAGE: 229; OBJECTIVE: 1; TYPE: concept

50. _____ Although a direct approach is sometimes necessary, most effective persuasion uses an indirect approach.

ANSWER: True. Most persuasive messages use an indirect approach and explain the reasons before revealing the purpose.
DIFFICULTY: moderate; PAGE: 230; OBJECTIVE: 1; TYPE: concept

51. _____ Naming your sources and supporting your message with facts will help you to establish credibility.

ANSWER: True. The more specific and relevant your proof, the better. Naming your sources allows your audience to know who agrees with you and where your information comes from.
DIFFICULTY: easy; PAGE: 232; OBJECTIVE: 2; TYPE: concept

52. _____ Being clear and objective can help you gain credibility with your audience.

ANSWER: True. Other techniques include using facts, naming sources, being an expert, establish common ground, and having good intentions.
DIFFICULTY: difficult; PAGE: 232; OBJECTIVE: 2; TYPE: concept

53. _____ The AIDA approach focuses on appealing to your audience's fears.

ANSWER: False. The AIDA approach focuses on appealing to audience interests and needs.
DIFFICULTY: moderate; PAGE: 233; OBJECTIVE: 3; TYPE: concept

54. _____ The AIDA plan for persuasion can use either a direct or an indirect approach.

ANSWER: True. Your main idea can come last as an action step or first as the attention getter.
DIFFICULTY: difficult; PAGE: 233; OBJECTIVE: 3; TYPE: concept

55. _____ Most persuasive messages contain both emotional and logical appeals.

ANSWER: True. Finding the right balance between emotional and logical appeals is important, but most messages contain elements of both.
DIFFICULTY: moderate; PAGE: 235; OBJECTIVE: 4; TYPE: concept

56. _____ When you are persuading someone to make a large and important decision, it is best to rely primarily on emotional appeals.

ANSWER: False. Appeals that provide logical support are usually better for serious and important issues.
DIFFICULTY: moderate; PAGE: 235; OBJECTIVE: 4; TYPE: concept

57. _____ In general, emotional appeals should be tempered with logical support.

ANSWER: True. Emotional appeals aren't necessarily effective by themselves.
DIFFICULTY: moderate; PAGE: 235; OBJECTIVE: 4; TYPE: concept

58. _____ Induction and deduction are two types of reasoning techniques that help you make a logical appeal to the audience.

ANSWER: True. The third technique is analogy.
DIFFICULTY: moderate; PAGE: 235; OBJECTIVE: 4; TYPE: concept

59. _____ Going from a generalization to a specific conclusion is the inductive approach to reasoning.

ANSWER: False. This is a definition of the deductive approach.
DIFFICULTY: moderate; PAGE: 235; OBJECTIVE: 4; TYPE: concept

60. _____ Most claim letters should use the direct approach.

ANSWER: True. Most claim letters are routine; it is in the company's interest to keep you satisfied.
DIFFICULTY: moderate; PAGE: 237; OBJECTIVE: 3; TYPE: application

61. _____ When writing a claim letter, you should strive for a calm, reasonable tone.

ANSWER: True. This will greatly increase your chance of getting the result you want.
DIFFICULTY: moderate; PAGE: 238; OBJECTIVE: 3; TYPE: application

62. _____ A good claim letter should show the audience that they are responsible for the problem.

ANSWER: True. This will give the readers a good reason for granting the claim.
DIFFICULTY: difficult; PAGE: 238; OBJECTIVE: 3; TYPE: concept

63. _____ Selling points focus on the product; benefits focus on the buyers.

ANSWER: True. Selling points are the most attractive features of an idea or product; benefits are the particular advantages that readers will realize from those features.
DIFFICULTY: moderate; PAGE: 239-40; OBJECTIVE: 6; TYPE: concept

64. _____ You should always phrase the selling points in terms of what the product can do for potential customers.

ANSWER: True. Sales letters should reflect the "you" attitude and be written to address customer needs and benefits.
DIFFICULTY: easy; PAGE: 239-40; OBJECTIVE: 6; TYPE: concept

65. _____ A sales message should always downplay the importance of price.

ANSWER: False. Price can be a key selling feature. You may want to highlight it.
DIFFICULTY: moderate; PAGE: 240; OBJECTIVE: 3; TYPE: concept

66. _____ Stating the price of a product after describing the product's key selling points is one technique for de-emphasizing the price.

ANSWER: True. Other techniques include embedding the price in the middle of a paragraph or leaving it out altogether.
DIFFICULTY: moderate; PAGE: 240; OBJECTIVE: 3; TYPE: concept

67. _____ Providing a sample or demonstration of the product is usually an effective way of catching the reader's attention.

ANSWER: True. A sample will get your product immediately into your reader's hands.
DIFFICULTY: easy; PAGE: 241; OBJECTIVE: 3; TYPE: concept

68. _____ Persuasion is sometimes associated with dishonest and unethical practices.

ANSWER: True. Coaxing, urging, and tricking people into accepting an idea or buying a product, or taking an unwanted or unneeded action are kinds of dishonest persuasion.
DIFFICULTY: easy; PAGE: 242; OBJECTIVE: 1; TYPE: concept

69. _____ Because sales letters are advertisements they cannot be considered binding legal contracts.

ANSWER: False. In many states, sales letters are binding contracts. You must be able to do what you say you can do.
DIFFICULTY: moderate; PAGE: 242; OBJECTIVE: 7; TYPE: concept

70. _____ Because sales letters are advertisements, it is expected that you will make exaggerated claims about your product.

ANSWER: False. Misrepresenting any information about your product is considered fraud and is illegal.
DIFFICULTY: moderate; PAGE: 242; OBJECTIVE: 7; TYPE: concept

71. _____ The final section of a sales letter should always ask the reader to take action promptly.

ANSWER: True. Readers are less likely to respond if they wait.
DIFFICULTY: difficult; PAGE: 242; OBJECTIVE: 3; TYPE: application

72. _____ Most readers will not read the postscript (P.S.) section of a sales letter, so it is best not to include one.

ANSWER: False. The postscript is often one of the first and last parts people read, so it is a good place to emphasize the key benefit you have to offer and to emphasize the advantages of ordering soon.
DIFFICULTY: moderate; PAGE: 242; OBJECTIVE: 3; TYPE: application

Fill-in the Blank

73. The attempt to change an audience's attitudes, beliefs or actions is known as _____.

ANSWER: Persuasion
DIFFICULTY: moderate; PAGE: 228; OBJECTIVE: 1; TYPE: concept

74. Information about the age, gender, occupation, income, education and other quantifiable characteristics of your audience is called _____.

ANSWER: Demographics
DIFFICULTY: difficult; PAGE: 229; OBJECTIVE: 1; TYPE: concept

75. Information about the personality, attitudes, lifestyle and other psychological characteristics of an individual is called _____.

ANSWER: Psychographics
DIFFICULTY: difficult; PAGE: 229; OBJECTIVE: 1; TYPE: concept

76. Most persuasive messages use the _____ approach, explaining the reasoning and building interest before revealing their purpose.

ANSWER: Indirect
DIFFICULTY: difficult; PAGE: 230; OBJECTIVE: 1; TYPE: concept

77. Your _____ is your capability of being believed because you're reliable and worthy of confidence.

ANSWER: Credibility
DIFFICULTY: moderate; PAGE: 231-32; OBJECTIVE: 2; TYPE: concept

78. Identifying your sources is one way to enhance your _____.

ANSWER: Credibility
DIFFICULTY: moderate; PAGE: 232; OBJECTIVE: 2; TYPE: concept

79. The four-step plan for writing persuasive messages is called the _____ plan.

ANSWER: AIDA (attention, interest, desire, and action)
DIFFICULTY: difficult; PAGE: 233; OBJECTIVE: 3; TYPE: concept

80. The AIDA approach can work with both the _____ and _____ approaches to organizing persuasive messages.

ANSWER: Direct, Indirect OR Indirect, Direct
DIFFICULTY: easy; PAGE: 233; OBJECTIVE: 3; TYPE: concept

81. A/An _____ appeal calls on human reason.

ANSWER: Logical
DIFFICULTY: easy; PAGE: 235; OBJECTIVE: 4; TYPE: concept

82. Basing your argument on the audience's needs or sympathy is one way to make a/an _____ appeal.

ANSWER: Emotional
DIFFICULTY: moderate; PAGE: 235; OBJECTIVE: 4; TYPE: concept

83. When you use specific evidence to support a general conclusion, the type of persuasive reasoning you are using is called _____.

ANSWER: Induction
DIFFICULTY: difficult; PAGE: 235; OBJECTIVE: 4; TYPE: concept

84. One example of faulty logic to avoid in persuasive message is _____ reasoning, which occurs when you try to support your claim by restating it in different words.

ANSWER: Circular
DIFFICULTY: moderate; PAGE: 235; OBJECTIVE: 3; TYPE: application

85. A common mistake people make in trying to persuade readers is resisting _____--forgetting that persuasion is a process of give and take.

ANSWER: Compromise
DIFFICULTY: moderate; PAGE: 236; OBJECTIVE: 5; TYPE: concept

86. The most attractive features of an idea or product are its _____.

ANSWER: Selling Points
DIFFICULTY: moderate; PAGE: 239; OBJECTIVE: 6; TYPE: concept

87. Unlike marketing letters (which usher potential buyers through the purchasing process), _____ letters ask potential buyers to make an immediate decision about the product or service.

ANSWER: Sales
DIFFICULTY: moderate: PAGE: 239; OBJECTIVE: 3; TYPE: concept

88. In many states, marketing and sales messages are considered binding _____, which makes it illegal to misrepresent your product.

ANSWER: Contracts
DIFFICULTY: moderate; PAGE: 242; OBJECTIVE: 7; TYPE: concept

89. A "P.S." at the bottom of a letter stands for _____--one of the first and last sections of the letter many people will read.

ANSWER: Postscript
DIFFICULTY: easy; PAGE: 242; OBJECTIVE: 3; TYPE: concept

90. An _____ e-mail newsletter is sent only to those people who have specifically requested information.

ANSWER: Opt-In
DIFFICULTY: moderate; PAGE: 244; OBJECTIVE: 7; TYPE: concept

Short Answer/Essay

91. Briefly explain the difference between demographics and psychographics.

ANSWER: Demographics are the age, gender, occupation, income, education, and other quantifiable characteristics of your audience. Psychographics, in contrast, are qualitative characteristics such as personality, attitudes, and lifestyle.
DIFFICULTY: moderate; PAGE: 229; OBJECTIVE: 1; TYPE: concept

92. List seven techniques for establishing your credibility in persuasive messages.

ANSWER: 1) Use clear language that your audience can easily understand. 2) Support your message with facts rather than empty promises and extravagant claims. 3) Identify your sources. 4) Be an expert on the subject (or find one to support your message.) 5) Establish common ground. The things that you have in common with your audience will help them to identify with you. 6) Be objective. 7) Display your good intentions.
DIFFICULTY: difficult; PAGE: 232; OBJECTIVE: 1; TYPE: concept

93. Describe the four steps of the AIDA plan for persuasive messages.

ANSWER: 1) Attention: Make your audience want to hear about your idea. Find some common ground on which to build your case. 2) Interest: Explain the relevance of your message to your audience. 3) Desire: Make readers want to change by explaining how the change will benefit them. Answer questions that your audience might have in advance. Back up your claims with evidence that supports your point. 4) Action: Ask your audience to take the action you suggest.
DIFFICULTY: difficult; PAGE: 233; OBJECTIVE: 3; TYPE: application

94. When your AIDA message uses an indirect approach and is delivered by memo or e-mail, what are two goals to keep in mind as you write the subject line?

ANSWER: One challenge in this situation is to make the subject line interesting and relevant enough to capture reader attention. At the same time, however, you have to do that without revealing your main idea.
DIFFICULTY: difficult; PAGE: 233-34; OBJECTIVE: 3; TYPE: concept

95. Rewrite the following e-mail subject line in order to make it more interesting without revealing the main idea: "Proposal to switch to new medical insurance provider"

ANSWER: "Instant savings on medical insurance premiums"
DIFFICULTY: moderate; PAGE: 233-34; OBJECTIVE: 3; TYPE: application

96. Describe the three main types of logical appeals.

ANSWER: 1) Analogy—using comparisons to persuade. 2) Induction—reasoning from specific evidence to a general conclusion. 3) Deduction—reasoning from a generalization to a specific conclusion.
DIFFICULTY: difficult; PAGE: 235; OBJECTIVE: 4; TYPE: concept

97. Describe the best way to write a claim request using the AIDA approach.

ANSWER: Use the direct approach. Begin by getting the reader's attention by clearly stating the basic problem. Be as specific as possible about what you want to happen. Give your reader a good reason for granting your claim. Show that the audience is responsible for the problem. Explain the situation calmly and reasonably. Don't make threats. Make sure that your request is a logical response to the problem. Close by specifying a deadline for action and reminding your audience of the benefit of granting your claim.
DIFFICULTY: difficult; PAGE: 238-39; OBJECTIVE: 3; TYPE: application

98. Briefly explain the difference between selling points and benefits, then give an example of each.

ANSWER: Selling points are the most attractive features of an idea or product. Benefits are the particular advantages that readers will realize from those features. The fact that a television comes with a remote control is a selling point, but the convenience the buyer will enjoy *because of* the remote control is a benefit.
DIFFICULTY: moderate; PAGE: 239-40; OBJECTIVE: 6; TYPE: concept/application

99. Describe the ways that you can minimize the importance of price in a sales letter.

ANSWER: You can leave out any mention of price or place it in a less important location in the letter, near the end or mid-paragraph after you have described the benefits and selling points. You can compare the price to some other product or activity in an attempt to make the price of your product seem small and affordable in comparison. You can also compare the price to the potential costs of *not* buying the product.
DIFFICULTY: moderate; PAGE: 240; OBJECTIVE: 3; TYPE: application

100. List at least three common mistakes communicators make when preparing persuasive arguments.

ANSWER: Some common mistakes are using an up-front hard sell, resisting compromise, relying solely on great arguments (but ignoring audience needs), and assuming that persuasion is a one-shot effort instead of a process.
DIFFICULTY: moderate; PAGE: 241; OBJECTIVE: 5; TYPE: concept

101. List at least five common techniques for attracting an audience's attention at the beginning of a sales letter.

ANSWER: 1) Your product's strongest feature or benefit. 2) A piece of genuine news. 3) A point of common ground with the audience. 3) A personal appeal to the reader's emotions and values. 4) The promise of insider information. 5) The promise of savings. 6) A sample or demonstration of the product. 7) A solution to a problem.
DIFFICULTY: difficult; PAGE: 241; OBJECTIVE: 3; TYPE: concept

CHAPTER 10
UNDERSTANDING AND PLANNING REPORTS AND PROPOSALS

Multiple Choice

1. The basic purpose of informational reports is
   a. to persuade the audience to act.
   b. to present recommendations and conclusions.
   c. to present data, facts, feedback, and other types of information, without analysis or recommendations.
   d. to convince the reader of the soundness of your thinking.

ANSWER: c. Informational reports do not contain analysis of data.
DIFFICULTY: easy; PAGE: 266; OBJECTIVE: 2; TYPE: concept

2. An analytical report
   a. often requires a more comprehensive statement of purpose than an informational report.
   b. presents data, but does not draw conclusions about the data.
   c. does not include recommendations.
   d. all of the above

ANSWER: a. Options b and c describe informational reports.
DIFFICULTY: moderate; PAGE: 266; OBJECTIVE: 2; TYPE: concept

3. Despite the variety among them, many analytical reports include a
   a. standard opening.
   b. section of recommendations.
   c. "this is how it's done" quality.
   d. standard middle section.

ANSWER: b. Many analytical reports recommend actions as part of their analysis of the data.
DIFFICULTY: moderate; PAGE: 266; OBJECTIVE: 2; TYPE: concept

4. The best way to phrase the purpose statement of a report is with
   a. complex language.
   b. an infinitive phrase.
   c. a controversial statement.
   d. jargon.

ANSWER: b. This helps clarify exactly what you need to accomplish.
DIFFICULTY: moderate; PAGE: 267; OBJECTIVE: 1; TYPE: concept

5. Which of the following is the least clear statement of purpose?
   a. The purpose of this report to determine which of four alternative investments will have the highest return.
   b. The purpose of this report is to analyze four potential investments.
   c. The purpose of this report is to answer the question, 'Which of four investments will provide the highest return?'
   d. The goal of this report is to evaluate the return on four investments.

ANSWER: b. This statement provides no information on how the investments will be evaluated.
DIFFICULTY: moderate; PAGE: 267-68; OBJECTIVE: 1; TYPE: application

6. Which of the following is an infinitive phrase?
   a. updating clients
   b. update clients
   c. updated clients
   d. to update clients

ANSWER: d. Infinitive phrases contain 'to' and a verb.
DIFFICULTY: moderate; PAGE: 267-68; OBJECTIVE: 1; TYPE: application

7. A formal work plan includes all of the following *except*
   a. a statement of the problem or opportunity addressed in your report.
   b. a list of all the sources you will use.
   c. plans for following up after delivering the report.
   d. a statement of the purpose and scope of your investigation.

ANSWER: b. A work plan does not normally include this.
DIFFICULTY: moderate; PAGE: 269; OBJECTIVE: 1; TYPE: concept

8. Which of the following is *not* a typical element in a formal work plan?
   a. a list of tasks to be accomplished
   b. a schedule
   c. conclusions and recommendations
   d. none of the above

ANSWER: c. Conclusions and recommendations are not normally included in a work plan.
DIFFICULTY: moderate; PAGE: 269; OBJECTIVE: 1; TYPE: concept

9. When selecting a medium for a report
   a. you should choose the ones that are most convenient.
   b. you should choose the ones that are most economical.
   c. your decisions should reflect your audience and your purpose.
   d. you should always present your report in writing.

ANSWER: c. This is part of the audience-centered approach.
DIFFICULTY: moderate; PAGE: 270; OBJECTIVE: 1; TYPE: concept

10. Delivering a business report as an electronic file
    a. is useful if readers will need to search the report frequently.
    b. costs too much to be practical.
    c. is usually an inconvenience for readers.
    d. is rarely, if ever, necessary.

ANSWER: a. Your choice of medium should reflect your audience's needs.
DIFFICULTY: moderate; PAGE: 270; OBJECTIVE: 1; TYPE: application

11. For business reports,
    a. the direct approach is usually best.
    b. it is sometimes acceptable to combine the direct and indirect
       approaches.
    c. the indirect approach is less effective if the report is lengthy.
    d. all of the above.

ANSWER: d. All of these statements are true.
DIFFICULTY: moderate; PAGE: 270; OBJECTIVE: 1; TYPE: concept

 12. A problem statement for a business report
    a. is basically the same thing as a purpose statement.
    b. is generally unnecessary.
    c. defines the purpose of your research.
    d. none of the above

ANSWER: c. A problem statement defines the purpose of your research.
DIFFICULTY: moderate; PAGE: 271; OBJECTIVE: 3; TYPE: concept

13. In evaluating sources as you do research for a report, it is important to avoid
    sources that are
    a. not current.
    b. very recent.
    c. very objective.
    d. none of the above

**ANSWER: a. It is important to make sure you are using the most current
information available.**
DIFFICULTY: moderate; PAGE: 272; OBJECTIVE: 5; TYPE: concept

 14. Which of the following is usually treated as a primary source?
    a. books
    b. articles
    c. observations
    d. websites

**ANSWER: c. Although books, articles, and websites can qualify as primary
sources (depending on how they are used), interviews, observations, and surveys are
more popular forms of primary sources.**
DIFFICULTY: moderate; PAGE: 272; OBJECTIVE: 4; TYPE: concept

15. Unlike search engines, web directories
    a. search only American websites.
    b. always require subscription fees.
    c. use human editors to categorize and evaluate websites.
    d. none of the above

ANSWER: c. This is the primary advantage of using a web directory.
DIFFICULTY: moderate; PAGE: 273; OBJECTIVE: 3; TYPE: concept

16. An online database
    a. is basically the same thing as a search engine.
    b. provides access to newspapers, magazines, and journals.
    c. is an obsolete research tool.
    d. is too technical for most people to use.

ANSWER: b. Online databases give you access to materials that standard search engines may not include.
DIFFICULTY: moderate; PAGE: 273; OBJECTIVE: 3; TYPE: concept

17. A _____ search lets you define a query with words such as AND, OR, or NOT.
    a. keyword
    b. forms-based
    c. Boolean
    d. none of the above

ANSWER: c. This is the definition of a Boolean search.
DIFFICULTY: moderate; PAGE: 274; OBJECTIVE: 3; TYPE: concept

18. Monitor/control reports include
    a. policies and procedures.
    b. plans, operating reports, and personal activity reports.
    c. solicited and unsolicited sales proposals.
    d. research, justification, and troubleshooting reports.

ANSWER: b. These are all types of monitor/control reports.
DIFFICULTY: moderate; PAGE: 277; OBJECTIVE: 2; TYPE: concept

19. Policy and procedure reports are used for
    a. documenting compliance with government regulations.
    b. monitoring and controlling operations.
    c. conveying guidelines and other organizational decisions.
    d. presenting and analyzing the alternative solutions to a problem.

ANSWER: c. These are the primary uses.
DIFFICULTY: moderate; PAGE: 277; OBJECTIVE: 2; TYPE: concept

20. A public corporation filing a quarterly tax report would be providing a
    a. progress report.
    b. compliance report.
    c. justification report.
    d. periodic operating report.

ANSWER: b. A tax report is a form of compliance report.
DIFFICULTY: moderate; PAGE: 278; OBJECTIVE: 2; TYPE: application

21. Compliance reports are most often written
    a. in response to government regulations.
    b. to explain rules and guidelines.
    c. to protest unfair treatment.
    d. in response to employee grievances.

ANSWER: a. Compliance reports document adherence to regulations, usually those mandated by a government agency.
DIFFICULTY: moderate; PAGE: 278; OBJECTIVE: 2; TYPE: concept

22. A contractor submitting a weekly report on work done to date would be providing the client with
    a. an interim progress report.
    b. an interim compliance report.
    c. a justification report.
    d. a periodic operating report.

ANSWER: a. An interim progress report documents work at various stages of completion.
DIFFICULTY: moderate; PAGE: 278; OBJECTIVE: 2; TYPE: application

23. Topical organization strategies for informational reports include all of the following *except:*
    a. complexity
    b. spatial orientation
    c. importance
    d. comparison

ANSWER: a. This is not a type of topical organization.
DIFFICULTY: moderate; PAGE: 278; OBJECTIVE: 1; TYPE: concept

24. A report that examines the financial aspects of a proposed decision, such as acquiring another company, is known as a _____ report.
    a. troubleshooting
    b. hypothetical
    c. due diligence
    d. justification

ANSWER: c. This type of report precedes major financial decisions.
DIFFICULTY: moderate; PAGE: 278; OBJECTIVE: 2; TYPE: concept

25. Unlike a failure analysis report, a troubleshooting report is written
   a. before a failure occurs.
   b. while a failure is occurring.
   c. after a failure occurs.
   d. by management.

ANSWER: b. These reports are designed to solve current problems.
DIFFICULTY: moderate; PAGE: 278; OBJECTIVE: 2; TYPE: concept

26. A justification report
   a. provides the history of a problem, then presents and analyzes possible solutions.
   b. describes what has happened in a department or division during a particular period.
   c. is written after a course of action has been taken to justify what was done.
   d. does all of the above.

ANSWER: c. Unlike a proposal, a justification report is written after the action has been taken.
DIFFICULTY: moderate; PAGE: 278; OBJECTIVE: 2; TYPE: concept

27. Unlike proposals and feasibility reports, justification reports
   a. are designed to support products, plans, or projects after they have been implemented.
   b. are internal as opposed to external reports.
   c. are always in memo format.
   d. do not require a great deal of supporting data.

ANSWER: a. This is the definition of a justification report.
DIFFICULTY: moderate; PAGE: 278; OBJECTIVE: 2; TYPE: concept

28. A report that explores the ramifications of a proposed course of action is known as a _____ report.
   a. justification
   b. feasibility
   c. troubleshooting
   d. due diligence

ANSWER: b. This type of report analyzes the benefits and drawbacks of a possible action.
DIFFICULTY: moderate; PAGE: 278; OBJECTIVE: 2; TYPE: concept

29. One potential drawback of focusing on conclusions in a report is that you may
    a. take too long to reach the main idea of your report.
    b. alienate audiences that are skeptical.
    c. offend your audience.
    d. do all of the above.

ANSWER: b. Audiences that are skeptical may not read on to see how you have justified your conclusions.
DIFFICULTY: moderate; PAGE: 279; OBJECTIVE: 8; TYPE: concept

30. Which of the following is *not* a common organizational format for analytical reports?
    a. focusing on conclusions
    b. focusing on recommendations
    c. focusing on information
    d. focusing on logical argument

ANSWER: c. The other three formats can all be used for analytical reports.
DIFFICULTY: moderate; PAGE: 279-81; OBJECTIVE: 8; TYPE: concept

31. Reports that focus on recommendations should
    a. establish the need for action.
    b. list the benefits that can be achieved if the recommendations are adopted.
    c. list the steps needed to achieve the benefits.
    d. all of the above

ANSWER: d. All of these statements are true of reports focused on recommendations.
DIFFICULTY: moderate; PAGE: 280; OBJECTIVE: 7; TYPE: concept

32. A report focused on recommendations should
    a. follow the direct approach.
    b. not include conclusions.
    c. avoid mentioning any potential risks.
    d. outline costs, but not in detail.

ANSWER: a. A report focused on recommendations uses the direct approach.
DIFFICULTY: moderate; PAGE: 280; OBJECTIVE: 8; TYPE: concept

33. Any risks involved with your recommendations should
    a. not be addressed since they may discourage your audience.
    b. be discussed in your report, but only in vague, general terms.
    c. be addressed clearly in your report, along with how they can be minimized.
    d. be outlined before you reveal the benefits that can be achieved.

ANSWER: c. Not addressing risks limits the effectiveness of your report.
DIFFICULTY: moderate; PAGE: 280; OBJECTIVE: 8; TYPE: concept

34. Reports focusing on logical arguments
    a. never use the indirect approach.
    b. are not very convincing.
    c. are generally best when readers are hostile or skeptical to your recommendations.
    d. do not include outside evidence.

ANSWER: c. Logical arguments are often effective for overcoming audience resistance to your report.
DIFFICULTY: moderate; PAGE: 281; OBJECTIVE: 8; TYPE: concept

35. Which of the following is *not* a strategy for structuring reports focused on logical arguments?
    a. 2+2 approach
    b. direct approach
    c. yardstick approach
    d. none of the above

ANSWER: b. Reports focused on logical arguments do not follow the direct approach.
DIFFICULTY: moderate; PAGE: 281; OBJECTIVE: 8; TYPE: concept

36. The 2+2 approach
    a. generally works only with lengthy, nonroutine reports.
    b. shows readers how all the evidence adds up to your conclusion.
    c. is far more complicated than any other organizational strategy.
    d. is the only approach that is appropriate for any business report.

ANSWER: b. This approach leads readers to understand the logic of your main idea.
DIFFICULTY: moderate; PAGE: 281; OBJECTIVE: 8; TYPE: concept

37. If a client requests a proposal and then provides a list of criteria the solution must meet, the _____ approach will probably be the best way to organize your report.
    a. 2+2
    b. scientific
    c. direct
    d. yardstick

ANSWER: d. The yardstick approach illustrates how your proposal meets each of the audience's criteria.
DIFFICULTY: moderate; PAGE: 281; OBJECTIVE: 8; TYPE: concept

38. Whereas _____ proposals seek funds from private parties, _____ proposals seek funds from government agencies.
    a. grant; investment
    b. investment; grant
    c. internal; external
    d. external; internal

ANSWER: b. Investment proposals are aimed at individual investors, while grant proposals target government agencies.
DIFFICULTY: moderate; PAGE: 283; OBJECTIVE: 2; TYPE: concept

39. Solicited proposals are generally prepared by
    a. companies attempting to obtain business.
    b. government regulatory agencies.
    c. companies at the request of clients who require a product or service.
    d. clients who wish to acquire the services of highly regarded companies.

ANSWER: c. Solicited proposals reflect the demands of the person(s) who request them.
DIFFICULTY: moderate; PAGE: 284; OBJECTIVE: 2; TYPE: concept

40. "RFP" stands for
    a. request for proposals.
    b. reconciliation for protocol.
    c. receipt for proposal.
    d. rejection from proposal.

ANSWER: a. This is the standard term for a document that invites business proposals.
DIFFICULTY: moderate; PAGE: 284; OBJECTIVE: 2; TYPE: concept

41. A request for proposals generally specifies
    a. the exact type of work to be performed.
    b. how the work should be completed.
    c. when the work should be completed.
    d. all of the above

ANSWER: d. An RFP specifies everything needed to produce an accurate bid on a project.
DIFFICULTY: moderate; PAGE: 284; OBJECTIVE: 2; TYPE: concept

42. In an unsolicited proposal, the writer
   a. explains why the client should take action.
   b. analyzes the client's business in light of the competition.
   c. uses a style approved by the American Association of Business Writers.
   d. enumerates the client's options regarding such business decisions as product-line expansion.

ANSWER: a. Unlike a solicited proposal, an unsolicited proposal must first convince readers that there is a problem that needs to be solved.
DIFFICULTY: moderate; PAGE: 284; OBJECTIVE: 2; TYPE: concept

True/False

43. An analytical report may end by presenting a recommendation.

ANSWER: True. Analytical reports offer information and analysis, and may provide recommendations.
DIFFICULTY: easy; PAGE: 266; OBJECTIVE: 2; TYPE: concept

44. Analytical reports provide both information and analysis.

ANSWER: True. This is what distinguishes analytical reports from informational reports.
DIFFICULTY: moderate; PAGE: 266; OBJECTIVE: 2; TYPE: concept

45. Analytical reports are solely intended to inform readers.

ANSWER: False. Analytical reports present data, but also interpret the data.
DIFFICULTY: moderate; PAGE: 266; OBJECTIVE: 2; TYPE: concept

46. For a business document to be considered a report, it must be at least six pages long.

ANSWER: False. Business reports vary in length.
DIFFICULTY: easy; PAGE: 267; OBJECTIVE: 1; TYPE: concept

47. The statement of purpose for a report is always presented as a question.

ANSWER: False. The most useful way to phrase a statement of purpose is to begin with an infinitive phrase (*to* plus a verb).
DIFFICULTY: moderate; PAGE: 267; OBJECTIVE: 2; TYPE: concept

48. The statement of purpose for analytical reports will usually need to be more comprehensive than one for informational reports.

ANSWER: True. Analytical reports go beyond merely presenting data.
DIFFICULTY: moderate; PAGE: 268; OBJECTIVE: 2; TYPE: concept

49. Very few reports require a work plan.

ANSWER: False. You will want to prepare a work plan for most reports.
DIFFICULTY: moderate; PAGE: 269; OBJECTIVE: 1; TYPE: concept

50. Some work plans include a tentative outline.

ANSWER: True. An outline can be included.
DIFFICULTY: moderate; PAGE: 269; OBJECTIVE: 1; TYPE: concept

51. An executive dashboard is a customized online presentation of key report elements.

ANSWER: True. This is the correct definition.
DIFFICULTY: moderate; PAGE: 270; OBJECTIVE: 1; TYPE: concept

52. In today's business environment, adding multimedia to reports is always desirable.

ANSWER: False. For some reports, this would be a waste of resources.
DIFFICULTY: easy; PAGE: 270; OBJECTIVE: 1; TYPE: concept

53. The direct approach is the most popular strategy for business reports.

ANSWER: True. It saves time, makes the rest of the report easy to follow, and produces a more forceful report.
DIFFICULTY: moderate; PAGE: 270; OBJECTIVE: 1; TYPE: concept

54. Depending on your status in the organization, using the direct approach can be misconstrued as arrogance.

ANSWER: True. This is one risk of using the direct approach.
DIFFICULTY: moderate; PAGE: 270; OBJECTIVE: 1; TYPE: concept

55. For longer reports, the indirect approach tends to be less effective than the direct approach.

ANSWER: True. The longer the report, the less effective an indirect approach is likely to be.
DIFFICULTY: moderate; PAGE: 270; OBJECTIVE: 1; TYPE: concept

56. In business reports, it is never appropriate to combine the direct and indirect approaches by revealing conclusions and recommendations as you go along.

ANSWER: False. This is a common practice.
DIFFICULTY: moderate; PAGE: 270; OBJECTIVE: 1; TYPE: concept

57. A problem statement specifies the challenges you expect to face in preparing a formal business report.

ANSWER: False. A problem statement defines the purpose of your research.
DIFFICULTY: moderate; PAGE: 271; OBJECTIVE: 1; TYPE: concept

58. Secondary research includes sources such as books, articles, websites, and newspapers.

ANSWER: True. These are all types of secondary sources.
DIFFICULTY: moderate; PAGE: 272; OBJECTIVE: 4; TYPE: concept

59. The key difference between primary research and secondary research is that primary research is more important.

ANSWER: False. The key difference is that primary research is new research done specifically for your current project.
DIFFICULTY: moderate; PAGE: 272; OBJECTIVE: 4; TYPE: concept

60. The publication date of a source is unimportant, as long as the source contains interesting information.

ANSWER: False. It is important to make sure you use the most recent information available.
DIFFICULTY: moderate; PAGE: 272; OBJECTIVE: 5; TYPE: concept

61. Trade journals provide information about specific industries, whereas academic journals provide research-oriented articles from researchers and educators.

ANSWER: True. This is the correct definition of each type of source.
DIFFICULTY: moderate; PAGE: 273; OBJECTIVE: 3; TYPE: concept

62. A search engine and a web directory are essentially the same things.

ANSWER: False. Unlike a search engine, a web directory uses human editors to categorize and evaluate websites.
DIFFICULTY: moderate; PAGE: 273; OBJECTIVE: 3; TYPE: concept

63. NewsGator and NewzCrawler are examples of forms-based search engines.

ANSWER: False. These are both news aggregators, which enable you to subscribe to specific information channels at thousands of websites, blogs, and newsgroups.
DIFFICULTY: moderate; PAGE: 274; OBJECTIVE: 3; TYPE: application

64. A survey is reliable if it would produce identical results if repeated.

ANSWER: True. This is the correct definition.
DIFFICULTY: moderate; PAGE: 274; OBJECTIVE: 3; TYPE: concept

65. The following is a closed question: "Why do you think South Africa represents a better opportunity than Europe for this product line?"

ANSWER: False. This is an open-ended question because it does not elicit a specific answer, such as yes or no.
DIFFICULTY: moderate; PAGE: 275; OBJECTIVE: 6; TYPE: concept

66. The main difference between summarizing and paraphrasing is that summarizing presents only the gist of the material in fewer words.

ANSWER: True. A paraphrase restates the original in your own words, but with the same level of detail.
DIFFICULTY: moderate; PAGE: 276; OBJECTIVE: 3; TYPE: concept

67. A memo summarizing an employee's trip to a trade show would be an example of a personal activity report.

ANSWER: True. This is one type of personal activity report.
DIFFICULTY: moderate; PAGE: 277; OBJECTIVE: 2; TYPE: application

68. Operating reports often provide feedback on sales and expenses.

ANSWER: True. This is one function of operating reports.
DIFFICULTY: moderate; PAGE: 277; OBJECTIVE: 2; TYPE: concept

69. Position papers are a type of compliance report.

ANSWER: False. Position papers do not demonstrate compliance. Instead, they fall within the category of reports to implement policies and procedures.
DIFFICULTY: moderate; PAGE: 277; OBJECTIVE: 2; TYPE: concept

70. Position papers spell out company procedures.

ANSWER: False. This is the definition of a policy report.
DIFFICULTY: moderate; PAGE: 277; OBJECTIVE: 2; TYPE: concept

71. Compliance reports, progress reports, and monitoring/control reports are all types of informational reports.

ANSWER: True. These are all types of information reports.
DIFFICULTY: easy; PAGE: 277-78; OBJECTIVE: 2; TYPE: concept

72. Progress reports are never more than simple updates in memo or e-mail format.

ANSWER: False. Sometimes this is all that is required.
DIFFICULTY: moderate; PAGE: 278; OBJECTIVE: 2; TYPE: concept

73. The indirect approach is never appropriate for informational reports.

ANSWER: False. If the report contains disappointing information, the indirect approach may be best.
DIFFICULTY: moderate; PAGE: 278; OBJECTIVE: 1; TYPE: concept

74. Reports that examine the financial aspects of a proposed decision, such as acquiring another company, are called due diligence reports.

ANSWER: True. This is the correct definition.
DIFFICULTY: moderate; PAGE: 278; OBJECTIVE: 2; TYPE: concept

75. Whereas troubleshooting reports deal with problems as they occur, failure analysis reports seek to prevent problems before they happen.

ANSWER: False. A failure analysis report studies an event that happened in the past, with the hope of showing how to avoid similar failures in the future.
DIFFICULTY: moderate; PAGE: 278; OBJECTIVE: 2; TYPE: concept

76. A justification report is an internal report designed to persuade top management to approve a proposed investment or project.

ANSWER: False. Justification reports explain decisions that have already been made.
DIFFICULTY: moderate; PAGE: 278; OBJECTIVE: 2; TYPE: concept

77. Managers use feasibility reports to examine the ramifications of a decision they are about to make.

ANSWER: True. This is the correct definition.
DIFFICULTY: moderate; PAGE: 278; OBJECTIVE: 2; TYPE: concept

78. Focusing on conclusions in an analytical report involves using the direct approach to organization.

ANSWER: True. This approach is best for addressing a receptive audience.
DIFFICULTY: moderate; PAGE: 279; OBJECTIVE: 8; TYPE: concept

79. In reports focused on recommendations, it is best to avoid the direct approach.

ANSWER: False. The direct approach is most appropriate for reports that focus on recommendations.
DIFFICULTY: moderate; PAGE: 280; OBJECTIVE: 8; TYPE: concept

80. The primary purpose of an internal proposal is either to request funds and management support for new projects or to obtain permission to take action on specific projects.

ANSWER: True. These are common functions of internal proposals.
DIFFICULTY: moderate; PAGE: 283; OBJECTIVE: 7; TYPE: concept

Fill-in-the-Blank

81. Whereas _____ reports focus on facts, _____ reports offer interpretation and can also include recommendations.

ANSWER: Informational, Analytical
DIFFICULTY: moderate; PAGE: 266; OBJECTIVE: 2; TYPE: concept

82. The statement of _____ defines why you are preparing the report and what you plan to deliver.

ANSWER: Purpose
DIFFICULTY: moderate; PAGE: 267; OBJECTIVE: 1; TYPE: concept

83. In organizing their reports, business people often combine the _____ and _____ approaches—revealing their conclusions and recommendations as they go along instead of putting them first or last.

ANSWER: Direct, Indirect OR Indirect, Direct
DIFFICULTY: moderate; PAGE: 270; OBJECTIVE: 1; TYPE: concept

84. A common monitor/control report is the _____ plan, which summarizes a proposed business venture, communicates the company's goals, highlights how management intends to achieve those goals, and explains why customers will be motivated to buy the company's products or services.

ANSWER: Business
DIFFICULTY: moderate; PAGE: 277; OBJECTIVE: 2; TYPE: concept

85. _____ reports such as tax returns often demonstrate that a company's practices follow established government regulations.

ANSWER: Compliance
DIFFICULTY: moderate; PAGE: 278; OBJECTIVE: 2; TYPE: concept

86. A _____ report is written to validate a decision that has already been made.

ANSWER: Justification
DIFFICULTY: moderate; PAGE: 278; OBJECTIVE: 2; TYPE: concept

87. _____ _____ reports study events that happened in the past, with the hope of learning how to avoid similar failures in the future.

ANSWER: Failure Analysis
DIFFICULTY: moderate; PAGE: 278; OBJECTIVE: 2; TYPE: concept

88. In reports focusing on logical arguments, the _____ approach is often the most persuasive and efficient way to develop an analytical report for skeptical readers since it demonstrates that everything adds up.

ANSWER: 2+2 = 4 OR Indirect
DIFFICULTY: moderate; PAGE: 281; OBJECTIVE: 8; TYPE: concept

89. With the _____ approach to structuring analytical reports, you use a number of criteria to decide which option to select from two or more possibilities.

ANSWER: Yardstick
DIFFICULTY: moderate; PAGE: 281; OBJECTIVE: 8; TYPE: concept

90. Whereas _____ proposals are used to request decisions from managers within an organization, _____ proposals are directed to parties outside the organization.

ANSWER: Internal, External
DIFFICULTY: easy; PAGE: 283; OBJECTIVE: 2; TYPE: concept

91. One type of external proposal is the _____ proposal, which requests funds from government agencies and other sponsoring organizations.

ANSWER: Grant
DIFFICULTY: moderate; PAGE: 283; OBJECTIVE: 2; TYPE: concept

92. A formal invitation to bid on a contract is called a _____ for _____, or RFP.

ANSWER: Request, Proposals
DIFFICULTY: moderate; PAGE: 284; OBJECTIVE: 2; TYPE: concept

93. In a(n) _____ proposal, the author must convince readers that a problem or opportunity exists before providing a solution or plan of action.

ANSWER: Unsolicited
DIFFICULTY: moderate; PAGE: 284; OBJECTIVE: 2; TYPE: concept

Short Answer/Essay

94. Describe the ways that analytical and informational reports differ.

ANSWER: These two types of reports differ in terms of content and aims. Analytical reports offer information and analysis, and can also include recommendations. Informational reports present unbiased information; they do not offer analysis or recommendations.
DIFFICULTY: moderate; PAGE: 266; OBJECTIVE: 2; TYPE: concept

95. Briefly explain the primary function of a statement of purpose, then indicate the most useful way to phrase one.

ANSWER: A statement of purpose defines why you are preparing your report and what you plan to deliver in the report. The best way to phrase a purpose statement is to begin with an infinitive phrase, such as "to analyze."
DIFFICULTY: moderate; PAGE: 267; OBJECTIVE: 1; TYPE: concept

96. You have been asked to help a company find ways to reduce the amount it spends on employee health and dental benefits. Write a purpose statement for the report that you will produce.

ANSWER: (Answers may vary.) To analyze the employee health and dental benefits and suggest ways to reduce expenses.
DIFFICULTY: moderate; PAGE: 267; OBJECTIVE: 1; TYPE: application

97. Define "work plan" and briefly describe the elements it often contains.

ANSWER: For simpler reports, the work plan can be an informal list of tasks and a simple schedule. However, if you're preparing a lengthy report, particularly when you're collaborating with others, you'll want to develop a more detailed work plan.
DIFFICULTY: moderate; PAGE: 269; OBJECTIVE: 1; TYPE: concept

98. Describe several benefits and one potential drawback of organizing business reports using the direct approach.

ANSWER: The direct approach is the most popular and convenient format for business reports because it saves time, makes the rest of the report easy to follow, and produces a more forceful report. In some cases, however, the confidence implied by the direct report may be misconstrued as arrogance. Depending on your relationship with your audience and on their probable reaction to your report, the indirect approach may be more appropriate.
DIFFICULTY: difficult; PAGE: 270; OBJECTIVE: 1; TYPE: concept

99. List three common types of monitor/control reports.

ANSWER: (1) Plans, (2) operating reports, and (3) personal activity reports.
DIFFICULTY: moderate; PAGE: 277; OBJECTIVE: 2; TYPE: concept

100. Provide at least five examples of topical organization strategies for business reports.

ANSWER: (1) Comparison, (2) importance, (3) sequence, (4) chronology, (5) geography, and (6) category.
DIFFICULTY: difficult; PAGE: 278; OBJECTIVE: 1; TYPE: concept

101. What is the primary difference between a feasibility report and a justification report?

ANSWER: Whereas a feasibility report studies proposed options, a justification report is written after an action, to justify what was done.
DIFFICULTY: moderate; PAGE: 278; OBJECTIVE: 2; TYPE: concept

102. Give three reasons that writing analytical reports presents a greater challenge than writing informational reports.

ANSWER: (1) The quality of your reasoning—you're doing more than just delivering information; (2) the quality of your writing—you need to present your thinking in a compelling and persuasive manner; and (3) the responsibility that comes with persuasion.
DIFFICULTY: difficult; PAGE: 278-79; OBJECTIVE: 2; TYPE: concept

103. List the three most common strategies for structuring analytical reports.

ANSWER: (1) Focusing on conclusions; (2) focusing on recommendations; (3) focusing on logical arguments.
DIFFICULTY: moderate; PAGE: 279-81; OBJECTIVE: 8; TYPE: concept

104. Describe the basic function of internal proposals.

ANSWER: *Internal proposals* request decisions from managers within the organization, such as proposals to buy new equipment or launch new research projects.
DIFFICULTY: moderate; PAGE: 283; OBJECTIVE: 2; TYPE: concept

105. Explain the three basic categories of analytical business reports and provide at least one example of each type.

ANSWER: The first category includes reports written to assess opportunities. One example of this type is the market analysis report, which judges the likelihood of success for new products or sales initiatives by suggesting potential opportunities in a given market and identifying competitive threats and other risks. Due diligence reports, which examine the financial aspects of a proposed decision, are also in this category. The second category includes reports written to solve problems. Examples of these are troubleshooting reports (which managers assign when they need to understand why something isn't working properly) and failure analysis reports (which study past failures in an effort to avoid similar ones in the future). The third category of analytical business reports includes reports written to support decisions. Feasibility reports are one type in this category. They are called for when managers need to explore the ramifications of a decision they're about to make. Justification reports (written to justify decisions that have already been made) also fall into this group.
DIFFICULTY: difficult; PAGE: 278; OBJECTIVE: 1; TYPE: concept

CHAPTER 11
WRITING AND COMPLETING REPORTS AND PROPOSALS

Multiple Choice

1. To make your business reports more effective, do all of the following *except*
   a. be sensitive to audience needs.
   b. make the report lengthy.
   c. adopt the "you" attitude.
   d. use bias-free language.

ANSWER: b. All of the other strategies increase the effectiveness of business reports.
DIFFICULTY: moderate; PAGE: 299; OBJECTIVE: 1; TYPE: concept

2. When you write in a formal style, you
   a. eliminate all references to *I* and *me*.
   b. remain businesslike and unemotional.
   c. use very few colorful adjectives or adverbs.
   d. do all of the above.

ANSWER: d. Each of these techniques increases the formality of your writing.
DIFFICULTY: moderate; PAGE: 299; OBJECTIVE: 1; TYPE: concept

3. The writing style for a report should probably be more formal if
   a. you know your readers reasonably well.
   b. your report is internal.
   c. your audience includes people in other cultures.
   d. the report is relatively short.

ANSWER: c. Informal elements (such as humor) often do not translate well from one culture to another.
DIFFICULTY: moderate; PAGE: 299; OBJECTIVE: 1; TYPE: concept

4. Which of the following statements is the most formal?
   a. The financial analysis clearly shows that buying TramCo is the best alternative.
   b. I think we should buy TramCo.
   c. In my opinion, we should consider the purchase of TramCo.
   d. We therefore conclude that acquiring TramCo would (based on information we have gathered) be in our company's best interest.

ANSWER: a. This version emphasizes objectivity and avoids references to *you, I, we,* and *us*.
DIFFICULTY: moderate; PAGE: 299; OBJECTIVE: 1; TYPE: application

5. When writing business reports for people from other cultures, it is best to
   a. use a more formal tone than you would for a U.S. audience.
   b. use a less formal tone than you would for a U.S. audience.
   c. include personal references such as "you" and "us."
   d. use a great deal of idiomatic language.

ANSWER: a. This can help prevent miscommunication.
DIFFICULTY: moderate; PAGE: 299; OBJECTIVE: 1; TYPE: concept

6. The introduction (or opening) of a business report or proposal should always
   a. outline your conclusions or recommendations.
   b. list all the sources from which you draw information.
   c. provide a detailed description of your qualifications to write the report.
   d. tie your report to a problem or an assignment.

ANSWER: d. This is one function of an effective introduction.
DIFFICULTY: moderate; PAGE: 300; OBJECTIVE: 1; TYPE: concept

7. The information needed to support your conclusions and recommendations should appear in the _____ of your report.
   a. opening
   b. body
   c. close
   d. appendix

ANSWER: b. The body presents, analyzes, and interprets the information gathered during your investigation and supports your recommendations or conclusions.
DIFFICULTY: moderate; PAGE: 301; OBJECTIVE: n/a; TYPE: concept

8. The close of a report should
   a. emphasize the main points of the message.
   b. summarize reader benefits if the document suggests a change.
   c. refer to all the pieces and remind readers how those pieces fit together.
   d. achieve all of the above.

ANSWER: d. The close should achieve all of these functions.
DIFFICULTY: easy; PAGE: 301; OBJECTIVE: n/a; TYPE: concept

9. In the introduction, explaining the historical conditions or factors that led up to your report
   a. may take several pages or a few sentences, depending on the length of your report.
   b. is unnecessary in internal reports.
   c. diminishes your credibility by wasting readers' time.
   d. is necessary only in very formal reports.

ANSWER: a. The overall length of the report helps determine how much space to devote to each topic in the introduction.
DIFFICULTY: moderate; PAGE: 303; OBJECTIVE: 1; TYPE: concept

10. Terms in your report that are unfamiliar to your audience should most often be defined in the
    a. introduction
    b. body
    c. explanatory notes
    d. any of the above

ANSWER: a. The introduction is generally the best place to define unfamiliar terms.
DIFFICULTY: moderate; PAGE: 303; OBJECTIVE: 1; TYPE: concept

11. In the close of a report that proposes a specific course of action, you should
    a. provide hints on what the audience should do so you don't sound like you're giving orders
    b. instruct your audience to contact you about what they should do next
    c. make sure your readers understand exactly what's expected of them and when it's expected
    d. any of the above

ANSWER: c. This is an important component of reports that propose specific actions.
DIFFICULTY: moderate; PAGE: 303; OBJECTIVE: 2; TYPE: concept

12. The writing for a proposal should
    a. follow the AIDA plan.
    b. follow the plan for good-news messages.
    c. avoid the "you" attitude.
    d. be as vague as possible.

ANSWER: a. This format is useful for persuasive messages such as proposals.
DIFFICULTY: moderate; PAGE: 304; OBJECTIVE: 2; TYPE: concept

13. The introduction of a solicited proposal
    a. need not be as detailed as that of an unsolicited proposal.
    b. should refer specifically to the RFP that initiated it.
    c. should downplay the magnitude of the problem you're addressing.
    d. is expected to be much longer than that of an unsolicited proposal.

ANSWER: b. This makes it easy for readers to know exactly which RFP you're responding to.
DIFFICULTY: moderate; PAGE: 304; OBJECTIVE: 2; TYPE: concept

14. "Delimitations" are
    a. market conditions that allow a company to adopt your proposal.
    b. employee restraints that have recently been lifted.
    c. the boundaries of your proposal.
    d. harsh realities that may prevent your audience from adopting your proposal.

ANSWER: c. 'Delimitations' and 'boundaries' are terms that describe the scope of your proposal.
DIFFICULTY: moderate; PAGE: 304; OBJECTIVE: 2; TYPE: concept

15. Which of the following is *not* an element normally included in the introduction section of a proposal?
    a. Background/statement of the problem
    b. Proposed solution to the problem
    c. The scope of the report
    d. Statement of qualifications

ANSWER: d. All the other elements usually appear in the introduction of a proposal.
DIFFICULTY: moderate; PAGE: 304; OBJECTIVE: 2; TYPE: concept

16. In a proposal, the work plan
    a. is presented in the conclusion.
    b. is contractually binding.
    c. outlines the costs of the proposed actions.
    d. involves all of the above.

ANSWER: b. This makes it especially important not to promise more than you can deliver.
DIFFICULTY: moderate; PAGE: 304; OBJECTIVE: n/a; TYPE: concept

17. In the body of a proposal, the section describing the concept, product, or service you have to offer could be called
    a. Technical Proposal.
    b. Research Design.
    c. Issues for Analysis.
    d. any of the above.

ANSWER: d. Any of these titles are acceptable.
DIFFICULTY: moderate; PAGE: 304; OBJECTIVE: n/a ; TYPE: concept

18. In a proposal to install and monitor a security system, statements such as "Our company has over 25 years of experience" should appear in what section?
    a. Introduction
    b. Body
    c. Close
    d. Appendix

ANSWER: b. Describing your organization's qualifications is appropriate for the body of a proposal.
DIFFICULTY: moderate; PAGE: 305; OBJECTIVE: n/a; TYPE: application

19. Describing your organization's qualifications in a formal proposal is
    a. considered arrogant and should be avoided.
    b. appropriate, but only in the introduction.
    c. an essential part of the body.
    d. a good idea only when your recommendations are controversial.

ANSWER: c. This can make your proposal more persuasive.
DIFFICULTY: moderate; PAGE: 305; OBJECTIVE: n/a; TYPE: concept

20. The close of a proposal should
    a. ask for a decision from the client.
    b. restate why you or your firm are the ones to perform the service in question.
    c. emphasize the benefits readers will realize from your solution.
    d. do all of the above.

ANSWER: d. The close should accomplish all of these tasks.
DIFFICULTY: moderate; PAGE: 306; OBJECTIVE: n/a; TYPE: concept

21. In an online report, hyperlinks
    a. should be used only for headings and subheadings.
    b. are a useful way to provide access to additional information that supports one of your arguments.
    c. are considered trendy and should usually be avoided.
    d. complicate the organization of your report by enabling readers to jump from section to section.

ANSWER: b. Hyperlinks can make it easy for readers to navigate your report.
DIFFICULTY: moderate; PAGE: 308; OBJECTIVE: 3; TYPE: concept

22. Transitional words and phrases
    a. tie ideas together and show how one thought is related to another.
    b. usually frustrate and confuse the audience.
    c. are essential to analytical reports but unnecessary in informational reports.
    d. involve all of the above.

ANSWER: a. Transitions make your report easier to read and understand.
DIFFICULTY: easy; PAGE: 308; OBJECTIVE: 3; TYPE: concept

23. Effective transitions in a business reports
    a. should never be longer than a short phrase.
    b. may be as long as a sentence.
    c. may be as long as a paragraph.
    d. are included only between major sections—never within each section.

ANSWER: c. In long reports, an entire paragraph might be used to highlight transitions from one section to the next.
DIFFICULTY: moderate; PAGE: 308; OBJECTIVE: 3; TYPE: concept

24. Preview sections in a report
    a. should always appear in narrative form, not as lists
    b. help prepare readers for new information
    c. should never be used in combination with review sections
    d. all of the above

ANSWER: b. This is the primary function of preview sections.
DIFFICULTY: moderate; PAGE: 308; OBJECTIVE: 3; TYPE: concept

25. Which of the following would be an effective preview in a formal report?
   a. Our sales in the eastern region have plummeted.
   b. First, let me begin by introducing our team.
   c. The next section discusses the advantages of advertising on the Internet.
   d. Before we proceed, however, I need to alert you to some important issues.

ANSWER: c. This statement prepares readers for upcoming information.
DIFFICULTY: moderate; PAGE: 308; OBJECTIVE: 3; TYPE: application

26. Using templates in preparing reports
   a. limits your creativity and makes your report look ordinary.
   b. is a sign of incompetence.
   c. saves time by providing a format and identifying the specific sections required for the type of report you are writing.
   d. is costly and time-consuming.

ANSWER: c. Templates can even identify the specific sections required for each type of report and insert headings for each section.
DIFFICULTY: moderate; PAGE: 308; OBJECTIVE: 4; TYPE: concept

27. In an online report regarding your region's productivity, the best way to include a spreadsheet containing figures that are updated daily would be to
   a. embed the spreadsheet in your report.
   b. include the spreadsheet in an appendix.
   c. simply insert the spreadsheet using Microsoft Word.
   d. link the spreadsheet to your report.

ANSWER: d. Embedding the spreadsheet would not allow it to get updated as easily.
DIFFICULTY: difficult; PAGE: 308; OBJECTIVE: 4; TYPE: application

28. The primary difference between linking and embedding files in your report is that
   a. linked files are automatically updated, but embedded files are not.
   b. embedded files are automatically updated, but linked files are not.
   c. it is more difficult to link files than to embed them.
   d. none of the above are true.

ANSWER: a. It is best to embed documents only when they do not need to be updated very often. Otherwise, linking is the better option.
DIFFICULTY: difficult; PAGE: 308; OBJECTIVE: 4; TYPE: concept

29. Electronic forms
   a. are easy to fill out but difficult to post and distribute.
   b. combine boilerplate with text boxes that allow users to input new information.
   c. require special software to create and use.
   d. are all of the above.

ANSWER: b. This is the primary function of electronic forms.
DIFFICULTY: moderate; PAGE: 308; OBJECTIVE: 4; TYPE: concept

30. Saving your report in PDF format
    a. makes it easy to share electronically.
    b. drastically limits the number of people who can access it.
    c. will make most of the graphics impossible to read.
    d. should only be used as a backup measure.

ANSWER: a. PDF documents have become a universal replacement for printed documents.
DIFFICULTY: moderate; PAGE: 308; OBJECTIVE: 4; TYPE: concept

31. To create an online form on which customers can type answers to questions about their dining habits, you would need to use
    a. Acrobat Reader.
    b. a scanner.
    c. text boxes.
    d. embedding software.

ANSWER: c. Text boxes enable users to input new text.
DIFFICULTY: moderate; PAGE: 308; OBJECTIVE: 4; TYPE: application

32. When deciding which points to illustrate with visuals in your report,
    a. it is best to avoid sections that require extensive description or explanation.
    b. consider using visuals in sections that require extensive explanation.
    c. avoid using visuals if you are communicating with a multilingual audience.
    d. all of the above

ANSWER: b. Visuals can make it easier to convey complex ideas concisely.
DIFFICULTY: moderate; PAGE: 309; OBJECTIVE: 5; TYPE: concept

33. The best type of visual aid for presenting detailed, specific information is a
    a. table.
    b. line chart.
    c. pie chart.
    d. variegated bar chart.

ANSWER: a. A table is best for presenting detailed, exact values.
DIFFICULTY: moderate; PAGE: 309; OBJECTIVE: 6; TYPE: concept

34. Prefatory parts of a formal report include the
    a. cover.
    b. title page.
    c. table of contents.
    d. all of the above

ANSWER: d. All of these are prefatory parts.
DIFFICULTY: moderate; PAGE: 317; OBJECTIVE: 7; TYPE: concept

35. The primary difference between a synopsis and an executive summary is
   a. an executive summary is a more detailed, fully developed "mini" version of the report itself.
   b. a synopsis is a more detailed, fully developed "mini" version of the report itself.
   c. an executive summary never includes headings, but a synopsis does.
   d. none of the above

ANSWER: d. An executive summary is more detailed than a synopsis.
DIFFICULTY: moderate; PAGE: 325-26; OBJECTIVE: 8; TYPE: concept

True/False

36. Using words such as "I" and "we" decrease the formality of your report.

ANSWER: True. To increase formality, avoid references to *you* and *I*.
DIFFICULTY: moderate; PAGE: 299; OBJECTIVE: n/a; TYPE: concept

37. Communicating with people in other cultures often calls for more formality than one would use in the U.S.

ANSWER: True. Communicating with people in other cultures generally calls for more formality in reports.
DIFFICULTY: moderate; PAGE: 299; OBJECTIVE: n/a; TYPE: concept

38. To make your report effective, it is best to leave out any information that does not support your line of reasoning.

ANSWER: False. Include all essential information, even if it does not support your line of reasoning.
DIFFICULTY: moderate; PAGE: 301; OBJECTIVE: n/a; TYPE: concept

39. All formal business reports should include all of the following elements in the introduction: authorization, problem/purpose, scope, background, sources/methods, definitions, limitations, and report organization.

ANSWER: False. It is best to pick and choose from these elements based on the particular report you're writing.
DIFFICULTY: moderate; PAGE: 302; OBJECTIVE: 1; TYPE: concept

40. In a business report, you should not introduce new facts as part of a conclusion or recommendation.

ANSWER: True. Your audience should have all the information they need by the time they reach this point.
DIFFICULTY: moderate; PAGE: 303; OBJECTIVE: 2; TYPE: concept

41. Combining conclusions and recommendations under one heading is not acceptable in business reports.

ANSWER: False. These can appear under a single heading.
DIFFICULTY: moderate; PAGE: 303; OBJECTIVE: n/a; TYPE: concept

42. Most RFPs spell out exactly what you should cover in your report and in what order.

ANSWER: True. It is important to follow the instructions in every detail.
DIFFICULTY: moderate; PAGE: 304; OBJECTIVE: 2; TYPE: concept

43. In solicited proposals, you have more freedom in terms of scope and organization than you do in unsolicited proposals.

ANSWER: False. You have less latitude in a solicited proposal, since the expectations are spelled out in an RFP.
DIFFICULTY: moderate; PAGE: 304; OBJECTIVE: 2; TYPE: concept

44. The general purpose of any proposal is to inform the audience.

ANSWER: False. The general purpose of a proposal is to persuade readers to do something.
DIFFICULTY: moderate; PAGE: 304; OBJECTIVE: 2; TYPE: concept

45. Your writing approach for a proposal should be similar to that used for persuasive messages.

ANSWER: True. The AIDA format is often effective for proposals.
DIFFICULTY: moderate; PAGE: 304; OBJECTIVE: 2; TYPE: concept

46. The general purpose of any proposal is to get your audience to change their minds about some important issue.

ANSWER: False. **The general purpose of a proposal is to persuade readers to do something.**
DIFFICULTY: moderate; PAGE: 304; OBJECTIVE: 2; TYPE: concept

47. Using the "you" attitude is inappropriate when writing proposals.

ANSWER: False. Relating your proposal to the audience's exact needs can make it more persuasive.
DIFFICULTY: moderate; PAGE: 304; OBJECTIVE: 2; TYPE: concept

48. If your proposal is solicited, its introduction should refer to the RFP specifically.

ANSWER: True. This makes it easy for readers to know exactly which RFP you're responding to.
DIFFICULTY: moderate; PAGE: 304; OBJECTIVE: 2; TYPE: concept

49. The body of a proposal has the same purpose as the body of other reports.

ANSWER: True. The body of a proposal gives complete details on the proposed solution and specifies anticipated results.
DIFFICULTY: moderate; PAGE: 304; OBJECTIVE: n/a; TYPE: concept

50. The scope of a report is sometimes called its 'delimitations.'

ANSWER: True. This is another term for boundaries or scope.
DIFFICULTY: moderate; PAGE: 304; OBJECTIVE: 2; TYPE: concept

51. Once your proposal is accepted, you can start altering the work plan to make the schedule and costs more realistic.

ANSWER: False. The work plan is contractually binding.
DIFFICULTY: moderate; PAGE: 304; OBJECTIVE: n/a; TYPE: concept

52. In formal proposals, the close should be the longest section.

ANSWER: False. The close should be brief, assertive, and confident.
DIFFICULTY: moderate; PAGE: 306; OBJECTIVE: n/a; TYPE: concept

53. It is unprofessional to point out your company's qualifications in the body of a formal report.

ANSWER: False. Doing so can enhance your credibility.
DIFFICULTY: moderate; PAGE: 305; OBJECTIVE: n/a; TYPE: concept

54. Statements such as, "Cyberdyne has more than 25 years of experience providing effective software solutions" are inappropriate for formal proposals.

ANSWER: False. This would be an appropriate statement of your organization's qualifications.
DIFFICULTY: moderate; PAGE: 305; OBJECTIVE: n/a; TYPE: application

55. The close of a proposal is the right place to discuss any costs associated with your recommendations.

ANSWER: False. Costs should be discussed in the body of the report.
DIFFICULTY: moderate; PAGE: 305; OBJECTIVE: 2; TYPE: concept

56. The close of a proposal is not the place to ask for a decision from the client.

ANSWER: False. This is the correct place to request a decision.
DIFFICULTY: moderate; PAGE: 306; OBJECTIVE: 2; TYPE: concept

57. In the close of a proposal, it is not necessary to emphasize reader benefits if you think they are obvious.

ANSWER: False. The close of a proposal should emphasize benefits the readers will realize from your solution.
DIFFICULTY: moderate; PAGE: 306; OBJECTIVE: 2; TYPE: concept

58. Headings and subheadings are vital for online reports, but not necessary for those distributed on paper.

ANSWER: False. Headings are especially important in online reports, but are also helpful in other media.
DIFFICULTY: moderate; PAGE: 308; OBJECTIVE: 3; TYPE: concept

59. In business environments, you can usually assume that most members of your audience will read your entire report.

ANSWER: False. Readers today often lack the time or inclination to plow through long reports.
DIFFICULTY: easy; PAGE: 308; OBJECTIVE: 3; TYPE: concept

60. Including phrases such as "As you can see" in a business report is helpful to readers as they seek to understand the document.

ANSWER: True. This is an example of a transitional phrase.
DIFFICULTY: moderate; PAGE: 308; OBJECTIVE: 3; TYPE: application

61. Report templates often identify the specific sections required for each type of report.

ANSWER: True. This is one benefit of using templates in preparing reports.
DIFFICULTY: moderate; PAGE: 308; OBJECTIVE: 4; TYPE: concept

62. Linked documents and embedded documents are essentially the same things.

ANSWER: False. Linked documents are automatically updated, but embedded documents are not.
DIFFICULTY: moderate; PAGE: 308; OBJECTIVE: 4; TYPE: concept

63. When sharing a report electronically, sending it in Portable Document Format (PDF) will severely limit the number of readers who can access it.

ANSWER: False. PDF files have become a universal replacement for printed documents.
DIFFICULTY: moderate; PAGE: 308; OBJECTIVE: 4; TYPE: concept

64. A flowchart is the best type of visual aid to illustrate trends over time.

ANSWER: False. A line chart is best to illustrate trends over time. A flowchart illustrates a sequence of events.
DIFFICULTY: moderate; PAGE: 310; OBJECTIVE: 6; TYPE: concept

65. In a pie chart, the segment you want to emphasize is placed at the three o'clock position.

ANSWER: False. The most important slice of the pie is placed at the twelve o'clock position.
DIFFICULTY: moderate; PAGE: 313; OBJECTIVE: 6; TYPE: concept

66. It is appropriate to include the letter of authorization among the prefatory parts of your report.

ANSWER: True. If you received written authorization to prepare the report, you may want to include the letter (or memo).
DIFFICULTY: moderate; PAGE: 321; OBJECTIVE: 7; TYPE: concept

67. In formal reports, the list of illustrations should never appear on the same page as the table of contents.

ANSWER: False. If you have enough space on a single page, include the list of illustrations directly beneath the table of contents.
DIFFICULTY: moderate; PAGE: 323-24; OBJECTIVE: 7; TYPE: concept

68. In business reports, a synopsis is basically the same thing as an executive summary.

ANSWER: False. A synopsis is a brief overview of a report's most important points. An executive summary is a more detailed, fully developed "mini" version of the report itself.
DIFFICULTY: moderate; PAGE: 325-26; OBJECTIVE: 8; TYPE: concept

Fill-in-the-Blank

69. A more _____ tone often is appropriate for reports that will be sent to people in other cultures.

ANSWER: Formal
DIFFICULTY: moderate; PAGE: 299; OBJECTIVE: n/a; TYPE: concept

70. The introduction or opening of a business report should put the report in a broader context by tying it to a _____ or an assignment.

ANSWER: Problem
DIFFICULTY: moderate; PAGE: 300; OBJECTIVE: 1; TYPE: concept

71. The _____ is the section of a business report that contains the detailed information necessary to support your conclusions and recommendations.

ANSWER: Body
DIFFICULTY: moderate; PAGE: 301; OBJECTIVE: n/a; TYPE: concept

72. The general _____ of any proposal is to persuade readers to do something, such as purchase goods or services, fund a project, or implement a program.

ANSWER: Purpose
DIFFICULTY: moderate; PAGE: 304; OBJECTIVE: n/a; TYPE: concept

73. The introduction of a proposal should state the _____ or boundaries of the proposal—what you will and will not do.

ANSWER: Scope OR Delimitations
DIFFICULTY: moderate; PAGE: 304; OBJECTIVE: 1; TYPE: concept

74. The _____ _____ of a proposal describes (among other things) how you'll accomplish what must be done, when the work will begin, and when it will be completed.

ANSWER: Work Plan
DIFFICULTY: moderate; PAGE: 304; OBJECTIVE: n/a; TYPE: concept

75. In an online report, _____ enable readers to navigate your report and access additional information.

ANSWER: Hyperlinks OR Links
DIFFICULTY: moderate; PAGE: 308; OBJECTIVE: 4; TYPE: concept

76. Smooth _____ are useful tools for tying ideas together in business reports and for showing how one thought is related to another.

ANSWER: Transitions
DIFFICULTY: moderate; PAGE: 308; OBJECTIVE: 3; TYPE: concept

77. _____ sections introduce important topics by helping readers get ready for new information.

ANSWER: Preview
DIFFICULTY: moderate; PAGE: 308; OBJECTIVE: 3; TYPE: concept

78. Use _____ sections after a body of material in a report to summarize the information for your readers.

ANSWER: Review
DIFFICULTY: moderate; PAGE: 308; OBJECTIVE: 3; TYPE: concept

79. A _____ can save time by identifying the specific sections required for the type of report you are writing.

ANSWER: Template
DIFFICULTY: moderate; PAGE: 308; OBJECTIVE: 4; TYPE: concept

80. A file that is _____ to a report will get updated automatically when you or someone else updates the file.

ANSWER: Linked
DIFFICULTY: moderate; PAGE: 308; OBJECTIVE: 4; TYPE: concept

81. Files that are _____ in a report are not connected to their original versions and will not be updated automatically.

ANSWER: Embedded
DIFFICULTY: moderate; PAGE: 308; OBJECTIVE: 4; TYPE: concept

82. A _____ chart is the best visual aid to illustrate changes in the composition of something over time.

ANSWER: Surface OR Area
DIFFICULTY: moderate; PAGE: 311; OBJECTIVE: 6; TYPE: concept

83. To illustrate a sequence of events from start to finish, a _____ is the best type of visual aid.

ANSWER: Flowchart
DIFFICULTY: moderate; PAGE: 313; OBJECTIVE: 6; TYPE: concept

84. The _____ parts of a report come before the main text and help readers decide whether and how to read the report.

ANSWER: Prefatory
DIFFICULTY: moderate; PAGE: 318; OBJECTIVE: 7; TYPE: concept

85. Unlike a more detailed executive summary, a _____ (or 'abstract') is a brief overview of a report's most important points.

ANSWER: Synopsis
DIFFICULTY: moderate; PAGE: 325-26; OBJECTIVE: 8; TYPE: concept

Short Answer/Essay

86. List at least three strategies for increasing the formality of your writing in business reports.

ANSWER: (1) Avoid referring to yourself as "I" and to your readers as "you." (2) Do not include jokes. (3) similes, or (4) metaphors. (5) Try to minimize the use of colorful adjectives or adverbs.
DIFFICULTY: moderate; PAGE: 299; OBJECTIVE: n/a; TYPE: concept

87. What are the three main sections of a business report?

ANSWER: The introduction (or opening), the body, and the close.
DIFFICULTY: easy; PAGE: 299; OBJECTIVE: n/a; TYPE: concept

88. What are the four functions of a report introduction?

ANSWER: An effective introduction 1) puts the report or proposal in context by tying it to a problem or an assignment, 2) introduces the subject or purpose of the report and explains why it is important, 3) previews the main ideas and the order in which they'll be covered, and 4) establishes the tone of the document and the writer's relationship with the audience.
DIFFICULTY: difficult; PAGE: 300; OBJECTIVE: 1; TYPE: concept

89. List at least three functions of the close in a business report.

ANSWER: The close of a report (1) emphasizes the main points of the message, (2) summarizes the benefits to the reader if the message proposes a change or course of action, (3) refers back to all the pieces and reminds the reader of how all the pieces fit together, and (4) brings all the action items together and specifies who should do what, when, where, and how.
DIFFICULTY: difficult; PAGE: 301; OBJECTIVE: 2; TYPE: concept

90. If you find relevant information that does not support your line of reasoning, should you still include it in your report? Why or why not?

ANSWER: Yes, you should include it. Omitting relevant information or facts can bias your report and detract from your credibility.
DIFFICULTY: moderate; PAGE: 301; OBJECTIVE: n/a; TYPE: concept

91. What four topics are commonly covered in the introduction to a business proposal? Briefly explain each one.

ANSWER: The introduction to a business proposal normally provides some background or simply a statement of the problem. Here the author reviews the reader's situation and establishes a need for action and emphasize how his or her goals align with those of the audience. It also offers a brief description of the solution—outlining the change you propose along with your key selling points and their benefits. The introduction also describes the scope or "delimitations" of the proposal, clearly defining its boundaries and explaining what you will and will not do. Finally, the introduction explains how the proposal is organized, orienting the reader to the remainder of the proposal and calling attention to the major divisions of information.
DIFFICULTY: difficult; PAGE: 304; OBJECTIVE: 2; TYPE: concept

92. In a formal proposal, where does the Work Plan section normally appear and what information does it contain? Can it be changed later?

ANSWER: The Work Plan section normally appears in the body of a formal proposal. It describes how you'll accomplish what must be done, explains the steps you'll take, their timing, the methods or resources you'll use, and the person(s) responsible. It also specifies when the work will begin, how it will be divided into stages, when you will finish, and whether any follow-up is involved. If the proposal is accepted, the work plan is contractually binding, so you cannot change it later in the midst of the project.
DIFFICULTY: difficult; PAGE: 304; OBJECTIVE: n/a; TYPE: concept

93. Briefly explain at least one difference between the introduction of a proposal and the introduction of an informational or analytical report.

ANSWER: The primary differences are that the introduction of a proposal refers specifically to the RFP on which the proposal is based, clearly establishes a need for action, and outlines the change you propose along with key selling points and their benefits to your audience.
DIFFICULTY: difficult; PAGE: 304; OBJECTIVE: 2; TYPE: concept

94. Briefly explain at least one difference between the close of a proposal and the close of an informational or analytical report.

ANSWER: The key difference is that the close of a proposal emphasizes the benefits readers will realize from your solution, summarizes the merits of your approach, restates why you and your firm are a good choice, and asks for a decision from the client. The close of an informational or analytical report may not need to incorporate all of these components.
DIFFICULTY: difficult; PAGE: 306; OBJECTIVE: 2; TYPE: concept

95. What elements can report writers use to help readers navigate long reports and proposals?

ANSWER: Elements that help readers find their way include headings and links, transitional words and phrases, and previews and reviews.
DIFFICULTY: moderate; PAGE: 308; OBJECTIVE: 3; TYPE: concept

96. Briefly explain the primary difference between linking and embedding files in business reports.

ANSWER: These are both strategies for combining graphics, spreadsheets, and other elements with the text of your report. The primary difference is that linked files are automatically updated, while embedded documents are not.
DIFFICULTY: difficult; PAGE: 308; OBJECTIVE: 4; TYPE: concept

97. List and explain the function of five technological tools for developing effective reports and proposals.

ANSWER: (1) Templates save report writers time by helping with formatting and even identifying the specific sections required for each type of report. (2) Linked and embedded documents make it easy to include graphics, spreadsheets, databases, and other elements created in a variety of software packages. (3) Electronic forms are word processor files that combine boilerplate text—for material that doesn't change from report to report—with form tools such as text boxes and check boxes to accommodate input that does change. The completed file can then be printed, e-mailed, or posted to an intranet, like any other document. (4) The simple process of converting reports to electronic documents in portable document format (PDF) allows writers to share their reports quickly and economically with a widespread audience. (5) Multimedia documents combine the text of the report with video clips, animation, presentation software slides, and other elements.
DIFFICULTY: difficult; PAGE: 308; OBJECTIVE: 4; TYPE: concept

98. What are the "five Cs" to keep in mind when deciding which points to illustrate with visuals in a business report?

ANSWER: The five Cs are 1) Clear: if you're having difficulty conveying an idea in words, see if a visual can do the job better; 2) Complete: visuals can be a great way to provide the supporting details for your main idea or recommendation; 3) Concise: if a particular section seems to require extensive description or explanation, see if there's a way to convey the information visually; 4) Connected: visuals can help readers understand connections such as similarities or differences; 5) Compelling: visuals can make your report more compelling to readers since we live in a highly visual world.
DIFFICULTY: difficult; PAGE: 309; OBJECTIVE: 5; TYPE: concept

99. List at least two specific guidelines to follow in creating effective pie charts.

ANSWER: When creating pie charts, 1) limit the number of slices in the pie, 2) place the most important segment at the twelve o'clock position, and 3) arrange the other segments clockwise either in order of size or in some other logical progression.
DIFFICULTY: difficult; PAGE: 313; OBJECTIVE: 6; TYPE: concept

100. Explain the difference between a synopsis and an executive summary.

ANSWER: A synopsis is simply a brief overview of the main points of a report. An executive summary, on the other hand, is a more detailed, fully developed "mini" version of the entire report. It may even include headings, transitions, and visual aids.
DIFFICULTY: difficult; PAGE: 325-26; OBJECTIVE: 8; TYPE: concept

CHAPTER 12
PLANNING, WRITING, AND COMPLETING ORAL PRESENTATIONS

Multiple Choice

1. Speeches and oral presentations are much like other business messages in that
   a. they require similar planning.
   b. the size of the groups to which they are delivered is similar.
   c. the interaction between the audience and speaker is similar.
   d. they deal with emotional or personal issues to a similar extent.

ANSWER: a. It is important to plan presentations with as much care as you would plan other types of business messages.
DIFFICULTY: moderate; PAGE: 355; OBJECTIVE: 2; TYPE: concept

2. When you prepare a speech or presentation, your first step involves
   a. analyzing the situation.
   b. choosing the right words.
   c. planning the content, length, and style of your speech or presentation.
   d. all of the above.

ANSWER: a. This involves defining your purpose and developing an audience profile.
DIFFICULTY: moderate; PAGE: 355; OBJECTIVE: 2; TYPE: concept

3. The two most common purposes of business presentations are to
   a. analyze and synthesize.
   b. regulate and validate.
   c. inform and persuade.
   d. illustrate and entertain.

ANSWER: c. A less common purpose of oral presentations is to collaborate.
DIFFICULTY: moderate; PAGE: 355; OBJECTIVE: 1; TYPE: concept

4. Analyzing your audience helps you
   a. determine whether your audience is comfortable listening to the language you speak.
   b. remember to keep your speech or oral presentation short.
   c. define your purpose.
   d. prepare a detailed, informative outline.

ANSWER: a. This is one benefit of conducting an audience analysis.
DIFFICULTY: moderate; PAGE: 356; OBJECTIVE: 2; TYPE: concept

5. Selecting the right medium for your presentation is
    a. easy—you're simply giving a speech.
    b. an important decision since technology offers a number of choices.
    c. only an issue when addressing audiences from other cultures.
    d. not something you need to think about early on.

ANSWER: b. Technology offers a variety of options from live, in-person presentations to webcasts that people either view live or download later from your website.
DIFFICULTY: moderate; PAGE: 356; OBJECTIVE: 2; TYPE: concept

6. When organizing a speech or presentation, your first step is to
    a. develop an outline.
    b. define the main idea.
    c. write the introduction.
    d. decide on the delivery style.

ANSWER: b. This is the first step in organizing a speech or presentation.
DIFFICULTY: moderate; PAGE: 356; OBJECTIVE: 2; TYPE: concept

7. The best way to clarify your main idea in a presentation is to
    a. provide a lengthy handout for your audience to review during your presentation.
    b. describe it using jargon and complicated language to emphasize its importance.
    c. develop a single sentence that links your subject and purpose to your audience's frame of reference.
    d. allow your audience to gradually figure it out on their own.

ANSWER: c. This helps keep the audience's attention and convince them that your points are relevant.
DIFFICULTY: moderate; PAGE: 357; OBJECTIVE: 2; TYPE: concept

8. For business presentations, time restraints are usually
    a. rigid, permitting little or no flexibility.
    b. meaningless—audiences expect presenters to take a little more time than they're allotted.
    c. imposed only on lower-level employees.
    d. not important if you are presenting to your colleagues.

ANSWER: a. There are often problems associated with violating time limits in business presentations.
DIFFICULTY: moderate; PAGE: 357; OBJECTIVE: 2; TYPE: concept

9. When using electronic slides, try to average one slide for
    a. each minute you speak.
    b. every 3 minutes you speak.
    c. every 10 minutes you speak.
    d. every 20 minutes you speak.

ANSWER: b. If you move through the slides any more quickly, you are probably not engaging the audience.
DIFFICULTY: moderate; PAGE: 357; OBJECTIVE: 2; TYPE: concept

10. The average speaker talks at a rate of about
    a. 50 words a minute.
    b. 10 double-spaced pages an hour.
    c. 2,000 words an hour.
    d. between 125 and 150 words per minute.

ANSWER: d. Most people speak at this rate.
DIFFICULTY: moderate; PAGE: 357; OBJECTIVE: 2; TYPE: application

11. If you have 10 minutes or less to deliver a presentation, you should
    a. speak as quickly as you possibly can.
    b. limit yourself to four or five main points.
    c. assume your audience is already interested.
    d. organize your presentation as you would a letter or brief memo.

ANSWER: d. This is the most effective approach when your time is limited.
DIFFICULTY: moderate; PAGE: 357; OBJECTIVE: 2; TYPE: concept

12. When organizing a speech, use the indirect order if your purpose is to
    a. entertain and the audience is resistant.
    b. motivate and the audience is receptive.
    c. persuade and the audience is resistant.
    d. inform and the audience is receptive.

ANSWER: c. Resistant audiences tend to respond more favorably if you use the indirect approach.
DIFFICULTY: moderate; PAGE: 357-58; OBJECTIVE: 2; TYPE: application

13. Longer speeches and presentations are organized like
    a. reports.
    b. memos.
    c. letters.
    d. e-mail messages.

ANSWER: a. The organization strategies are similar for both media.
DIFFICULTY: moderate; PAGE: 358; OBJECTIVE: 2; TYPE: concept

14. When preparing an outline for your speech, keep in mind that
   a. it should generally include a title that is compelling and audience-centered.
   b. you should keep each item to two- to three-word descriptions of what you will say.
   c. you can leave out all transitions.
   d. this is not the place to include "stage directions."

ANSWER: a. Even if the title will not be published, it helps you focus your thoughts around your main idea.
DIFFICULTY: moderate; PAGE: 359; OBJECTIVE: 2; TYPE: application

15. To reduce the formality of a talk
   a. deliver your remarks in a conversational tone.
   b. use a large room.
   c. seat the audience in rows.
   d. do all of the above.

ANSWER: a. This is particularly appropriate when speaking to a small group.
DIFFICULTY: moderate; PAGE: 361; OBJECTIVE: 2; TYPE: application

16. Formal speeches differ from informal ones in that
   a. formal speeches always include obscure, unfamiliar vocabulary.
   b. formal speeches are always much longer.
   c. formal speeches are often delivered from a stage or platform.
   d. all of the above are the case.

ANSWER: c. This makes it easier for the speaker's remarks to be heard throughout the room.
DIFFICULTY: moderate; PAGE: 361; OBJECTIVE: 2; TYPE: concept

17. In the introduction to your speech, you should
   a. discuss the three or four main points on your outline.
   b. establish credibility.
   c. ask for audience input.
   d. boast about your qualifications.

ANSWER: b. It is important to do so quickly, since audiences tend to decide within a few minutes whether you're worth listening to.
DIFFICULTY: moderate; PAGE: 361; OBJECTIVE: 3; TYPE: concept

18. As a speaker, your credibility depends on
   a. using jargon and a complex vocabulary.
   b. shocking the audience with a disturbing fact.
   c. quickly establishing a good relationship with the audience.
   d. boasting about your accomplishments.

ANSWER: c. Audiences do not wait very long to form an opinion of a speaker or presenter.
DIFFICULTY: moderate; PAGE: 361; OBJECTIVE: 3; TYPE: concept

19. To arouse interest at the start of a speech, whether it's serious or light, you should
   a. always start things off with a joke.
   b. do something dramatic.
   c. tease the audience by not mentioning specifically what you'll be talking about.
   d. do none of the above.

ANSWER: d. These strategies are not effective.
DIFFICULTY: moderate; PAGE: 361-62; OBJECTIVE: 3; TYPE: concept

20. "Now that we've reviewed the problem, let's take a look at some solutions" is an example of
   a. a poor transition.
   b. a good transition between major sections of a speech.
   c. a small link between sentences or paragraphs in a speech.
   d. the kind of wording that should never appear in a speech.

ANSWER: b. This is an example of an effective transition.
DIFFICULTY: moderate; PAGE: 363; OBJECTIVE: 2; TYPE: application

21. To hold your audience's attention during the body of your speech
   a. make at least seven or eight main points.
   b. include numerous abstract ideas.
   c. relate your subject to your audience's needs.
   d. do all of the above.

ANSWER: c. This is one of several techniques for keeping your audience's attention.
DIFFICULTY: moderate; PAGE: 363; OBJECTIVE: 4; TYPE: concept

22. At the close of a business presentation
   a. audience attention tends to reach its lowest point.
   b. you should clearly indicate that you're about to finish.
   c. you should avoid making it obvious that you're about to finish.
   d. audiences resent being reminded of the presentation's main ideas.

ANSWER: b. This helps the audience make one final effort to listen closely.
DIFFICULTY: moderate; PAGE: 363; OBJECTIVE: 2; TYPE: concept

23. When you have covered all the main points in your speech, you should
   a. reinforce your theme by repeating and summarizing the three or four main supporting points.
   b. wrap up as quickly as possible.
   c. avoid using such phrases as "To sum it all up" and "In conclusion."
   d. do all of the above.

ANSWER: a. It is important to restate and reinforce your main points as you close your presentation.
DIFFICULTY: moderate; PAGE: 363; OBJECTIVE: 2; TYPE: concept

24. If there is a lack of consensus among the audience at the end of your presentation, you should
   a. gloss over it as quickly as possible.
   b. make the disagreement clear and be ready to suggest a method for resolving the differences.
   c. identify the individuals causing the disagreement and ask them pointed questions.
   d. do all of the above.

ANSWER: b. This is the best approach if there is disagreement at the end of our presentation.
DIFFICULTY: moderate; PAGE: 364; OBJECTIVE: 2; TYPE: application

25. If your speech or presentation requires the audience to reach a decision or take some specific action
   a. go directly to the question-and-answer session after you cover the main points of your speech.
   b. close your speech on a note of uncertainty.
   c. close your speech by explaining who is responsible for doing what.
   d. lead people to believe that the decision will be easy to carry out.

ANSWER: c. This public commitment to action is good insurance that something will happen.
DIFFICULTY: moderate; PAGE: 364; OBJECTIVE: 2; TYPE: concept

26. Research shows that visual aids can improve learning by up to
   a. 25%.
   b. 100%
   c. 400%
   d. none of the above

ANSWER: c. Humans can process visuals 60,000 times faster than text.
DIFFICULTY: moderate; PAGE: 364; OBJECTIVE: 5; TYPE: concept

27. When adapting graphics for slides
   a. reduce the amount of detail.
   b. use full numbers, such as 2006, rather than '06.
   c. avoid using arrows or boldface type.
   d. don't use more than eight or nine graph lines.

ANSWER: a. It is best to eliminate any detail that is not absolutely essential.
DIFFICULTY: moderate; PAGE: 365; OBJECTIVE: 6; TYPE: concept

28. When choosing a background for your slides, the most effective approach is to
    a. use dark colors such as blue.
    b. pair complex patterns with intricate borders.
    c. choose a simple design.
    d. use all of the above.

ANSWER: c. Generally speaking, the less your background does, the better.
DIFFICULTY: moderate; PAGE: 367; OBJECTIVE: 6; TYPE: concept

29. When choosing fonts and type styles for slides, be sure to
    a. use script fonts for emphasis.
    b. limit your fonts to no more than two per slide.
    c. avoid boldface type.
    d. do all of the above.

ANSWER: b. Including more than two fonts can make the slide look cluttered.
DIFFICULTY: moderate; PAGE: 367; OBJECTIVE: 6; TYPE: concept

30. In today's business environment, giving online presentations is
    a. simply impractical for most professionals.
    b. more common than ever before.
    c. so costly that only large companies can afford to do it.
    d. viewed as a passing fad.

ANSWER: b. Online presentations make it easy to meet at a moment's notice and to communicate with a geographically dispersed audience at a fraction of the cost of travel.
DIFFICULTY: moderate; PAGE: 369; OBJECTIVE: 7; TYPE: concept

31. Probably the most effective and easiest mode of speech delivery is
    a. memorization.
    b. reading from a prepared script.
    c. speaking from notes.
    d. impromptu speaking.

ANSWER: c. This approach gives you something to refer to and still allows for plenty of eye contact and interaction with the audience.
DIFFICULTY: moderate; PAGE: 371; OBJECTIVE: n/a; TYPE: concept

32. Which of the following is *not* a good way to deal with speaking anxiety?
    a. Prepare more material than necessary.
    b. Concentrate on your nervousness.
    c. Take a few deep breaths before speaking.
    d. Have your first sentence memorized and on the tip of your tongue.

ANSWER: b. This is likely to worsen your anxiety.
DIFFICULTY: moderate; PAGE: 372-73; OBJECTIVE: n/a; TYPE: application

33. A question-and-answer period after a speech is
    a. usually unnecessary.
    b. helpful only if the purpose of the speech is to motivate or entertain.
    c. one of the most important parts of any presentation.
    d. included only for small audiences.

ANSWER: c. This portion may even consume most of the time allotted for your presentation.
DIFFICULTY: moderate; PAGE: 373; OBJECTIVE: n/a; TYPE: concept

34. Repeating an audience member's question before you answer it is
    a. helpful because it confirms your understanding of the question.
    b. a waste of your audience's valuable time.
    c. a surefire way to lose credibility with your audience.
    d. none of the above.

ANSWER: a. Repeating the question also ensures that the entire audience has heard it.
DIFFICULTY: moderate; PAGE: 373; OBJECTIVE: 8; TYPE: concept

35. If you don't know the answer to a question someone asks following your presentation,
    a. it is vital to make the audience think you do know the answer.
    b. the best approach is to dismiss the question as irrelevant.
    c. don't pretend that you do.
    d. none of the above

ANSWER: c. Instead, say something like, "I don't have those figures. I'll get them for you as quickly as possible."
DIFFICULTY: moderate; PAGE: 373; OBJECTIVE: 8; TYPE: concept

36. When your allotted time is up, prepare your audience for the end of the question-and-answer period by
    a. packing up your belongings.
    b. refusing to acknowledge those who wish to speak.
    c. saying that you will take one more question.
    d. waving good-bye and leaving the podium.

ANSWER: c. This prepares the audience for the end of your presentation.
DIFFICULTY: moderate; PAGE: 374; OBJECTIVE: 8; TYPE: application

True/False

37. It's not as important to research your audience for an oral presentation as it is for a written one.

ANSWER: False. It is vitally important.
DIFFICULTY: moderate; PAGE: 355; OBJECTIVE: 2; TYPE: concept

38. Issues such as the room in which you'll give a presentation and the equipment you'll use should influence the style of your presentation, but not the content.

ANSWER: False. These issues can influence the content and style of your presentation.
DIFFICULTY: moderate; PAGE: 356; OBJECTIVE: 2; TYPE: concept

39. Organizing an oral message is similar to organizing a written message.

ANSWER: True. It involves the same tasks.
DIFFICULTY: moderate; PAGE: 356; OBJECTIVE: 2; TYPE: concept

40. You should be able to summarize the main idea for a speech in a single sentence that links your subject and purpose to the audience's frame of reference.

ANSWER: True. This is the best way to define your main idea.
DIFFICULTY: moderate; PAGE: 357; OBJECTIVE: 2; TYPE: concept

41. Most speakers can comfortably deliver at least 200 words per minute.

ANSWER: False. Most speakers speak between 125 and 150 words per minute.
DIFFICULTY: moderate; PAGE: 357; OBJECTIVE: 2; TYPE: concept

42. Even when you expect your audience to be skeptical, the direct approach is always best for presentations.

ANSWER: False. The indirect approach is best if the subject involves bas news or persuasion.
DIFFICULTY: moderate; PAGE: 357-58; OBJECTIVE: 2; TYPE: concept

43. If you have 10 minutes or less to deliver your message, you should organize it like a report.

ANSWER: False. You should organize it as you would a letter or a brief memo.
DIFFICULTY: moderate; PAGE: 357; OBJECTIVE: 2; TYPE: concept

44. If your purpose is to analyze, persuade, or collaborate, you should organize your speech around conclusions and recommendations or a logical argument.

ANSWER: True. These are the best strategies for presentations designed to analyze, persuade, or collaborate.
DIFFICULTY: moderate; PAGE: 358; OBJECTIVE: 2; TYPE: concept

45. If you plan to use a speaking outline for your speech, you should condense points and transitions to keywords or phrases.

ANSWER: True. It is best to use keywords or phrases that will prompt you to remember what each point is about.
DIFFICULTY: moderate; PAGE: 360; OBJECTIVE: 2; TYPE: concept

46. The speech outline is not an appropriate place to include notes about the visual aids.

ANSWER: False. It is helpful to add delivery cues and notes about visual aids.
DIFFICULTY: moderate; PAGE: 360; OBJECTIVE: 2; TYPE: concept

47. If you plan to use PowerPoint during your presentation, you can use the "notes" field on each slide for your speaking notes.

ANSWER: True. This is an effective delivery strategy.
DIFFICULTY: moderate; PAGE: 360; OBJECTIVE: 2; TYPE: concept

48. In general, you should use a casual style when speaking to small groups and a formal style for large groups.

ANSWER: True. It is important to adapt your style to your audience.
DIFFICULTY: moderate; PAGE: 361; OBJECTIVE: 2; TYPE: concept

49. In a formal speech, it is important to impress your audience with your extensive and even obscure vocabulary.

ANSWER: False. You should use simple, familiar vocabulary.
DIFFICULTY: moderate; PAGE: 361; OBJECTIVE: 2; TYPE: concept

50. Of the total time you spend writing your oral presentation, you should devote a large amount to writing your introduction.

ANSWER: True. The introduction can get your presentation off to a great start.
DIFFICULTY: moderate; PAGE: 361; OBJECTIVE: 3; TYPE: concept

51. Even if you will be discussing a topic that will have a profound effect on your audience, you need to come up with an attention-getting introduction.

ANSWER: False. If you're discussing matters that are already important to the audience, they will probably listen regardless of how you begin.
DIFFICULTY: moderate; PAGE: 361; OBJECTIVE: 4; TYPE: concept

52. The beginning of an effective presentation should be carefully staged.

ANSWER: False. Nothing turns off the average audience more than a trite, staged beginning.
DIFFICULTY: moderate; PAGE: 361; OBJECTIVE: 4; TYPE: concept

53. Audiences tend to decide within only a few minutes whether or not someone is worth listening to.

ANSWER: True. Audiences make this decision early in your presentation.
DIFFICULTY: moderate; PAGE: 361; OBJECTIVE: 4; TYPE: concept

54. Having someone else introduce you can help establish your credibility as a speaker.

ANSWER: True. This helps you avoid sounding boastful about your qualifications.
DIFFICULTY: moderate; PAGE: 361-62; OBJECTIVE: 2; TYPE: concept

55. The introduction of your presentation should arouse the audience's interest in your topic, but the body of the speech is the best place to establish your credibility.

ANSWER: False. It is vital to establish credibility quickly in the introduction.
DIFFICULTY: moderate; PAGE: 361-62; OBJECTIVE: 3; TYPE: concept

56. It is never appropriate to use humor in a business presentation to get the audience's attention.

ANSWER: False. As long as it is relevant and not offensive, humor can be an effective attention-getter.
DIFFICULTY: moderate; PAGE: 362; OBJECTIVE: 4; TYPE: concept

57. One way to arouse audience interest is to state a startling statistic during the introduction of your presentation.

ANSWER: True. This is one way to wake up your audience.
DIFFICULTY: moderate; PAGE: 362; OBJECTIVE: 4; TYPE: concept

58. Giving your audience a preview of what you'll be talking about will reduce their interest and attention.

ANSWER: False. Doing so helps them understand how the individual facts and figures are related to your main idea.
DIFFICULTY: moderate; PAGE: 362; OBJECTIVE: n/a; TYPE: concept

59. Transitional words and sentences are less important in oral presentations than in written reports.

ANSWER: False. Transitions are even more important in oral presentations.
DIFFICULTY: moderate; PAGE: 362; OBJECTIVE: n/a; TYPE: concept

60. To keep your audience's attention, try to present every point in light of the audience's needs and values.

ANSWER: True. This is one effective strategy.
DIFFICULTY: moderate; PAGE: 363; OBJECTIVE: 4; TYPE: concept

61. The ending is the least important part of a speech.

ANSWER: False. It is critical.
DIFFICULTY: moderate; PAGE: 363; OBJECTIVE: n/a; TYPE: concept

62. As you end your presentation, it is best to avoid obvious clues such as, "In conclusion" or "To sum it all up."

ANSWER: False. You should make it clear that you are about to conclude the presentation.
DIFFICULTY: moderate; PAGE: 363; OBJECTIVE: n/a; TYPE: application

63. When concluding a speech, don't bore your audience by restating points you already made in the body of the speech.

ANSWER: False. It is important to restate and reinforce your main points.
DIFFICULTY: moderate; PAGE: 363; OBJECTIVE: n/a; TYPE: concept

64. If you are unsure about how your audience will respond to a presentation, prepare two closes, one that acknowledges agreement and one that accommodates the fact that the audience didn't reach consensus.

ANSWER: True. This is a good way to prepare when you are not sure how the audience will react.
DIFFICULTY: moderate; PAGE: 364; OBJECTIVE: 2; TYPE: concept

65. Even if parts of your speech have been downbeat, it's always best to close on a positive note.

ANSWER: True. This will be the section of your presentation that most of the audience will remember.
DIFFICULTY: moderate; PAGE: 364; OBJECTIVE: 2; TYPE: concept

66. Using visual aids in your presentation can improve learning by up to 400%.

ANSWER: True. Humans process visuals 60,000 times faster than text.
DIFFICULTY: moderate; PAGE: 364; OBJECTIVE: 5; TYPE: concept

67. To increase readability, presenters should use contrasting colors for the background and text of electronic slides.

ANSWER: True. Contrast makes it easier for the audience to read and understand your slides.
DIFFICULTY: moderate; PAGE: 367; OBJECTIVE: 6; TYPE: concept

68. A slide master enables you to choose the fonts and other design elements for every slide in your electronic presentation.

ANSWER: True. These choices automatically show up on every slide in the presentation.
DIFFICULTY: moderate; PAGE: 367; OBJECTIVE: 6; TYPE: concept

69. Giving presentations online makes it easier for presenters to tell when an audience is bored or confused.

ANSWER: False. Online presentations make it more difficult to tell.
DIFFICULTY: moderate; PAGE: 369; OBJECTIVE: 7; TYPE: concept

70. The best way to prepare for a speech is to memorize the whole thing.

ANSWER: False. Memorization is usually not a good choice because you'll sound stilted even in the best circumstances.
DIFFICULTY: moderate; PAGE: 371; OBJECTIVE: n/a; TYPE: concept

71. A good way to deal with nervousness over speaking is to prepare more material than you really need.

ANSWER: True. This is an effective strategy for dealing with nervousness.
DIFFICULTY: moderate; PAGE: 372; OBJECTIVE: n/a; TYPE: concept

72. Good speakers will never admit that they do not know the answer to a question during the question and answer period following a presentation.

ANSWER: False. Do not pretend you know the answer if you don't.
DIFFICULTY: easy; PAGE: 373; OBJECTIVE: 8; TYPE: concept

73. During the question and answer period following a presentation, it is often helpful if the speaker repeats each audience member's question before answering.

ANSWER: True. This confirms the speaker's understanding of the question and ensures that the entire audience has heard it.
DIFFICULTY: moderate; PAGE: 373; OBJECTIVE: 8; TYPE: concept

Fill-in-the-Blank

74. The purpose of most business presentations is to inform or _____.

ANSWER: Persuade
DIFFICULTY: easy; PAGE: 355; OBJECTIVE: 2; TYPE: concept

75. Early in the planning stages of a speech, you should develop a (an) _____ profile.

ANSWER: Audience
DIFFICULTY: moderate; PAGE: 356; OBJECTIVE: 2; TYPE: concept

76. The _____ _____ of a speech is a one-sentence statement that links your subject and purpose to your audience's frame of reference.

ANSWER: Main Idea
DIFFICULTY: moderate; PAGE: 357; OBJECTIVE: 2; TYPE: concept

77. Many speakers prepare both a detailed _____ outline and a simpler speaking outline prior to giving a presentation.

ANSWER: Planning
DIFFICULTY: moderate; PAGE: 359; OBJECTIVE: 2; TYPE: application

78. For a large audience and an important event, your tone will generally be more _____ than it would be for a smaller audience.

ANSWER: Formal
DIFFICULTY: moderate; PAGE: 361; OBJECTIVE: 2; TYPE: concept

79. The _____ to your speech must capture the audience's attention.

ANSWER: Introduction
DIFFICULTY: moderate; PAGE: 361; OBJECTIVE: 3; TYPE: concept

80. At the beginning of a speech, you need to establish _____ with your audience.

ANSWER: Credibility
DIFFICULTY: moderate; PAGE: 361; OBJECTIVE: 3; TYPE: concept

81. A good introduction gives the audience a _____ of what's ahead in your speech.

ANSWER: Preview
DIFFICULTY: moderate; PAGE: 362; OBJECTIVE: 3; TYPE: concept

82. In the body of your presentation, it is important to hold your audience's _____ by continually relating your topic to the audience's needs.

ANSWER: Attention OR Interest
DIFFICULTY: moderate; PAGE: 363; OBJECTIVE: 4; TYPE: concept

83. Even if parts of your presentation are downbeat, you should always try to end on a _____ note.

ANSWER: Positive OR Strong
DIFFICULTY: moderate; PAGE: 364; OBJECTIVE: 2; TYPE: concept

84. To make the text on your slides more readable, write short _____ phrases instead of long sentences or blocks of text.

ANSWER: Bulleted
DIFFICULTY: moderate; PAGE: 365; OBJECTIVE: 6; TYPE: concept

85. _____ control how one electronic slide replaces another on screen.

ANSWER: Transitions
DIFFICULTY: moderate; PAGE: 368; OBJECTIVE: 6; TYPE: concept

86. You can overcome _____ by concentrating on your message and your audience, not on your fears.

ANSWER: Anxiety OR Stage Fright
DIFFICULTY: moderate; PAGE: 373; OBJECTIVE: n/a; TYPE: application

87. Although _____ presentations make it easy for teams to meet at a moment's notice, they also present important challenges, mainly because they make it harder to tell whether the audience is bored or confused.

ANSWER: Online
DIFFICULTY: moderate; PAGE: 369; OBJECTIVE: 7; TYPE: application

88. The _____ and _____ period following a presentation gives you a chance to build enthusiasm for your point of view, work in material that didn't fit into the formal presentation, and obtain important feedback from your audience.

ANSWER: Question, Answer
DIFFICULTY: moderate; PAGE: 373; OBJECTIVE: 8; TYPE: concept

Short Answer/Essay

89. Briefly explain the importance of oral presentations in your career success.

ANSWER: Oral presentations offer important opportunities to put all your communication skills on display, and let you demonstrate your ability to think on your feet, grasp complex issues, and handle challenging situations—all attributes that executives look for when searching for talented employees to promote.
DIFFICULTY: difficult; PAGE: 354-55; OBJECTIVE: 1; TYPE: concept

90. List the four steps involved in planning an oral presentation.

ANSWER: (1) Analyze the situation. (2) Gather information. (3) Select the right medium. (4) Organize the information.
DIFFICULTY: moderate; PAGE: 355; OBJECTIVE: 2; TYPE: concept

91. When planning a presentation, what does it mean to "analyze the situation?" Briefly explain each of the tasks involved.

ANSWER: Analyzing the situation involves defining your purpose and developing an audience profile. The purpose of most business presentations is to inform or to persuade, although some may involve collaboration. Developing an audience profile requires anticipating what sort of emotional state your audience is likely to be in and determining whether your audience is comfortable listening in the language you speak.
DIFFICULTY: difficult; PAGE: 355-56; OBJECTIVE: 2; TYPE: concept

92. Describe the four steps to organizing a presentation effectively.

ANSWER: (1) Define the main idea—what do you want the audience to walk away with? (2) Limit your scope—tailor the material to fit the time limit. (3) Choose your approach—direct for supportive audiences and indirect for resistant audiences. (4) Prepare your outline—keep it audience-centered for maximum effectiveness.
DIFFICULTY: difficult; PAGE: 356-58; OBJECTIVE: 2; TYPE: concept

93. What two-step process helps you define the main idea of your presentation?

ANSWER: The first step is to figure out the one message you want audience members to walk away with. Then compose a one-sentence summary that links your subject and purpose to your audience's frame of reference.
DIFFICULTY: moderate; PAGE: 357; OBJECTIVE: 2; TYPE: concept

94. In a longer presentation, how does your purpose influence the way you organize your material?

ANSWER: If the purpose is to entertain, motivate, or inform, use direct order and a structure imposed naturally by the subject (importance, sequence, etc.). If the purpose is to analyze, persuade, or collaborate, organize the material around conclusions and recommendations or around a logical argument.
DIFFICULTY: difficult; PAGE: 358; OBJECTIVE: 2; TYPE: concept

95. Briefly explain the difference between a planning outline and a speaking outline.

ANSWER: Whereas a planning outline is very detailed and includes all the points you plan to cover in your presentation, a speaking outline is much simpler and provides only the cues and reminders you need to present your material.
DIFFICULTY: moderate; PAGE: 359; OBJECTIVE: 2; TYPE: concept

96. What three tasks should an effective speech introduction accomplish?

ANSWER: (1) Arouse audience interest in your topic. (2) Establish your credibility. (3) Prepare the audience for what will follow.
DIFFICULTY: moderate; PAGE: 361; OBJECTIVE: 3; TYPE: concept

97. List two goals to achieve in the body of a business presentation.

ANSWER: (1) Make sure that the organization of your presentation is clear and (2) hold your audience's attention.
DIFFICULTY: moderate; PAGE: 362; OBJECTIVE: 2; TYPE: concept

98. List at least three types of visuals commonly used in business presentations.

ANSWER: (1) Overhead transparencies, (2) electronic slides, (3) chalkboards and whiteboards, and (4) flip charts.
DIFFICULTY: moderate; PAGE: 364-65; OBJECTIVE: 5; TYPE: concept

99. Generally speaking, what font sizes are best for the text in an electronic presentation?

ANSWER: A good rule of thumb is to use between 24- and 36-point type, reserving the larger size for titles and the smaller size for text items.
DIFFICULTY: moderate; PAGE: 367; OBJECTIVE: 6; TYPE: concept

100. Briefly describe the benefits and challenges of giving business presentations online.

ANSWER: Online presentations enable you to communicate easily with a geographically dispersed audience, and make it easy for a team to meet at a moment's notice. However, they often eliminate the "human moments" that guide and encourage you through a face-to-face presentation, and the technology itself can cause problems.
DIFFICULTY: moderate; PAGE: 369; OBJECTIVE: 7; TYPE: concept

101. List at least three guidelines for effectively handling questions following a business presentation.

ANSWER: 1) Pay attention to the questioner's body language to help determine what the person really means. 2) Repeat the question to confirm your understanding and to ensure that the entire audience has heard it. 3) If the question is vague or confusing, ask for clarification. 4) If you're asked to choose between two alternatives, don't feel you must do so. Instead, offer your own choice if it makes more sense. 5) Be sure to answer the question you're asked, rather than sidestepping or ignoring it. 6) If you don't know the answer to a question, don't pretend that you do.
DIFFICULTY: difficult; PAGE: 373-74; OBJECTIVE: 8; TYPE: concept

102. List and briefly explain at least four strategies for holding your audience's attention.

ANSWER: (1) Relate your subject to your audience's needs—present every point in light of how it will affect the listeners. (2) Anticipate your audience's questions— anticipate listener questions and address them in the body of your speech. (3) Use clear, vivid language— familiar words, short sentences, and concrete examples. (4) Explain the relationship between your subject and familiar ideas—show how your subject is related to ideas that your listeners already understand. (5) Ask opinions or pause for questions or comments—doing so lets the audience change from listening to participating. 6) Illustrate your ideas with visuals, which enliven your message, help you connect with the audience, and help them remember your message more effectively.
DIFFICULTY: difficult; PAGE: 363; OBJECTIVE: 4; TYPE: concept

103. Explain the content and function of the three types of navigational slides.

ANSWER: Navigational slides help the audience follow the flow of a presentation. The first type is the cover slide, which is the equivalent of a report's title page. The second type is the introduction slide, which defines and clarifies the topic of your presentation, emphasizes why you are speaking on this topic, and establishes any expectations you may have of the audience. Finally, blueprint slides make up the third category of navigational slides. These tell your audience where you are in the presentation.
DIFFICULTY: difficult; PAGE: 371; OBJECTIVE: 6; TYPE: concept

104. Give at least ten suggestions for becoming a more confident speaker.

ANSWER: (1) Prepare more material than necessary. Extra knowledge will reduce your anxiety. (2) Practice. The more familiar you are with your material, the less nervous you will be. (3) Think positively. Imagine yourself giving a polished and professional presentation. (4) Visualize your success. Use the few minutes before you start to tell yourself that you're ready. (5) Take a few deep breaths. (6) Be ready. Have your first sentence memorized and ready to go. (7) Be comfortable. (8) Don't panic. (9) Concentrate on your message and audience. Think about your subject and your audience. (10) Maintain eye contact with friendly audience members. (11) Keep going. Don't stop if you make a mistake.
DIFFICULTY: difficult; PAGE: 372-73; OBJECTIVE: n/a; TYPE: concept

CHAPTER 13
BUILDING CAREERS AND WRITING RÉSUMÉS

Multiple Choice

1. Today's changing workplace has affected the job market in all of the following ways *except*
   - a. most people now do not plan to work at one company for their whole life.
   - b. most jobs are being created by large companies.
   - c. many employers are looking for temporary workers or consultants.
   - d. employers want workers who are able to adapt to diverse situations.

ANSWER: b. Small business continues to be the primary engine of job creation in the U.S.
DIFFICULTY: moderate; PAGE: 385; OBJECTIVE: 1; TYPE: concept

2. When you begin to look for a job, your first step should be to
   - a. identify what you want to do.
   - b. write your résumé.
   - c. interview with some potential employers.
   - d. set up informational interviews.

ANSWER: a. This is the first step in adapting to today's job market.
DIFFICULTY: moderate; PAGE: 386; OBJECTIVE: 2; TYPE: concept

3. When you consider what you want to do, you should think about all of the following *except*
   - a. how much money you want to make.
   - b. what size of company would suit you.
   - c. whether there are any openings in the field you are interested in.
   - d. what location would you like.

ANSWER: c. This is not something to consider at this early stage.
DIFFICULTY: moderate; PAGE: 386; OBJECTIVE: 2; TYPE: concept

4. It is important to consider not only how much money you hope to make during your first year on the job but also
   - a. your ultimate earnings goal.
   - b. whether you would take less money to do a job you really love.
   - c. what location you would like.
   - d. all of the above

ANSWER: d. All of these are important to consider.
DIFFICULTY: moderate; PAGE: 386; OBJECTIVE: 2; TYPE: concept

5. Which of the following is an example of corporate culture?
    a. Modern office space
    b. A competitive environment
    c. Computer-assisted customer relations
    d. Profit-making status

ANSWER: b. This is an example of a corporate culture.
DIFFICULTY: moderate; PAGE: 386; OBJECTIVE: 2; TYPE: application

6. Before trying to identify employers who are likely to want you and vice versa, you begin by
    a. limiting your search to a particular industry or functional specialty.
    b. talking to friends who have interesting jobs.
    c. analyzing what you have to offer in terms of skills and abilities.
    d. reading carefully through company literature from a wide variety of firms.

ANSWER: c. This is an important step in preparing to apply for employment.
DIFFICULTY: moderate; PAGE: 386; OBJECTIVE: 2; TYPE: application

7. As part of your search for employment you should
    a. research specific companies.
    b. seek career counseling.
    c. network.
    d. do all of the above.

ANSWER: d. All of these are valuable strategies.
DIFFICULTY: easy; PAGE: 388-89; OBJECTIVE: 2; TYPE: application

8. When conducting a job search, you can use the Internet to
    a. stay abreast of business and financial news.
    b. research specific companies.
    c. search for job postings.
    d. do all of the above.

ANSWER: d. The internet can be useful in all of these tasks.
DIFFICULTY: moderate; PAGE: 388-90; OBJECTIVE: 2; TYPE: application

9. The purpose of a résumé is to
    a. induce the reader to hire you.
    b. list all your skills and abilities.
    c. get you an interview.
    d. take the place of an application letter.

ANSWER: c. This is the primary purpose of a résumé.
DIFFICULTY: moderate; PAGE: 391; OBJECTIVE: 4; TYPE: concept

10. Your résumé mainly emphasizes
    a. your work experience.
    b. your education.
    c. information that clearly aligns your career objectives with the needs of your target employers.
    d. your long-term career goals.

ANSWER: c. Although the other items are important, an audience-centered resume focuses on how you can meet the employer's needs.
DIFFICULTY: moderate; PAGE: 392; OBJECTIVE: 4; TYPE: concept

11. The main qualities that all employers seek include all of the following *except*
    a. analytical abilities.
    b. the ability to be a team player.
    c. diversified skills.
    d. flexibility and willingness to learn throughout one's career.

ANSWER: a. Although this is a valuable quality, it is generally not as much of a priority as the others.
DIFFICULTY: moderate; PAGE: 392; OBJECTIVE: 3; TYPE: concept

12. The most common way to organize a résumé is
    a. chronologically.
    b. functionally.
    c. geographically.
    d. alphabetically.

ANSWER: a. This is the most common format.
DIFFICULTY: moderate; PAGE: 393; OBJECTIVE: 4; TYPE: application

13. The best organization for the résumé of someone with a strong employment history along a progressive career path would be
    a. chronological.
    b. functional.
    c. targeted.
    d. portfolio.

ANSWER: a. This format highlights growth and career progression.
DIFFICULTY: moderate; PAGE: 393; OBJECTIVE: 4; TYPE: application

14. A _____ résumé emphasizes a candidate's skills and capabilities, but many employment professionals are suspicious of this type.
    a. chronological
    b. functional
    c. targeted
    d. indirect

ANSWER: b. Monster.com lists the functional resume as one of employers' "Top 10 Pet Peeves."
DIFFICULTY: moderate; PAGE: 393; OBJECTIVE: 4; TYPE: concept

15. A type of résumé that emphasizes a candidate's skills and accomplishments while also including a complete job history is termed
    a. a chronological résumé.
    b. a functional résumé.
    c. a combination résumé.
    d. an indirect résumé.

ANSWER: c. This format includes the best features of the chronological and functional approaches.
DIFFICULTY: moderate; PAGE: 393; OBJECTIVE: 4; TYPE: concept

16. If you are still a student and have little work experience, your résumé should emphasize
    a. summer jobs you have held.
    b. your educational background.
    c. your hobbies and interests.
    d. volunteer work you've done and service organizations in which you've been active.

ANSWER: b. One way to do so on a chronological resume is to list your educational qualifications before your experience.
DIFFICULTY: moderate; PAGE: 393; OBJECTIVE: 4; TYPE: application

17. When you describe your work experience on your résumé, you should
    a. start with your most recent job and work back chronologically.
    b. describe one or two jobs in detail so that employers get an idea of your work ethic.
    c. list only full-time positions.
    d. try to come up with fancier titles for the jobs you've held.

ANSWER: a. This is the most widely accepted strategy.
DIFFICULTY: moderate; PAGE: 393; OBJECTIVE: 4; TYPE: application

18. Which of the following would be the most desirable wording to use on a résumé?
    a. "I was in charge of a staff of six employees."
    b. "I supervised six employees."
    c. "Was in charge of entire departmental staff."
    d. "Supervised staff of six employees."

ANSWER: d. It's best to use short, crisp phrases and to avoid "I" on résumés.
DIFFICULTY: moderate; PAGE: 397; OBJECTIVE: 4; TYPE: application

19. When listing activities and achievements, you should probably avoid mentioning
    a. participation in athletics.
    b. involvement in fund-raising or community service activities.
    c. membership in political or religious organizations.
    d. speaking, writing, or tutoring experience.

ANSWER: c. This information can be a red flag to an employer with different views.
DIFFICULTY: moderate; PAGE: 400; OBJECTIVE: 5; TYPE: application

20. In describing activities and achievements on your résumé, you should
    a. use mild exaggerations—everyone else does, so you'll be at an unfair disadvantage if you don't.
    b. explain how the skills you've learned are related to the job for which you're applying.
    c. use significant amounts of jargon and technical terms.
    d. leave out any awards you've won unless they are specifically relevant to your current career objective.

ANSWER: b. Doing so helps employers better understand your qualifications.
DIFFICULTY: moderate; PAGE: 400; OBJECTIVE: 5; TYPE: concept

21. In the "Personal Data" section of your résumé, you list
    a. hobbies or miscellaneous experiences that may help you get the job.
    b. any health problems or disabilities you have, whether or not they may affect your job performance.
    c. your age, marital status, race, color, religion, and national origin, which are required by law.
    d. any experience in the military, whether or not it has a bearing on the job.

ANSWER: a. Experts advise candidates not to list personal interests unless including them enhances the employer's understanding of why you are the best candidate.
DIFFICULTY: moderate; PAGE: 400; OBJECTIVE: 5; TYPE: application

22. Do not include on your résumé items that could encourage discrimination, such as
    a. home address.
    b. hobbies.
    c. marital status.
    d. military service.

ANSWER: c. It is best to leave this information out.
DIFFICULTY: moderate; PAGE: 400; OBJECTIVE: 5; TYPE: concept

23. Military service relevant to the position you're seeking should be listed in the _____ section of your résumé.
    a. Education
    b. Work Experience
    c. Personal Data
    d. any of the above

ANSWER: d. It's appropriate to list it in any of these sections.
DIFFICULTY: moderate; PAGE: 400; OBJECTIVE: 5; TYPE: concept

24. Which of the following is *not* a common problem that employers see in résumés?
    a. too short or sketchy
    b. hard to read
    c. filled with misspellings and grammatical errors
    d. too straightforward

ANSWER: d. The other problems are all very common.
DIFFICULTY: moderate; PAGE: 401; OBJECTIVE: 5; TYPE: concept

25. Using a boastful tone in your résumé
    a. is the only way to avoid sounding unsure of your qualifications.
    b. helps you stand out among other applicants.
    c. causes prospective employers to question your self-evaluation.
    d. is expected in today's tight job market.

ANSWER: c. Boastful resumes are a turn-off for most employers.
DIFFICULTY: moderate; PAGE: 401; OBJECTIVE: 5; TYPE: concept

26. If design elements such as lists and white space cause your résumés to be more than one page long, you should
    a. still include those design elements since they make the document easier to read.
    b. add enough material to make it fill both the first and second pages.
    c. not include those design elements.
    d. cut whatever material you can in order to reduce it to one page.

ANSWER: a. Readability is of the utmost importance in a résumé.
DIFFICULTY: moderate; PAGE: 401; OBJECTIVE: n/a; TYPE: concept

27. To achieve the best physical appearance for your résumé, you should
    a. have it prepared by a professional résumé service.
    b. leave plenty of white space.
    c. use colored paper.
    d. use a variety of typefaces in various colors.

ANSWER: b. This enhances the readability of your résumé.
DIFFICULTY: moderate; PAGE: 401; OBJECTIVE: n/a; TYPE: application

28. The most common problem with résumé design is
    a. using excessive and distracting design elements.
    b. settling for an old-fashioned look.
    c. using the wrong type of paper.
    d. failing to include at least one graphic.

ANSWER: a. The most common way to get into trouble with résumé design is going overboard.
DIFFICULTY: moderate; PAGE: 401; OBJECTIVE: n/a; TYPE: concept

29. "OCR" stands for
    a. online character reference.
    b. optical character recognition.
    c. occupation criteria record.
    d. online chronological résumé.

ANSWER: b. This is a type of software used in scanning résumés and other documents.
DIFFICULTY: moderate; PAGE: 402; OBJECTIVE: 6; TYPE: concept

30. To prepare your résumé for the scanning process, you need to
    a. rewrite the whole thing.
    b. format it to be OCR-friendly.
    c. use a special software program.
    d. do all of the above.

ANSWER: b. If the OCR software can't make sense of fancy fonts or creative page layout, it will enter gibberish into the database.
DIFFICULTY: moderate; PAGE: 402-03; OBJECTIVE: 6; TYPE: application

31. A scannable résumé differs from a standard print résumé in that
    a. it includes a list of keywords.
    b. the Work Experience section always gets listed first.
    c. you leave out the Education section.
    d. it involves all of the above.

ANSWER: a. These keywords make it easy for employers to search for résumés of promising candidates.
DIFFICULTY: moderate; PAGE: 404; OBJECTIVE: 6; TYPE: application

32. The most common file format for uploading résumés directly to websites such as Monster.com is
    a. WordPerfect.
    b. PDF.
    c. Microsoft Word.
    d. Microsoft Publisher.

ANSWER: c. It is the de facto standard in business these days.
DIFFICULTY: moderate; PAGE: 404; OBJECTIVE: 6; TYPE: concept

33. When mailing a résumé, it is best to
    a. have it delivered via Priority Mail in a cardboard mailer.
    b. use a standard white #10 envelope.
    c. pay to have it delivered the next day.
    d. use a large kraft envelope.

ANSWER: a. This speeds the delivery and helps to ensure that your résumé arrives in good condition.
DIFFICULTY: moderate; PAGE: 405; OBJECTIVE: n/a; TYPE: application

34. When e-mailing your résumé to a prospective employer, you should
    a. always send it as a Microsoft Word attachment.
    b. make it less formal than you would for other formats.
    c. insert it as plain text into the body of the message unless you are specifically asked to send it as an attachment.
    d. use lots of colors to make your résumé stand out.

ANSWER: c. Otherwise it is not likely to be opened.
DIFFICULTY: moderate; PAGE: 405; OBJECTIVE: n/a; TYPE: concept

35. When posting your résumé on websites such as Monster.com, you should
    a. avoid including your Social Security number, student ID number, or driver's license number.
    b. make your résumé longer than you would for other formats.
    c. use a personal, "chummy" tone.
    d. do all of the above.

ANSWER: a. This information should never be posted online.
DIFFICULTY: moderate; PAGE: 406; OBJECTIVE: n/a; TYPE: application

True/False

36. When you are just starting out, it is unproductive to set future salary and career advancement goals.

ANSWER: False. This is an important consideration.
DIFFICULTY: moderate; PAGE: 386; OBJECTIVE: 2; TYPE: concept

37. Location should not be a factor in your choice of jobs. What you do is more important than where you do it.

ANSWER: False. This is an important consideration.
DIFFICULTY: moderate; PAGE: 386; OBJECTIVE: 2; TYPE: concept

38. When considering your ideal job, you should think about what kind of corporate culture you'd find most desirable.

ANSWER: True. This is an important consideration.
DIFFICULTY: moderate; PAGE: 386; OBJECTIVE: 2; TYPE: concept

39. Taking tests to identify your aptitudes, interests, and personality traits is not helpful in terms of seeking employment.

ANSWER: False. Doing so is particularly useful if you're having difficulty figuring out your interests, characteristics, or capabilities.
DIFFICULTY: moderate; PAGE: 386; OBJECTIVE: 2; TYPE: concept

40. Most employers refuse to look at unsolicited résumés.

ANSWER: False. Most employers accept and retain them.
DIFFICULTY: easy; PAGE: 388; OBJECTIVE: 3; TYPE: concept

41. As part of your job search, it's a good idea to stay abreast of business and financial news.

ANSWER: True. Online resources make it especially easy to do so. DIFFICULTY: moderate; PAGE: 388-89; OBJECTIVE: 2; TYPE: concept

42. You can find information about job hunting on the Internet, but it's not a reliable source for information on specific job openings.

ANSWER: False. It is an excellent source for this information.
DIFFICULTY: easy; PAGE: 389; OBJECTIVE: 2; TYPE: concept

43. The purpose of a résumé is to list all your skills and abilities.

ANSWER: False. The purpose is to stimulate a potential employer's interest in learning more about you.
DIFFICULTY: moderate; PAGE: 391; OBJECTIVE: 4; TYPE: concept

44. A good résumé can be customized for different situations and different employers.

ANSWER: True. It is vital to adapt your resume to your audience's needs.
DIFFICULTY: moderate; PAGE: 391-92; OBJECTIVE: 4; TYPE: concept

45. These days, preparing a basic paper resume is a waste of time.

ANSWER: False. You never know when someone will ask for a copy, and not all employers want to bother with technology when all they want to know is your basic profile.
DIFFICULTY: moderate; PAGE: 392; OBJECTIVE: 4; TYPE: concept

46. All résumés should be organized chronologically.

ANSWER: False. Other organization strategies may be more appropriate in some situations.
DIFFICULTY: moderate; PAGE: 393; OBJECTIVE: 4; TYPE: concept

47. A functional résumé is organized around a list of accomplishments and focuses on the person's areas of competence.

ANSWER: True. This is the correct definition.
DIFFICULTY: moderate; PAGE: 393; OBJECTIVE: 4; TYPE: concept

48. Most employers now prefer functional résumés to both chronological and combination résumés.

ANSWER: False. Monster.com lists the functional résumé as one of employers "Top 10 Pet Peeves."
DIFFICULTY: moderate; PAGE: 393; OBJECTIVE: 4; TYPE: concept

49. When giving your background and qualifications on a résumé, you always use complete sentences.

ANSWER: False. It is preferable to use short, crisp phrases that begin with action verbs.
DIFFICULTY: moderate; PAGE: 397; OBJECTIVE: 5; TYPE: application

50. If you have an e-portfolio, you should list its URL on your résumé under "Contact Information."

ANSWER: True. This is the best place to list that information.
DIFFICULTY: moderate; PAGE: 398; OBJECTIVE: 5; TYPE: concept

51. Experts agree that every résumé should include a statement of the applicant's career objective.

ANSWER: False. Experts disagree about the need to state a career objective.
DIFFICULTY: moderate; PAGE: 399; OBJECTIVE: 5; TYPE: concept

52. If you plan to include a career objective or summary of qualifications in your résumé, you should focus on your goals rather than the employer's needs.

ANSWER: False. The employer's needs should be of primary concern throughout the resume.
DIFFICULTY: moderate; PAGE: 399; OBJECTIVE: 5; TYPE: concept

53. An effective career objective is one such as, "A fulfilling position that provides ample opportunity for career growth and personal satisfaction."

ANSWER: False. Statements such as this do not reflect a "you" attitude.
DIFFICULTY: moderate; PAGE: 399; OBJECTIVE: 5; TYPE: concept

54. The education section of your résumé includes any relevant seminars or workshops you have attended.

ANSWER: True. This information should be included.
DIFFICULTY: moderate; PAGE: 399; OBJECTIVE: 5; TYPE: concept

55. You should always include your college GPA on your résumé.

ANSWER: False. Whether or not you do so depends on the job you want and the quality of your grades.
DIFFICULTY: easy; PAGE: 399; OBJECTIVE: 5; TYPE: concept

56. You should not list a college degree in the "Education" section of a résumé unless you have already graduated.

ANSWER: False. If you are working toward a degree, you should include in parentheses the expected date of completion.
DIFFICULTY: moderate; PAGE: 399; OBJECTIVE: 5; TYPE: concept

57. In the work experience section of your résumé, you should leave out any jobs that do not relate directly to your career objective.

ANSWER: False. You should list all positions, even if unrelated to your current career objective.
DIFFICULTY: moderate; PAGE: 400; OBJECTIVE: 5; TYPE: concept

58. Your résumé should list past jobs in chronological order, with the first job first and the current job last.

ANSWER: False. List your jobs in reverse chronological order.
DIFFICULTY: easy; PAGE: 400; OBJECTIVE: 5; TYPE: concept

59. When listing work experience on a résumé, you should not include any part-time jobs.

ANSWER: False. You should list part-time employment.
DIFFICULTY: moderate; PAGE: 400; OBJECTIVE: 5; TYPE: concept

60. It is inappropriate to mention community activities or volunteer work on a résumé.

ANSWER: False. These should be listed in the "Activities and Achievements" section.
DIFFICULTY: moderate; PAGE: 400; OBJECTIVE: 5; TYPE: concept

61. Prospective employers generally do not like résumés that are boastful.

ANSWER: True. This is one of the pitfalls to avoid.
DIFFICULTY: easy; PAGE: 401; OBJECTIVE: 3; TYPE: concept

62. Not all résumés need to be limited to one page in length.

ANSWER: True. Although you should try to keep it to one page, but this may not be practical if you have a great deal of experience and are applying for a higher-level position.
DIFFICULTY: moderate; PAGE: 401; OBJECTIVE: n/a; TYPE: concept

63. In today's high-tech business environment, it is essential to use various colors in designing your résumé.

ANSWER: False. This makes the resume appear unprofessional.
DIFFICULTY: moderate; PAGE: 401; OBJECTIVE: 3; TYPE: concept

64. To fit everything on one page, it's okay to sacrifice white space on your résumé.

ANSWER: False. White space increases the readability of your resume.
DIFFICULTY: moderate; PAGE: 401; OBJECTIVE: n/a; TYPE: concept

65. The most common problem with resume design is not using enough design elements.

ANSWER: False. The most common problem is going overboard. DIFFICULTY: moderate; PAGE: 401; OBJECTIVE: n/a; TYPE: concept

66. To get your résumé into an employer's database, it is helpful to convert it to plain-text format.

ANSWER: True. This format is less prone to errors than the scanning process. DIFFICULTY: moderate; PAGE: 404; OBJECTIVE: 6; TYPE: concept

67. Some examples of keywords to include in your electronic résumé would be "works hard," "manages time well," and "gets along well with others."

ANSWER: False. Employers tend to search for nouns since verbs tend to be generic rather than specific to a particular position or skill. DIFFICULTY: moderate; PAGE: 404; OBJECTIVE: 6; TYPE: application

68. When it comes to uploading résumés to websites such as Monster.com, WordPerfect is the most common format.

ANSWER: False. Microsoft Word is the de facto standard in business these days. DIFFICULTY: moderate; PAGE: 404; OBJECTIVE: 6; TYPE: concept

69. When e-mailing your résumé, it is best to attach it to the message as a Word document.

ANSWER: False. Unless you paste it into the main body of the message, it is not likely to be read. DIFFICULTY: moderate; PAGE: 405; OBJECTIVE: 6; TYPE: concept

70. When posting your résumé to a website, you should not provide photos or any information that reveals your age, gender, race, marital status, or religion.

ANSWER: True. This information should not be posted online. DIFFICULTY: moderate; PAGE: 406; OBJECTIVE: 6; TYPE: concept

Fill-in-the-Blank

71. _____ is the process of making informal connections with a broad sphere of mutually beneficial business contacts.

ANSWER: Networking DIFFICULTY: moderate; PAGE: 389; OBJECTIVE: 2; TYPE: concept

72. A (An) _____ is a form of self-advertisement designed to get you an interview.

ANSWER: Résumé DIFFICULTY: easy; PAGE: 391; OBJECTIVE: 2; TYPE: concept

73. The most common way to organize a résumé is _____.

ANSWER: Chronologically
DIFFICULTY: moderate; PAGE: 393; OBJECTIVE: 4; TYPE: concept

74. A _____ résumé is organized around a list of skills and capabilities.

ANSWER: Functional
DIFFICULTY: moderate; PAGE: 393; OBJECTIVE: 4; TYPE: concept

75. For a résumé, use short, crisp phrases starting with strong _____ verbs.

ANSWER: Action
DIFFICULTY: moderate; PAGE: 397-98; OBJECTIVE: 4; TYPE: concept

76. The Summary of _____ section of a résumé identifies the type of job you're interested in and gives employers a compelling reason to hire you.

ANSWER: Qualifications
DIFFICULTY: moderate; PAGE: 399; OBJECTIVE: 5; TYPE: concept

77. Even though the Career Objective section of a résumé states the applicant's \ objective, it is really focused on the needs of the _____.

ANSWER: Employer
DIFFICULTY: moderate; PAGE: 399; OBJECTIVE: 5; TYPE: concept

78. In the _____ section of your résumé you list schools you've attended and degrees you've received.

ANSWER: Education
DIFFICULTY: easy; PAGE: 399; OBJECTIVE: 5; TYPE: concept

79. In the _____ _____ section of your résumé, you list jobs you've had and responsibilities you've held on those jobs.

ANSWER: Work Experience
DIFFICULTY: moderate; PAGE: 400; OBJECTIVE: 5; TYPE: concept

80. Volunteer work that demonstrates your abilities should be listed in the _____ and _____ section of your résumé.

ANSWER: Activities, Achievements
DIFFICULTY: moderate; PAGE: 400; OBJECTIVE: 5; TYPE: concept

81. According to professional recruiters, a common problem with many résumés is that they are written in an overconfident or _____ tone.

ANSWER: Boastful OR Arrogant
DIFFICULTY: moderate; PAGE: 401; OBJECTIVE: n/a; TYPE: concept

82. To cope with the flood of unsolicited paper résumés in recent years, many companies now optically _____ incoming résumés into a database.

ANSWER: Scan
DIFFICULTY: moderate; PAGE: 402; OBJECTIVE: 6; TYPE: concept

83. Résumés prepared for an electronic database should include a list of 20 to 30 _____ that will help employers identify the applicant's skills.

ANSWER: Keywords
DIFFICULTY: moderate; PAGE: 404; OBJECTIVE: 6; TYPE: concept

84. To save your résumé in _____ format, simply use the "save as webpage" feature in your word processor.

ANSWER: HTML
DIFFICULTY: difficult; PAGE: 404; OBJECTIVE: 6; TYPE: concept

85. When e-mailing a copy of your résumé, it is generally best to include it within the _____ of the message.

ANSWER: Body
DIFFICULTY: moderate; PAGE: 405; OBJECTIVE: 6; TYPE: concept

Short Answer/Essay

86. Describe at least three factors that are likely to affect your entry into the job market and your career success in years to come.

ANSWER: The first important factor is stability. In today's business world, your career will be affected by globalization, mergers and acquisitions, short-term mentality driven by the demands of stockholders, ethical upheavals, and the relentless quest for lower costs. The second factor is the demise of lifetime employment: the idea that employees will spend their entire working lives with a single firm is all but gone in many industries. Most U.S. employees will not only change employers multiple times but will even change careers anywhere from three to five times over their working lives.

The third important factor is the growth of small business. Small business continues to be the primary engine of job creation in the United States. One expert predicts that before long, 80 percent of the U.S. labor force will be working for firms employing fewer than 200 people. The fourth factor is an increasing number of independent contractors. The nature of employment itself is changing for many people, with more employees leaving their companies and going into business for themselves.
DIFFICULTY: difficult; PAGE: 385; OBJECTIVE: 1; TYPE: concept

87. List at least five questions you might consider when you are deciding what you want to do.

ANSWER: (1) What would you like to do every day? (2) How would you like to work? (3) What specific compensation do you expect? (4) Can you establish some general career goals? (5) What size company would you prefer? (6) What sort of corporate culture would suit you? (7) What location would you like?
DIFFICULTY: difficult; PAGE: 386; OBJECTIVE: n/a; TYPE: concept

88. What three things must job seekers know in order to adapt to today's job market?

ANSWER: Adapting to today's job market requires knowing what you want to do, what you have to offer, and how to make yourself more attractive to employers.
DIFFICULTY: moderate; PAGE: 386; OBJECTIVE: 2; TYPE: concept

89. What is an e-portfolio, and how do you use it during the job search?

ANSWER: An e-portfolio is a multimedia presentation about your skills and experiences. It's an extensive résumé that links to an electronic collection of your student papers, projects, and anything else that demonstrates your accomplishments and activities. You can save it on CD-ROMs and send them out instead of résumés.
DIFFICULTY: difficult; PAGE: 386; OBJECTIVE: 2; TYPE: concept

90. Briefly describe four steps you can take to prepare for and successfully complete your search for employment.

ANSWER: (1) Stay abreast of business and financial news. (2) Research specific companies. (3) Network. (4) Find career counseling.
DIFFICULTY: difficult; PAGE: 388-89; OBJECTIVE: 2; TYPE: concept

91. Name at least three qualities you need to convey on any résumé.

ANSWER: On any résumé, you need to show that you (1) think in terms of results, (2) know how to get things done, (3) are well rounded, (4) show signs of progress, (5) have personal standards of excellence, (6) are flexible and willing to try new things, and (7) communicate effectively.
DIFFICULTY: moderate; PAGE: 392; OBJECTIVE: 3; TYPE: concept

92. Describe a strategy for handling gaps in your employment history when writing a résumé.

ANSWER: An effective way to deal with gaps in employment history when writing a résumé is to mention relevant experience and education you gained during employment gaps, such as volunteer or community work.
DIFFICULTY: moderate; PAGE: 393; OBJECTIVE: 4; TYPE: concept

93. List and describe the three methods for organizing a résumé along with the advantages and disadvantages of each one.

ANSWER: (1) Chronological—lists your employment history starting with the most recent job first. Advantages: Employers are familiar with it, it highlights growth and career progression, and it emphasizes continuity and stability. Disadvantages: It draws attention to gaps in your employment history. (2) Functional—lists your skills and accomplishments. Advantages: Employers can quickly see what you can do, you can emphasize earlier job experience, and de-emphasize any lack of career progress or lengthy unemployment. Disadvantages: Employers tend to assume that you are trying to hide something; it is harder for employers to quickly determine your employment history. (3) Combination—includes features of both chronological and functional approaches. Advantages: You can highlight both your skills and your employment history. Disadvantages: Employers are somewhat unfamiliar with it, and it can be repetitious and longer than other formats.
DIFFICULTY: difficult; PAGE: 393; OBJECTIVE: 4; TYPE: concept

94. Rewrite the following to make it a more active statement: "I was in charge of customer complaints and all ordering problems."

ANSWER: Handled all customer complaints and resolved all product order problems.
DIFFICULTY: moderate; PAGE: 397-98; OBJECTIVE: 5; TYPE: application

95. In addition to your name, what should be included in the Contact Information section of your résumé?

ANSWER: (1) Physical address, (2) e-mail address, (3) phone number(s), and (4) the URL of your personal webpage or e-portfolio if you have one.
DIFFICULTY: moderate; PAGE: 398; OBJECTIVE: 5; TYPE: concept

96. Describe the main sections or elements that are included on most résumés.

ANSWER: (1) Name and Contact Information—Include any information necessary to contact you including phone numbers, e-mail addresses, etc. (2) Career Objective—This section is optional. Including it allows you to clearly state your desired goal and to categorize yourself. (3) Education—Give your educational background, degrees earned, where you attended school, the dates attended, and the skills and abilities that you've developed in your course work. (4) Work Experience, Skills, and Accomplishments—List your jobs in chronological order with the current one first. Give the name and location of the employer as well as your title. Describe your skills and accomplishments and quantify them whenever possible. (5) Activities and Achievements—List volunteer activities that demonstrate your leadership, organization, teamwork, etc. Explain how the skills learned there are related to the job you're applying for. Note any awards you've received. (6) Personal Data—As with Career Objective, this section is optional. Include information about your interests and hobbies only if they enhance the employer's understanding of why you would be the best candidate for the job.
DIFFICULTY: difficult; PAGE: 398-400; OBJECTIVE: 5; TYPE: concept

97. What potential risk do some experts associate with including a career objective on your résumé?

ANSWER: Some experts maintain that such a statement labels you as being interested in only one thing and thus limits your possibilities as a candidate, especially if you want to be considered for a variety of openings.
DIFFICULTY: moderate; PAGE: 399; OBJECTIVE: 5; TYPE: concept

98. Name at least five types of information that should be excluded from all résumés in order to discourage discrimination.

ANSWER: Résumés should never include information about (1) marital or family status, (2) age, (3) race, (4) religion, (5) national origin, or (6) physical or mental disabilities.
DIFFICULTY: moderate; PAGE: 400; OBJECTIVE: 5; TYPE: concept

99. List at least five of the nine most common problems with résumés.

ANSWER: (1) Too long or too wordy. (2) Too short or sketchy. (3) Hard to read. (4) Poorly written. (5) Displaying a weak understanding of the business world or of a particular industry. (6) Poor quality printing or cheap paper. (7) Full of spelling and grammatical errors. (8) Boastful. (9) Gimmicky design.
DIFFICULTY: moderate; PAGE: 401; OBJECTIVE: n/a; TYPE: concept

100. Explain how to select keywords to include on a scannable résumé.

ANSWER: Include a keyword summary consisting of words and phrases that define your skills, experiences, education, and professional affiliations. Use mostly nouns, as verbs tend to be generic rather than specific to a particular position or skill. Underline all the skills listed in ads for the types of jobs you're interested in. Use those words that match your skills and qualifications. Use words that potential employers will understand, and use abbreviations sparingly.
DIFFICULTY: difficult; PAGE: 404; OBJECTIVE: 6; TYPE: concept

CHAPTER 14
APPLYING AND INTERVIEWING FOR EMPLOYMENT

Multiple Choice

1. You'll impress prospective employers with your application letter if you
    a. use a gimmicky layout.
    b. show that you understand the company and the position.
    c. use a personal, "chummy" tone.
    d. do all of the above.

ANSWER: b. The other strategies listed are not effective.
DIFFICULTY: moderate; PAGE: 419; OBJECTIVE: 1; TYPE: concept

2. Your cover letter should
    a. be specific.
    b. not repeat anything that you have discussed in your résumé.
    c. be short, upbeat, and professional.
    d. do all of the above.

ANSWER: d. All of these characterize an effective application letter.
DIFFICULTY: moderate; PAGE: 419; OBJECTIVE: 1; TYPE: concept

3. Cover letters submitted via e-mail should be
    a. longer than traditional cover letters.
    b. shorter than traditional application letters.
    c. the same length as traditional cover letters.
    d. less formal than traditional cover letters.

ANSWER: b. These should be no longer than two to three paragraphs.
DIFFICULTY: moderate; PAGE: 419; OBJECTIVE: 1; TYPE: concept

4. Sending an unsolicited application letter to an employer
    a. requires that you begin by capturing the reader's attention.
    b. is never a good idea.
    c. requires no special attention-getter in the opening paragraph.
    d. should only be done via e-mail.

ANSWER: a. This is an important task to achieve in the first paragraph of the letter.
DIFFICULTY: moderate; PAGE: 419; OBJECTIVE: 1; TYPE: concept

5. The main difference between solicited and unsolicited application letters is in
    a. the length.
    b. the way qualifications are presented.
    c. the way the letter begins.
    d. the way the letter closes.

ANSWER: c. An unsolicited letter begins with an attention-getting statement.
DIFFICULTY: moderate; PAGE: 419; OBJECTIVE: 1; TYPE: concept

6. In the middle section of a job application letter, you
   a. present your strongest selling points in terms of their potential benefit to the organization.
   b. give your entire work history, in case the employer doesn't read your résumé.
   c. mention any ways in which you do not meet the job qualifications but point out that you are willing to learn.
   d. do all of the above.

ANSWER: a. This is the primary goal of the Interest and Desire sections of the application letter.
DIFFICULTY: moderate; PAGE: 420; OBJECTIVE: 1; TYPE: concept

7. When writing a solicited application letter in response to a job announcement, you should
   a. clearly state which of the employer's requirements you do not meet.
   b. include a copy of the ad with your letter.
   c. discuss each of the requirements specified in the ad.
   d. do all of the above.

ANSWER: c. Doing so is the most audience centered approach to writing an effective application letter.
DIFFICULTY: moderate; PAGE: 421; OBJECTIVE: 1; TYPE: concept

8. If your application letter and résumé fail to bring a response within a month or so, you should
   a. call to find out why you haven't heard from the prospective employer.
   b. write a follow-up letter or e-mail message.
   c. cross this particular job possibility off your list.
   d. send another copy of your application letter and résumé.

ANSWER: b. It is important to let the company know you are still interested.
DIFFICULTY: moderate; PAGE: 423; OBJECTIVE: 1; TYPE: concept

9. Generally speaking, the best way to connect with smaller businesses is
   a. through a campus placement office.
   b. through a job search website.
   c. to contact the companies directly.
   d. to attend a job fair.

ANSWER: c. You should adapt your job search to each company's size and hiring practices.
DIFFICULTY: moderate; PAGE: 423-24; OBJECTIVE: 2; TYPE: concept

10. Most employers interview an applicant _____ time(s) before deciding to make a job offer.
    a. 1
    b. 2-3
    c. 4-5
    d. 5-6

ANSWER: b. Each of the interviews in this sequence has a different purpose.
DIFFICULTY: moderate; PAGE: 424; OBJECTIVE: 2; TYPE: concept

11. Employers use preliminary screening interviews to
    a. find out as much as possible about each job candidate.
    b. give employment tests.
    c. narrow the field of applicants.
    d. offer jobs to the best candidates.

ANSWER: c. The purpose of these interviews is to screen out unqualified candidates.
DIFFICULTY: moderate; PAGE: 424; OBJECTIVE: 2; TYPE: concept

12. During a screening interview, your best approach is to
    a. ask as many questions as possible.
    b. keep your answers short while differentiating yourself from other applicants.
    c. expand on your answers as much as possible so that the interviewer knows you are at ease.
    d. keep as low a profile as you can; this is not the time to try to differentiate yourself from other candidates.

ANSWER: b. Focusing on a few distinctive qualifications is the best approach.
DIFFICULTY: moderate; PAGE: 424; OBJECTIVE: 2; TYPE: concept

13. Your goal in the initial screening interview is to
    a. explain your greatest strengths in depth.
    b. differentiate yourself from other candidates.
    c. clinch the deal.
    d. show the interviewer that your personality fits well with the job.

ANSWER: b. This is the main priority in a screening interview.
DIFFICULTY: moderate; PAGE: 424; OBJECTIVE: 2; TYPE: concept

14. In the second round of interviews, your best approach is to
    a. stick to brief, yes and no answers to the interview questions.
    b. relate your training and experience to the organization's needs.
    c. inquire about salary and benefits.
    d. do all the above.

ANSWER: b. In the selection stage, it is important to accomplish this goal.
DIFFICULTY: moderate; PAGE: 424; OBJECTIVE: 2; TYPE: concept

15. If you are asked back for a final job interview, the interviewer will most likely be concerned with
    a. your previous job experience.
    b. selling you on the benefits of joining the organization.
    c. your educational background.
    d. checking your references.

ANSWER: b. This is often one of the employer's underlying objectives.
DIFFICULTY: moderate; PAGE: 424; OBJECTIVE: 2; TYPE: concept

16. An interview in which a job candidate is criticized or provoked is a type of
    a. stress interview.
    b. structured interview.
    c. screening interview.
    d. situational interview.

ANSWER: a. A stress interview is designed to unsettle the candidate.
DIFFICULTY: easy; PAGE: 424; OBJECTIVE: 2; TYPE: concept

17. Preparing for a video interview is generally
    a. the same as preparing for a face-to-face interview.
    b. not necessary.
    c. different from preparing for a face-to-face interview.
    d. virtually impossible.

ANSWER: c. Experts recommend, for example, that before a video interview you should request a preliminary phone interview to establish rapport.
DIFFICULTY: moderate; PAGE: 425; OBJECTIVE: 2; TYPE: concept

18. An interview in which a job candidate is placed in a hands-on scenario and asked to do job-related tasks is a type of
    a. stress interview.
    b. structured interview.
    c. screening interview.
    d. situational interview.

ANSWER: d. This type can also be called a behavioral interview.
DIFFICULTY: moderate; PAGE: 425; OBJECTIVE: 2; TYPE: concept

19. In general, employers are looking for two things: proof that a candidate can handle a specific job and
    a. excellent references.
    b. high employment test scores.
    c. evidence that the person will fit in with the organization.
    d. long-term commitment to the organization.

ANSWER: c. Employers use interviews to determine this.
DIFFICULTY: moderate; PAGE: 425; OBJECTIVE: 3; TYPE: concept

20. When it comes to drug and alcohol testing
    a. by law only government agencies can require it.
    b. nearly half of all U.S. companies now require it of all applicants.
    c. the great majority of companies now require it.
    d. the Supreme Court has declared it unconstitutional.

ANSWER: b. This percentage is expected to rise in the near future.
DIFFICULTY: moderate; PAGE: 426; OBJECTIVE: 3; TYPE: concept

21. When asking questions during job interviews, candidates should
    a. stick to neutral topics such as the weather.
    b. steer the discussion into areas where they can present their qualifications to peak advantage.
    c. stick to questions that elicit simple yes or no answers.
    d. put as much pressure on the interviewer as possible.

ANSWER: b. Doing so will enhance the effectiveness of your interview.
DIFFICULTY: moderate; PAGE: 429; OBJECTIVE: 4; TYPE: concept

22. The best way to counteract feelings of shyness, self-consciousness, or nervousness about job interviews is to
    a. focus on how you can help the organization succeed.
    b. use humor to mask these feelings.
    c. act overly confident to counteract these feelings.
    d. see a psychotherapist, since you obviously can't deal with such a serious problem on your own.

ANSWER: a. This is another way to maintain a "you" attitude during the interview.
DIFFICULTY: moderate; PAGE: 430; OBJECTIVE: 4; TYPE: concept

23. In the United States, you are more likely to have a successful interview if you
    a. refrain from smiling.
    b. maintain eye contact with the interviewer.
    c. avoid using hand gestures.
    d. do all of the above.

ANSWER: b. It is also important to smile frequently, sit in an attentive position, and use frequent hand gestures.
DIFFICULTY: moderate; PAGE: 430-31; OBJECTIVE: 4; TYPE: concept

24. If you are a smoker and must go to a job interview, you should
    a. ask the interviewer politely if you can smoke.
    b. smoke only if the interviewer smokes.
    c. refrain from smoking before and during the interview.
    d. smoke just prior to the interview to calm yourself.

ANSWER: c. Nonsmokers can smell smoke on the clothing of interviewees.
DIFFICULTY: moderate; PAGE: 431; OBJECTIVE: 4; TYPE: concept

25. When choosing the clothing you will wear for an interview, the best policy is to
    a. pick something that will make you stand out from the crowd.
    b. wear whatever makes you most comfortable.
    c. buy a new suit.
    d. dress conservatively.

ANSWER: d. This is especially true if you are unsure about what to wear.
DIFFICULTY: easy; PAGE: 431; OBJECTIVE: 4; TYPE: concept

26. When going in for a job interview, it's best to take
    a. a list of questions to ask the interviewer.
    b. gum or candy to eat during the question-and-answer period.
    c. a PDA.
    d. all of the above.

ANSWER: a. This will help to ensure that you do not forget to ask the questions you need to ask.
DIFFICULTY: moderate; PAGE: 432; OBJECTIVE: 4; TYPE: concept

27. When going to a job interview, you should
    a. take along samples of your work; recruiters are impressed by tangible evidence of job-related accomplishments.
    b. refrain from bringing copies of your résumé; you can assume the interviewer already has one.
    c. try not to be more than five or ten minutes late.
    d. do all of the above.

ANSWER: a. You may also want to take performance reviews and certificates of achievement.
DIFFICULTY: moderate; PAGE: 432; OBJECTIVE: 4; TYPE: concept

28. Many interviewers make a decision about the applicant
    a. within the first 20 seconds of the interview.
    b. during the question-and-answer stage.
    c. during the final minutes of the interview.
    d. after the candidate has left.

ANSWER: a. It is vitally important to make a good first impression.
DIFFICULTY: moderate; PAGE: 432; OBJECTIVE: 5; TYPE: concept

29. The longest phase of a job interview is
    a. the warm-up.
    b. the question-and-answer stage.
    c. the close.
    d. none; all are about the same length.

ANSWER: b. This portion consumes the greatest part of the interview.
DIFFICULTY: moderate; PAGE: 433; OBJECTIVE: 5; TYPE: concept

30. It is potentially illegal for employers to ask you questions about your
    a. marital status.
    b. national origin.
    c. religion.
    d. all of the above

ANSWER: d. Questions regarding these topics can lead to discrimination.
DIFFICULTY: easy; PAGE: 433-34; OBJECTIVE: 5; TYPE: concept

31. If your interviewer asks you inappropriate questions, how you answer depends mainly on
    a. how badly you want the job.
    b. what you think the interviewer will do with the information.
    c. how you feel about revealing the information requested.
    d. all of the above.

ANSWER: d. You have the option of refusing to answer, but it is likely to leave an unfavorable impression.
DIFFICULTY: moderate; PAGE: 433-34; OBJECTIVE: 5; TYPE: concept

32. When a job interviewer indicates the interview is coming to a close, you should
    a. try to prolong the interview, since the more the interviewer interacts with you, the better impression you'll make.
    b. leave as quickly as possible.
    c. prepare to leave but try to pin down what will happen next.
    d. ask how you did.

ANSWER: c. It is important to conclude gracefully.
DIFFICULTY: moderate; PAGE: 434; OBJECTIVE: 5; TYPE: concept

33. On your second or third visit to an organization, if you haven't been told by the end of an interview whether you got the job, you should
    a. not bring up the topic.
    b. mention that you have another job offer and need to give the other company an answer by a specific date.
    c. ask tactfully when you can expect to learn of the decision.
    d. ask whether you did anything wrong during the interview.

ANSWER: c. This is appropriate at the close of second or third interviews with the same organization.
DIFFICULTY: moderate; PAGE: 434; OBJECTIVE: 5; TYPE: concept

34. When you discuss salary requirements with a job recruiter, you should
    a. let the interviewer raise the topic first.
    b. say that you expect to receive a competitive compensation package.
    c. try to negotiate a higher salary if you are not satisfied with the offer and are in a good bargaining position.
    d. do all of the above.

ANSWER: d. All of these strategies can be effective.
DIFFICULTY: moderate; PAGE: 434-35; OBJECTIVE: 5; TYPE: concept

35. Within two days after an interview, you should
   a. have a friend call to see whether you got the job.
   b. write a follow-up letter (using the format for persuasive messages) and include another copy of your résumé.
   c. write a short note of thanks (using the format for routine messages).
   d. assume that you didn't get the job if you haven't heard anything.

ANSWER: c. You should send a thank-you message even if you feel you have little chance for the job.
DIFFICULTY: moderate; PAGE: 435; OBJECTIVE: 6; TYPE: concept

True/False

36. Unsolicited application letters are those sent in response to want ads for job openings.

ANSWER: False. This is the description of solicited application letters.
DIFFICULTY: easy; PAGE: 419; OBJECTIVE: 1; TYPE: concept

37. It is acceptable to send a solicited application letter via e-mail, but unsolicited letters should be sent only through regular mail.

ANSWER: False. Both types of application letters may be sent via e-mail.
DIFFICULTY: easy; PAGE: 419; OBJECTIVE: 1; TYPE: concept

38. An application letter follows the AIDA format for persuasive messages.

ANSWER: True. Since it is a persuasive message, this format is effective.
DIFFICULTY: moderate; PAGE: 419; OBJECTIVE: 1; TYPE: concept

39. The main difference between solicited and unsolicited application letters is in the opening paragraph.

ANSWER: True. An unsolicited letter should begin with an attention-getting statement.
DIFFICULTY: moderate; PAGE: 419; OBJECTIVE: 1; TYPE: concept

40. You should never volunteer salary information in a cover letter unless the employer has asked for it specifically.

ANSWER: True. It is best to let the employer bring up the subject.
DIFFICULTY: moderate; PAGE: 419; OBJECTIVE: 1; TYPE: concept

41. In the middle part of an application letter, you spell out your "selling points" and other potential benefits to your employer.

ANSWER: True. This is an important goal of the "Interest" and "Desire" sections of an application letter.
DIFFICULTY: moderate; PAGE: 420-22; OBJECTIVE: 1; TYPE: concept

42. In the final paragraph of your application letter, you should forcefully demand an interview.

ANSWER: False. You should respectfully request an interview, but not demand one.
DIFFICULTY: moderate; PAGE: 423; OBJECTIVE: 1; TYPE: concept

43. The campus placement office is the best way for applicants to connect with small businesses.

ANSWER: False. Often, the best way to connect with small businesses is to contact the company directly.
DIFFICULTY: moderate; PAGE: 423-24; OBJECTIVE: 2; TYPE: concept

44. Most employers interview an applicant two or three times before deciding whether to offer a person a job.

ANSWER: True. This is typical practice.
DIFFICULTY: moderate; PAGE: 424; OBJECTIVE: 2; TYPE: concept

45. A screening interview is usually used to gauge a job candidate's personality and personal qualities.

ANSWER: False. The usual goal of screening interviews is to eliminate unqualified applicants.
DIFFICULTY: moderate; PAGE: 424; OBJECTIVE: 2; TYPE: concept

46. Preliminary screening interviews tend to be structured, with each applicant being asked the same questions.

ANSWER: True. Many companies use standardized evaluation sheets to grade the applicants at this stage.
DIFFICULTY: moderate; PAGE: 424; OBJECTIVE: 2; TYPE: concept

47. During a screening interview, it is best to call attention to one key aspect of your background that will differentiate you from other candidates.

ANSWER: True. It is important to distinguish yourself in a screening interview.
DIFFICULTY: moderate; PAGE: 424; OBJECTIVE: 2; TYPE: concept

48. An open-ended interview tends to be formal and highly structured.

ANSWER: False. Open-ended interviews are less structured, and more like conversations between two peers.
DIFFICULTY: moderate; PAGE: 424; OBJECTIVE: 2; TYPE: concept

49. During a stress interview, you might be asked pointed questions designed to anger or unsettle you.

ANSWER: True. Stress interviews are intended to upset the applicant.
DIFFICULTY: moderate; PAGE: 424; OBJECTIVE: 2; TYPE: concept

50. You should prepare for a video interview the same way you would prepare for an in-person interview.

ANSWER: False. Experts recommend preparing differently for a video interview than for an in-person meeting.
DIFFICULTY: moderate; PAGE: 425; OBJECTIVE: 2; TYPE: concept

51. Nearly half of all companies now require job applicants to undergo drug and alcohol testing.

ANSWER: True. This percentage is expected to increase.
DIFFICULTY: moderate; PAGE: 426; OBJECTIVE: 3; TYPE: concept

52. It is not possible to anticipate what questions a potential employer will ask during an interview.

ANSWER: False. Employers usually gear their questions to specific organizational needs.
DIFFICULTY: moderate; PAGE: 427; OBJECTIVE: 3; TYPE: concept

53. Some employers will want to know about your hobbies and interests.

ANSWER: True. Some employers believe that personal background indicates how well the candidate will fit in.
DIFFICULTY: easy; PAGE: 427; OBJECTIVE: 3; TYPE: concept

54. Job applicants don't ask questions during an interview; they are there only to answer questions.

ANSWER: False. The questions you ask are just as important as the answers you provide.
DIFFICULTY: moderate; PAGE: 429; OBJECTIVE: 4; TYPE: concept

55. Because a job interview is a serious situation, you should try to smile as little as possible.

ANSWER: False. In the United States, you are more likely to have a successful interview if you smile frequently.
DIFFICULTY: moderate; PAGE: 430; OBJECTIVE: 4; TYPE: concept

56. Staging mock interviews can help you identify self-defeating nonverbal behaviors and speech mannerisms.

ANSWER: True. It is also helpful to tape record or videotape these mock interviews.
DIFFICULTY: moderate; PAGE: 430; OBJECTIVE: 4; TYPE: concept

57. Part of your preparation for job interviews is an evaluation of your voice tone and speaking habits.

ANSWER: True. The sound of your voice can profoundly impact your success.
DIFFICULTY: moderate; PAGE: 431; OBJECTIVE: 4; TYPE: concept

58. The appropriate clothing for most job interviews is something conservative and businesslike, such as a dark blue suit.

ANSWER: True. Your clothing reveals your ability to sense the unspoken "rules" of the situation.
DIFFICULTY: easy; PAGE: 431; OBJECTIVE: 4; TYPE: concept

59. It's a good idea to take extra copies of your résumé with you to an interview, as well as a list of questions to ask and any past correspondence about the position.

ANSWER: True. You should take all of these items with you.
DIFFICULTY: moderate; PAGE: 432; OBJECTIVE: 4; TYPE: concept

60. Most interviewers expect applicants to be a few minutes late for their appointment.

ANSWER: False. You should arrive early for the interview.
DIFFICULTY: moderate; PAGE: 432; OBJECTIVE: 4; TYPE: concept

61. Of the three stages of a job interview, the close is the most important.

ANSWER: False. The warm-up is the most important because many employers make a decision within 20 seconds of contact with a candidate.
DIFFICULTY: moderate; PAGE: 432; OBJECTIVE: 5; TYPE: concept

62. Many interviewers make up their mind about a candidate within the first 20 seconds of the interview.

ANSWER: True. Studies show that this is particularly true of employers who are poorly trained in interviewing techniques.
DIFFICULTY: moderate; PAGE: 432; OBJECTIVE: 5; TYPE: concept

63. Body language is particularly important during the warm-up phase of a job interview.

ANSWER: True. Because you won't have time to say much in the first minute or two, you must sell yourself nonverbally.
DIFFICULTY: easy; PAGE: 432; OBJECTIVE: 5; TYPE: concept

64. During the question-and-answer phase of an interview, try to keep your answers short; usually just a yes or no will do.

ANSWER: False. Don't limit yourself to yes-or-no answers.
DIFFICULTY: moderate; PAGE: 433; OBJECTIVE: 5; TYPE: concept

65. It is potentially illegal for an interviewer to ask about your religious affiliation, marital status, or number of children.

ANSWER: True. All of these topics can lead to discrimination.
DIFFICULTY: moderate; PAGE: 433-34; OBJECTIVE: 5; TYPE: concept

66. If you are asked a potentially discriminatory question during a job interview, you are legally obligated to refuse to answer.

ANSWER: False. You may respond in a variety of ways, depending primarily on how badly you want the job.
DIFFICULTY: moderate; PAGE: 433-34; OBJECTIVE: 5; TYPE: concept

67. At the close of an interview, you can impress the interviewer with your assertiveness by pressing for an immediate decision.

ANSWER: False. Although you should tactfully try to pin down what will happen next, you should not demand a decision.
DIFFICULTY: moderate; PAGE: 434; OBJECTIVE: 5; TYPE: concept

68. A job interviewer will expect you to raise the issue of salary.

ANSWER: False. Let the interviewer raise the subject.
DIFFICULTY: moderate; PAGE: 434; OBJECTIVE: 5; TYPE: concept

69. Once an interviewer states the salary for a job offer, you should never try to negotiate it.

ANSWER: False. If you are in a strong bargaining position, it is entirely appropriate to negotiate.
DIFFICULTY: moderate; PAGE: 434; OBJECTIVE: 5; TYPE: concept

70. Even if you feel that you have little chance for the job, you should still send a thank-you message within two days following the interview.

ANSWER: True. Not only is this good etiquette, but it leaves a positive impression.
DIFFICULTY: moderate; PAGE: 435; OBJECTIVE: 6; TYPE: concept

Fill-in-the-Blank

71. _____ interviews, such as those on college campuses, are a means of eliminating unqualified applicants.

ANSWER: Screening
DIFFICULTY: moderate; PAGE: 424; OBJECTIVE: 2; TYPE: concept

72. In _____ interviews, the interviewer controls the situation by asking a series of prepared questions in a set order.

ANSWER: Structured
DIFFICULTY: moderate; PAGE: 424; OBJECTIVE: 2; TYPE: concept

73. In _____ - _____ interviews, the interviewer poses broad questions and encourages the applicant to talk freely.

ANSWER: Open-Ended
DIFFICULTY: moderate; PAGE: 424; OBJECTIVE: 2; TYPE: concept

74. In _____ interviews, several candidates are interviewed simultaneously to see how they interact.

ANSWER: Group
DIFFICULTY: moderate; PAGE: 424; OBJECTIVE: 2; TYPE: concept

75. In _____ interviews, candidates answer pointed questions designed to upset or unsettle them.

ANSWER: Stress
DIFFICULTY: moderate; PAGE: 424; OBJECTIVE: 2; TYPE: concept

76. In _____ or *behavioral* interviews, candidates are asked how they would handle real-life work problems.

ANSWER: Situational
DIFFICULTY: moderate; PAGE: 425; OBJECTIVE: 2; TYPE: concept

77. _____ testing helps employers to improve the predictability of the employee selection process and reduce their reliance on the brief interaction that an interview allows.

ANSWER: Preemployment
DIFFICULTY: moderate; PAGE: 425; OBJECTIVE: 3; TYPE: concept

78. One way to practice and improve your interview skills is to stage _____ interviews with a friend.

ANSWER: Mock
DIFFICULTY: easy; PAGE: 430; OBJECTIVE: 4; TYPE: concept

79. Inquiries about an applicant's religious affiliation, national origin, marital status, and so on are considered to be _____ interview questions.

ANSWER: Discriminatory OR Illegal
DIFFICULTY: moderate; PAGE: 433; OBJECTIVE: 3; TYPE: concept

80. Following a job interview, send a (an) _____ - _____ message even if you feel you have little chance of landing the job.

ANSWER: Thank-You
DIFFICULTY: moderate; PAGE: 435; OBJECTIVE: 6; TYPE: concept

81. If you're not advised of the interviewer's decision by the promised date or within two weeks after an interview, send a message of _____.

ANSWER: Inquiry
DIFFICULTY: moderate; PAGE: 435-36; OBJECTIVE: 6; TYPE: concept

82. If you receive a job offer but are waiting to hear from other possible employers, request a time _____.

ANSWER: Extension
DIFFICULTY: moderate; PAGE: 436; OBJECTIVE: 6; TYPE: concept

83. When you receive a job offer that you want to accept, you should reply within _____ days.

ANSWER: Five
DIFFICULTY: moderate; PAGE: 436; OBJECTIVE: 6; TYPE: concept

84. A letter declining a job offer follows the organizational plan for _____ messages.

ANSWER: Negative
DIFFICULTY: moderate; PAGE: 438; OBJECTIVE: 6; TYPE: concept

85. When resigning from your current job, it is vital to give your employer at least _____ _____ notice.

ANSWER: Two Weeks'
DIFFICULTY: moderate; PAGE: 438; OBJECTIVE: 6; TYPE: concept

Short Answer/Essay

86. Briefly explain the primary differences between solicited application letters and unsolicited application letters.

ANSWER: Whereas a solicited application letter is written in response to an announced job opening, an unsolicited letter is sent to an organization that has not announced an opening. In terms of content, the main difference is in the opening paragraph, since the unsolicited letter should start with more of an attention-getter.
DIFFICULTY: moderate; PAGE: 419; OBJECTIVE: 1; TYPE: concept

87. Explain the function of each phase of an application letter written in the AIDA format.

ANSWER: (1) Getting Attention: The opening paragraph of your application letter has two important jobs to do: clearly stating your reason for writing and giving the recipient a reason to keep reading. (2) Building Interest and Increasing Desire: The middle section of the application letter presents your strongest selling points in terms of their potential benefit to the organization, thereby building interest in you and creating a desire to interview you. (3) Motivating Action: The final paragraph of your application letter has two important functions: to ask the reader for a specific action and to facilitate a reply. In almost all cases, the action you request is an interview.
DIFFICULTY: difficult; PAGE: 419-423; OBJECTIVE: 1; TYPE: concept

88. List the two functions of the final paragraph in an application letter.

ANSWER: This paragraph is designed to (1) ask the reader for a specific action and (2) facilitate a reply.
DIFFICULTY: moderate; PAGE: 423; OBJECTIVE: 1; TYPE: concept

89. Explain the dual purposes of employment interviews.

ANSWER: The organization is trying to find the best person available for the job by determining whether you and the organization are a good match. The applicant's main objective is to find the job best suited to his or her goals and capabilities.
DIFFICULTY: moderate; PAGE: 423; OBJECTIVE: 1; TYPE: concept

90. Explain how best to approach a selection interview.

ANSWER: Your best approach during this stage of interviews is to show interest in the job, relate your skills and experience to the organization's needs, listen attentively, ask insightful questions, and display enthusiasm.
DIFFICULTY: difficult; PAGE: 424; OBJECTIVE: 2; TYPE: concept

91. Briefly explain the difference between a structured interview and an open-ended interview.

ANSWER: In structured interviews, the employer asks a series of prepared questions in a set order. In less formal open-ended interviews, the employer asks broad questions, encouraging the applicant to talk freely.
DIFFICULTY: moderate; PAGE: 424; OBJECTIVE: 2; TYPE: concept

92. Describe each of the three stages in a typical sequence of interviews.

ANSWER: (1) Screening stage—These interviews usually occur on campus or via phone. They are focused on screening out unqualified applicants. (2) Selection stage—These are onsite interviews with several employees of the organization. They allow the applicant and the organization to decide if they will be a good fit for each other. (3) Final stage—This is usually an interview with a higher-level executive who can make the final decision and negotiate the terms of an offer.
DIFFICULTY: difficult; PAGE: 424; OBJECTIVE: 2; TYPE: concept

93. Describe six types of interviews.

ANSWER: (1) Structured interviews—Generally used in the screening stage, these interviews ask a series of prepared questions in a set order. All applicants are asked the same questions, and their answers are compared. (2) Open-ended interviews are less formal and structured, more like a conversation between peers. (3) Group interviews—To judge interpersonal skills, some employers meet with several candidates simultaneously to see how they interact. (4) Stress interviews—These interviews try to put applicants in a difficult or stressful situation and then observe how well they can handle that. (5) Video interviews—Many large companies use videoconferencing systems to screen middle-management candidates or to interview new recruits at universities. (6) Situational interviews—During these interviews, candidates may be asked how they would solve a particular business problem, or asked to lead a brainstorming session, engage in role playing, or even make a presentation.
DIFFICULTY: difficult; PAGE: 424-25; OBJECTIVE: 2; TYPE: concept

94. Briefly define "situational interview."

ANSWER: In a situational interview (or behavioral interview) the interviewer may ask you how you would solve a particular business problem, or ask you to lead a brainstorming session, engage in role playing, or even make a presentation.
DIFFICULTY: moderate; PAGE: 425; OBJECTIVE: 2; TYPE: concept

95. What six tasks do you need to complete to prepare for a successful job interview?

ANSWER: (1) Learn about the organization. (2) Think ahead about questions. (3) Bolster your confidence. (4) Polish your interview style. (5) Plan to look good. (6) Be ready when you arrive.
DIFFICULTY: moderate; PAGE: 426; OBJECTIVE: 4; TYPE: concept

96. List at least five things that you might want to find out during a job interview.

ANSWER: (1) Are these my kind of people? (2) Can I do this work? (3) Will I enjoy the work? (4) Is this the job I want? (5) Does the job pay what I'm worth? (6) What kind of person would I be working for? (7) What sort of future can I expect with this organization?
DIFFICULTY: difficult; PAGE: 429; OBJECTIVE: 4; TYPE: concept

97. In general, what are some guidelines to follow when deciding what to wear for an employment interview?

ANSWER: If you're not sure what to wear, dress conservatively in dark, solid colors. Wear the best quality clothing you can, but remember that clean and appropriate are far more important than expensive and flashy.
DIFFICULTY: moderate; PAGE: 431; OBJECTIVE: 4; TYPE: concept

98. List at least five items to you should take to every interview.

ANSWER: (1) Small notebook, (2) pen, (3) list of the questions you want to ask, (4) several copies of your résumé, (5) an outline of what you have learned about the organization, (6) any past correspondence about the position.
DIFFICULTY: moderate; PAGE: 432; OBJECTIVE: 4; TYPE: concept

99. Describe each of the three stages of a successful employment interview.

ANSWER: (1) The warm-up: This is the most important stage. Interviewers will make important decisions about you based on their first impression. Sell yourself nonverbally. Offer a firm but gentle handshake; use the interviewer's name; smile. Let the interviewer begin the discussion. (2) The question-and-answer session: Let the interviewer lead the conversation. Try to tailor your answers to make a favorable impression. Be sure to ask questions of your own about the job and the company. Explain how you will be able to help the company meet its needs. (3) The close: Respond promptly to the interviewer's signals that the interview is coming to a close. Thank the interviewer and express your interest in the organization.
DIFFICULTY: difficult; PAGE: 432-35; OBJECTIVE: 2; TYPE: concept

100. Describe at least three common employment messages that follow an interview.

ANSWER: (1) Thank-You Message: Send this type of message within two days of the interview. Acknowledge the interviewer's time and courtesy and express your continued interest in the job. (2) Message of Inquiry: If you have not heard back from the company within two weeks of your interview, you should send them a letter asking to be notified about the decision. Doing so shows that you are still interested in the position. (3) Request for a Time Extension: If you receive an offer while still waiting to hear back from another interview, you may write to the offering company and ask for a time extension on your decision. (4) Letter of Acceptance: Like the job offer itself, this message is legally binding. (5) Letter Declining a Job Offer: The plan for negative messages is ideally suited for this type of letter. (6) Letter of Resignation: If you get a job and are currently employed, send this type of message to let your immediate supervisor know that you will be changing jobs. You should give your current employer at least two weeks' notice, and the letter should follow the plan for negative messages.
DIFFICULTY: difficult; PAGE: 435-38; OBJECTIVE: 6; TYPE: concept

APPENDIX A
FORMAT AND LAYOUT OF BUSINESS DOCUMENTS

Multiple Choice

1. The quality of paper is measured by
    a. length and width.
    b. weight and cotton content.
    c. color and texture.
    d. whether or not it is imprinted with the name and address of the company.

ANSWER: b. These are two criteria.
DIFFICULTY: moderate; PAGE: A-1; TYPE: concept

2. The proper sequence for the standard parts of a letter is
    a. heading, date, inside address, salutation, body, complimentary close, signature block.
    b. date, heading, inside address, salutation, body, typewritten name, complimentary close.
    c. salutation, date, heading, inside address, body, complimentary close, signature block.
    d. inside address, heading, date, salutation, body, complimentary close, typewritten name.

ANSWER: a. This is the correct order.
DIFFICULTY: moderate; PAGE: A-2-A-6; TYPE: concept

3. Which of the following is a salutopening?
    a. Dear Professor Milford:
    b. Dear Esteemed Professor Milford,
    c. Thank you, Professor Milford,
    d. Attention: Professor J. J. Milford

ANSWER: c. A salutopening omits *Dear* but includes the first few words of the opening paragraph along with the recipient's name.
DIFFICULTY: moderate; PAGE: A-6; TYPE: application

4. You may place the attention line
    a. at the top of the page, centered under the letterhead.
    b. below the salutation.
    c. two lines below the complimentary close.
    d. on the first line of the inside address.

ANSWER: d. This is the correct location.
DIFFICULTY: moderate; PAGE: A-9; TYPE: concept

5. What is the correct format for reference initials?
   a. RSR/sm
   b. RSR:sm
   c. RSR:SM
   d. all of the above

ANSWER: d. Any of these formats is acceptable.
DIFFICULTY: moderate; PAGE: A-9-A-10; TYPE: application

6. The letter format in which all parts begin at the left margin is called
   a. block.
   b. modified block.
   c. simplified.
   d. mixed.

ANSWER: a. This is the definition of block letter format.
DIFFICULTY: moderate; PAGE: A-11; TYPE: concept

7. To meet the needs of U.S. postal equipment, envelopes
   a. are never made of colored paper.
   b. are addressed in capital letters, with no punctuation.
   c. include all mailing instructions below the address area.
   d. adhere to all of the above guidelines.

ANSWER: b. This format accommodates the optical scanners used by the Postal Service.
DIFFICULTY: moderate; PAGE: A-11-A-12; TYPE: concept

8. The top of a memo usually includes headings for
   a. to, from, date, subject.
   b. department, date, subject.
   c. attention, to, from, date.
   d. subject, to, date.

ANSWER: a. These are the standard headings.
DIFFICULTY: moderate; PAGE: A-15; TYPE: concept

9. When preparing a memo that deals with money or confidential matters, it is often a good idea to
   a. leave the subject line blank.
   b. include a complimentary close.
   c. use high-quality paper.
   d. sign it at the bottom.

ANSWER: d. It is acceptable to sign these types of memos.
DIFFICULTY: moderate; PAGE: A-16; TYPE: concept

10. When preparing a formal report, leave at least a
    a. uniform 2-inch margin on all sides.
    b. 2-inch margin at the top and bottom and a 1-inch margin on the sides.
    c. 1-inch margin on three sides and a 1-1/2-inch margin on the bound side.
    d. uniform 1-1/2-inch margin on all sides.

ANSWER: c. It is important to include sufficient white space along with the text of the report.
DIFFICULTY: moderate; PAGE: A-19; TYPE: concept

True or False

11. The design for letterhead stationery should be as simple as possible.

ANSWER: True. Letterhead design should not make the page look cluttered.
DIFFICULTY: easy; PAGE: A-1; TYPE: concept

12. In business documents, abbreviations such as U.S.A. and M.B.A. must always contain periods.

ANSWER: False. These abbreviations may or may not include periods, but should never have internal spaces.
DIFFICULTY: moderate; PAGE: A-2; TYPE: concept

13. "Sept. 10th, 2007" is the correct way to type the date in a letter.

ANSWER: False. There are several acceptable formats, but none would include *th* following the date.
DIFFICULTY: moderate; PAGE: A-2-A-3; TYPE: application

14. If you are writing a business letter to someone you know well, it is acceptable to use his or her first name in the salutation.

ANSWER: True. The formality of the salutation depends on your relationship with the addressee.
DIFFICULTY: moderate; PAGE: A-6; TYPE: concept

15. Three blank lines are left between the complimentary close and the sender's typed name.

ANSWER: True. This leaves enough room for the sender's written signature.
DIFFICULTY: moderate; PAGE: A-9; TYPE: concept

16. The second page of a letter includes a heading containing the name of the person or organization receiving the letter, the page number, and the date.

ANSWER: True. It may also include a reference number.
DIFFICULTY: moderate; PAGE: A-9; TYPE: concept

17. In the simplified letter format, commas follow both the salutation and the complimentary close.

ANSWER: False. This format does not include a salutation or a complimentary close.
DIFFICULTY: moderate; PAGE: A-11; TYPE: concept

18. Most envelopes used in business are No. 10 (9 1/2 inches long).

ANSWER: True. This is the standard for most businesses in the U.S.
DIFFICULTY: moderate; PAGE: A-11; TYPE: concept

19. A memo has a complimentary close and a signature.

ANSWER: False. Memos begin with headings.
DIFFICULTY: moderate; PAGE: A-15; TYPE: concept

20. E-mail messages can act as memos but not as letters.

ANSWER: False. E-mail messages can be used to carry information within your company or outside your company and around the world.
DIFFICULTY: moderate; PAGE: A-17; TYPE: concept

APPENDIX B
DOCUMENTATION OF REPORT SOURCES

Multiple Choice

1. With Chicago Humanities style, you use
    a. the author-date system.
    b. the author-page number system.
    c. footnotes or endnotes.
    d. full citations within the text itself.

ANSWER: c. This is one characteristic of Chicago Humanities style.
DIFFICULTY: moderate; PAGE: A-21; TYPE: concept

2. The purpose of a superscript in text is to let the reader know
    a. to read the marked line more carefully.
    b. how many sources the author consulted.
    c. that the report is scholarly.
    d. to look for source information in either a footnote or an endnote.

ANSWER: d. This is the function of an arabic numeral placed just above the line of type at the end of the reference.
DIFFICULTY: moderate; PAGE: A-21; TYPE: concept

3. A content note
    a. offers additional information or provides a cross-reference.
    b. documents direct quotes.
    c. documents paraphrased passages.
    d. documents visual aids.

ANSWER: a. Content notes may be included for the reader's convenience.
DIFFICULTY: moderate; PAGE: A-22; TYPE: concept

4. With Chicago Humanities style, the Bibliography
    a. lists only those works actually cited in the text.
    b. lists works in the order in which they were cited in the text.
    c. can include annotations.
    d. does all of the above.

ANSWER: c. This is true of Chicago Humanities style.
DIFFICULTY: moderate; PAGE: A-21; TYPE: concept

5. Entries for the Bibliography for a report following the Chicago style
   a. alphabetize magazine articles by the name of the magazine if no author is cited.
   b. use quotation marks around the titles of articles from newspapers and journals.
   c. capitalize only the first words of titles of books and articles.
   d. use only the name of the principal author, followed by "et al." to represent any other authors.

ANSWER: b. This is also true of articles from magazines.
DIFFICULTY: moderate; PAGE: A-23; TYPE: concept

6. With the APA style, you use
   a. the author-date system.
   b. the author-page number system.
   c. superscripts and footnotes or endnotes.
   d. full citations within the text itself.

ANSWER: a. This is a distinctive characteristic of APA style.
DIFFICULTY: moderate; PAGE: A-24; TYPE: concept

7. When preparing the list of references following the APA style
   a. include all the works you consulted, even if you didn't actually cite them anywhere in the text.
   b. include full information on any personal communications or interviews you conducted in your research.
   c. use the title "References."
   d. do all of the above.

ANSWER: c. This is the correct title.
DIFFICULTY: moderate; PAGE: A-24; TYPE: concept

8. When citing journal articles using the APA style
   a. use quotation marks around the title.
   b. capitalize only the first word of the title and the first word to follow an internal colon.
   c. you do not need to include the volume number.
   d. include only the first page of the article.

ANSWER: b. In this sense, capitalization standards of APA style differ from those of MLA and Chicago styles.
DIFFICULTY: moderate; PAGE: A-24; TYPE: concept

9. With the MLA style, you use
    a. the author-date system.
    b. the author-page number system.
    c. superscripts and footnotes or endnotes.
    d. full citations within the text itself.

ANSWER: b. MLA citations include the author's last name and a page reference following the cited material.
DIFFICULTY: moderate; PAGE: A-24; TYPE: concept

10. In the List of Works Cited following the MLA style
    a. the date comes immediately after the author's name.
    b. electronic sources are not included.
    c. the titles of books and periodicals are put in quotation marks.
    d. all the main words are capitalized in the titles of books and articles.

ANSWER: d. This is one characteristic that distinguishes MLA style from APA style.
DIFFICULTY: moderate; PAGE: A-25; TYPE: concept

True or False

11. Always use APA style for documentation in your reports, even if your employer or client normally uses a different form.

ANSWER: False. If your employer or client specifies a form, use it.
DIFFICULTY: moderate; PAGE: A-21; TYPE: concept

12. The Chicago style refers to the documentation style used by companies in the Chicago area.

ANSWER: False. It refers to a style of documentation recommended in the *Chicago Manual of Style*.
DIFFICULTY: moderate; PAGE: A-21; TYPE: concept

13. Footnotes and endnotes are identical; the only difference between the two is their placement.

ANSWER: True. This is the only difference.
DIFFICULTY: moderate; PAGE: A-21; TYPE: concept

14. The only format difference between endnotes and a bibliography is that the bibliography is in alphabetical order.

ANSWER: False. There are other important differences.
DIFFICULTY: moderate; PAGE: A-22-A-23; TYPE: concept

15. If a newspaper article doesn't have an author, your citation begins with the title of the newspaper.

ANSWER: False. The citation begins with the title of the article.
DIFFICULTY: moderate; PAGE: A-22; TYPE: concept

16. If you use unpublished materials, such as doctoral dissertations or public speeches, as resources, you do not need to cite them in your report.

ANSWER: False. You must cite these types of materials if you include information from them in your report.
DIFFICULTY: moderate; PAGE: A-22; TYPE: concept

17. The American Psychological Association style uses the author-date system.

ANSWER: True. This is a distinctive feature of APA style.
DIFFICULTY: moderate; PAGE: A-24; TYPE: concept

18. In the APA style, titles of articles are put in quotation marks and all important words are capitalized.

ANSWER: False. APA style requires listing these titles without quotation marks and capitalizing only the first word, any proper nouns, and the first word to follow a colon.
DIFFICULTY: moderate; PAGE: A-24; TYPE: concept

19. If you use the MLA style, your in-text citations include the author's last name and a page reference.

ANSWER: True. This is a distinctive feature of MLA style.
DIFFICULTY: moderate; PAGE: A-24; TYPE: concept

20. With the MLA style, you should wait to compile the Works Cited list until the rest of your report is completed.

ANSWER: False. The MLA Style Manual recommends preparing the list of works cited first so that you will know what information to give in the parenthetical citations throughout your report.
DIFFICULTY: moderate; PAGE: A-25; TYPE: concept

HANDBOOK OF GRAMMAR, MECHANICS, AND USAGE

Multiple Choice

1. Which of the following is the most gender-neutral (and correct) sentence?
    a. A manager must use his best judgment.
    b. Department heads must hire their own personnel.
    c. Every shopper will be issued her own personal credit card.
    d. Each technician has their own tool kit.

ANSWER: b. This is the only gender-neutral option.
DIFFICULTY: moderate; PAGE: H-5; TYPE: application

2. Which of the following possessive phrases is *not* correct?
    a. a year's recommendations
    b. two year's recommendations
    c. its recommendations
    d. one year's recommendations

ANSWER: b. The apostrophe should come after the 's' since "two years" is plural.
DIFFICULTY: moderate; PAGE: H-6; TYPE: application

3. What is the tense of the verb in this sentence? "We had issued the policy Monday afternoon."
    a. present
    b. past
    c. future
    d. past perfect

ANSWER: d. This is past perfect tense.
DIFFICULTY: easy; PAGE: H-7; TYPE: application

4. Which of the following words is an adjective?
    a. too
    b. silent
    c. into
    d. badly

ANSWER: b. This is the only adjective listed.
DIFFICULTY: moderate; PAGE: H-9; TYPE: application

5. Which of the following is a sentence fragment?
    a. The bigger they are, the harder they fall.
    b. Put it in the mail right away.
    c. Come here.
    d. Depending on the circumstances.

ANSWER: d. The other options are complete sentences.
DIFFICULTY: moderate; PAGE: H-15; TYPE: application

6. What is the problem with this sentence? "We can give him a small raise, he deserves it."
   - a. Comma splice
   - b. Sentence fragment
   - c. Dangling modifier
   - d. Nothing

ANSWER: a. A comma must not be used to separate two independent clauses.
DIFFICULTY: moderate; PAGE: H-16; TYPE: application

7. Which of the following punctuation marks is used to separate a dependent clause at the beginning of a sentence from the rest of the sentence?
   - a. semicolon
   - b. colon
   - c. comma
   - d. dash

ANSWER: c. This is one function of a comma.
DIFFICULTY: moderate; PAGE: H-19; TYPE: concept

8. Which of the following terms should *not* be hyphenated?
   - a. non-union
   - b. pro-Republican
   - c. self-assured
   - d. ex-wife

ANSWER: a. Omit hyphens from words that have prefixes such as pro-, anti-, non- and others.
DIFFICULTY: difficult; PAGE: H-20; TYPE: application

9. In the following sentence, which words should *not* be capitalized? "After talking with President Hilda Bruckner, he decided that the Insurance industry would provide a suitable career for someone who was a Graduate of the Department of Business at Gable University."
   - a. insurance, department
   - b. president, university
   - c. graduate, department
   - d. insurance, graduate

ANSWER: d. The other words are correctly capitalized.
DIFFICULTY: moderate; PAGE: H-22-H-23; TYPE: application

10. Which of the following words is misspelled?
   - a. accomodate
   - b. exaggerate
   - c. occurrence
   - d. receive

ANSWER: a. The other options are spelled correctly.
DIFFICULTY: moderate; PAGE: H-28; TYPE: application

True or False

11. The plural of "son-in-law" is "sons-in-law," but the possessive is "son-in-law's."

ANSWER: True.
DIFFICULTY: moderate; PAGE: H-4; TYPE: application

12. The pronoun "who" is in the nominative case; the pronoun "whom" is in the objective case.

ANSWER: True. The pronoun "who" is in the nominative case; the pronoun "whom" is in the objective case.
DIFFICULTY: moderate; PAGE: H-5; TYPE: application

13. The verb "to be" is an example of a regular verb.

ANSWER: False. "To be" is an irregular verb that does not follow the patterns of most other verbs.
DIFFICULTY: moderate; PAGE: H-7; TYPE: application

14. The difference between "lie" and "lay" is that "lie" is an intransitive verb and "lay" is a transitive verb.

ANSWER: True. The difference between "lie" and "lay" is that "lie" is an intransitive verb and "lay" is a transitive verb.
DIFFICULTY: moderate; PAGE: H-7-H-8; TYPE: application

15. Many adverbs are formed by adding "-ly" to adjectives.

ANSWER: True. Many adverbs are formed by adding "-ly" to adjectives.

DIFFICULTY: easy; PAGE: H-11; TYPE: concept

16. A linking verb is always followed by a noun, pronoun, or adjective.

ANSWER: True. A linking verb is always followed by a noun, pronoun, or adjective.

DIFFICULTY: moderate; PAGE: H-16; TYPE: concept

17. A semicolon is used to separate independent clauses when the second one begins with a word such as "however" or "therefore."

ANSWER: True. A semicolon is used to separate independent clauses when the second one begins with a word such as "however" or "therefore."
DIFFICULTY: moderate; PAGE: H-18; TYPE: application

18. You should include a comma when a date consists only of the month and year.

ANSWER: False. You should include a comma when the date includes the month, day, and year.
DIFFICULTY: moderate; PAGE: H-19; TYPE: concept

19. A period goes inside quotation marks if the whole sentence is quoted but outside the quotation marks if only the last part of the sentence is a quote.

ANSWER: False. The period always goes inside the quotation marks.
DIFFICULTY: moderate; PAGE: H-20; TYPE: concept

20. There are no mispelled words in this sentence.

ANSWER: False. The word "misspelled" is misspelled.
DIFFICULTY: moderate; PAGE: H-28; TYPE: application